Advance Praise for

Abbott Northwestern Hospital: 1882–Present
A Celebrated History

In what seems like a lifetime devoted to understanding why Minnesota medicine is the envy of so many around the world, I met many of the men and women you will discover in this celebrated history of the centerpiece of the largest health system in Minnesota. But here I also met Dr. Amos Wilson Abbott, born to medical missionary parents in India, and Harriet Walker and her women friends, who created our first women and children's hospital, and famed Australian Sister Elizabeth Kenny. Unlike medicine itself, this book about our first medical school, our first school of nursing, and the evolution of every health and medical specialty is easy to understand, and a real pleasure to read. I highly recommend it.

—*Dave Durenberger, U.S. Senator (MN) 1978-95*

When a physician joins a medical staff, they unwittingly accept a culture and a history of a hospital and those that helped create it. There is a special culture of excellence and caring at Abbott Northwestern Hospital that permeates the medical staff, hospital staff, and administrators alike. It is recognized by the community with overwhelming generosity in financial support of its programs. Reading this book provides a context for why that has been true, continues to be true, and will always be true. From the beginning of both Abbott and Northwestern Hospitals, excellence was fueled by an amazingly forward-thinking and philanthropic community, innovative care givers willing to push the boundaries, and nursing excellence that ensured a true commitment to patient-centered care. Thanks to Dr. Scott and his collaborators, we can now take an in depth look into the DNA of this amazing organization and hopefully use it to guide the history of the next 100 years.

—*Dr. Mark Migliori, Surgeon and Former Chief of Staff*
at Abbott Northwestern Hospital

It is the rare and thoughtful institution—in this case Abbott Northwestern—that makes the effort to tell its history. We are bent on doing our work, advancing our missions, and moving our organizations forward. Sometimes this important work is deferred to a milestone anniversary or is left unfulfilled because records haven't been kept or organized and those who could best tell the story are gone. Kudos to Abbott Northwestern and Dr. Robert Scott for this comprehensive initiative. Years from now staff and community will continue to be grateful that this busy group of authors paused long enough to provide valuable historical context for the world-class institution that thrives in our midst and benefits so many.

—*D. Stephen Elliott, Director/CEO,*
Minnesota Historical Society

Dr. Scott's book, *Abbott Northwestern Hospital: 1882-Present, A Celebrated History*, teaches people what it takes to create a care infrastructure that leads and lasts through an ever-changing environment. By harnessing the voices of key partners and change agents, like cardiologist Dr. Bob Van Tassel, who approached cardiovascular research and practice with the motto of "you can't think big enough," readers will marvel at what started in Minneapolis in the way of health care innovation. It is part history, part business, and, importantly, part human spirit.

—*Kristine Fortman, PhD, CEO,*
Minneapolis Heart Institute® Foundation

Abbott Northwestern Hospital

1882-Present

A Celebrated History

ISBN: 978-0-9978567-1-2

Contents

Dedicated to Belle—the love of my life—
and to Gordon Sprenger, who showed us the way.

— Dr. Robert Scott

Abbott Northwestern Hospital 1882-Present: A Celebrated History represents a compilation of writings and recollections by many of the leading members of the Abbott Northwestern Medical and Nursing Staffs. As gathered in this book, they strive to relay a comprehensive portrait of the breadth and depth of Abbott Northwestern and its storied history and legacy.

As is the case with a project of this scope and magnitude, it was necessary to identify specific individuals whose contribution to the book would reflect a representative voice and accurate historic perspective for the reader.

By nature of that same magnitude, it is unfortunately impossible to include the names of the countless number of dedicated doctors, nurses, board members, volunteers and administrators who have helped make Abbott Northwestern Hospital the world-class medical center it is today.*

To all who have shaped the history of the institution—named and otherwise—we offer our heartfelt appreciation and deep gratitude.

*While we have made every effort to correctly spell names and represent the events that occurred, some information was created from memory, and errors and omissions are, therefore, inevitable. We sincerely apologize for errors and omissions in this book.

Images

The graphic element on each chapter page is from Allina Health.

The image of Virginia Piper (page 72) is used courtesy of Gretchen Piper.

The image of Penny George (page 78) is used courtesy of the George Family Foundation.

The image of the Magnet Celebration (page 78) is used courtesy of Mary Petersen and Dr. Bill Petersen.

The images of hospital administrators (page 76) are used courtesy of Dr. Robert H. Scott.

The following images are copyright © of the Minnesotal Historical Society:
- p. 59: Abbott Hospital 1902-1911
- p. 60: Amos Wilson Abbott
- p. 61: Abbott Hospital staff (primarily student nurses) display banner honoring graduates who served in World War I
- p. 64: Northwestern Hospital Nursing School Class of 1897
- p. 65: Harriet Walker Home for Nurses, Minneapolis
- p. 66: Northwestern Hospital, Minneapolis
- p. 68: Sister Kenny demonstrates therapy techinques, Sister Kenny Institute
- p. 69: Sister Kenny Institute polio patients help Sister Kenny celebrate Institute's first birthday

The following images are copyright © of Abbott Northwestern Hospital:
- p. 67: Surgery image hanging on wall at Abbott Northwestern Hospital
- p. 70: The Healing Spirit Sculpture
- p. 72: Piper Building
- p. 77: The Mother Baby Center
- p. 79: Abbott Northwestern Hospital entrance
- p. 80: Emergency Room Sign

The following images are in the public domain:
- p. 63: Harriet Walker
- p. 68: Sister Elizabeth Kenny in 1915

Foreword

How fortunate we are that Dr. Robert H. Scott and the Abbott Northwestern Hospital Foundation have created this history of two great Minneapolis institutions – Abbott Hospital and Northwestern Hospital – and the evolution of Abbott Northwestern Hospital as a leading regional health center.

Institutions and organizations come and go. After a few decades, memories of their traditions and cultures are often lost. Institutional memories are tied to leaders and the decisions they made. This book preserves the history of the leadership of Abbott and Northwestern hospitals in creating and executing a vision of health care for the future.

Hospital leadership involves the Board of Directors, physicians, nurses, and administration. All four groups played a key role in the successful union of Abbott and Northwestern hospitals. In 1970, the leaders of these separate institutions, located two miles apart in the center of Minneapolis, determined that bringing their hospitals together would accomplish a number of things. It would eliminate inappropriate duplication of services and technology, and enable the clear vision that, together, the two hospitals could provide the highest quality medical care to the community.

This bold action to break from the status quo has been recognized over time for its wisdom. At the time of the merger, 25 independent hospitals served the Minneapolis-St. Paul area. Today a few of the 15 hospitals in the urban area are independent, but most are part of a health care system. The merger of Abbott and Northwestern hospitals was truly the beginning of the consolidation of independent hospitals into larger health care systems.

Combining these two facilities continued a rich history – in Minneapolis and in the State of Minnesota – of providing cutting-edge leadership in health care. This emerging medical center

Abbott Northwestern Hospital has led during a period of tremendous change in the delivery and financing of health care.

took the best of the past and developed the competence that allowed Abbott Northwestern Hospital to thrive. Abbott Northwestern Hospital has led during a period of tremendous change in the delivery and financing of health care. As you read this book, you will get a sense of its leadership's ability to anticipate the future and help shape the dramatic changes occurring in twentieth century health care.

The development and execution of a shared vision by the two institutions was not without its difficulties. These were two strong institutions. For each hospital to give up independence for the good of the collective whole was understandably difficult to accept. Members of the respective Boards of Directors had invested many years of volunteer service in developing each of these hospitals with their own traditions, values, and cultures. Physicians saw their independence and control of their medical practices being reduced. Since they thought things were going along fine, they questioned the necessity of the changes being proposed. The physicians at both Abbott Hospital and Northwestern Hospital worked in supportive environments. They felt in control of important decisions that affected them. For management, the blending of the two institutions, while intellectually acceptable, meant that some individuals would be changing their career paths or even lose their leadership roles entirely.

Where to locate the combined facilities was hotly contested, especially among the medical staffs as a result of the proposed merger. Some physicians would need to relocate their medical practices to another campus. For the Abbott medical staff, it meant leaving a well-loved environment. For the Northwestern medical staff, it meant welcoming new members into their physical space and leadership space. This was also true for the two Boards of Directors and management teams. Secret meetings of the medical staffs, with some Board members included, were held to strategize how to stop the consolidation.

The strength of the leaders of these institutions was tested. A number of those leaders are described in this book; a few leaders especially stand out. From the Board of Northwestern Hospital, Virginia and Bobby Piper were outstanding! From the Abbott Hospital side, Board members Conley Brooks, Herb Bissell, and Dean McNeal were exceptional! Physicians also served in key leadership roles. From the Abbott Hospital side, this was primarily Dr. Bill Petersen. From the Northwestern Hospital medical staff, two key leaders were

Dr. William Stromme and Dr. Frank Johnson. These physicians in leadership roles brought the medical staffs together and worked to provide the best outcome for everyone.

For decades, Abbott Hospital had been unique in that it was one of only a few hospitals in the nation owned by a single church. Abbott Hospital's Board of Directors were all men and all members of Westminster Presbyterian Church. Northwestern Hospital's uniqueness was in its founding by women to provide care to indigent women and children. From 1882 until 1967, its Board of Directors was composed entirely of women. The Board did have a men's advisory committee, but the men did not have a vote at the Board or Executive Committee meetings.

Board members from both institutions were close friends on a professional and social level. Members of the two medical staffs were medical colleagues in the community and respected each other. These relationships were significant in building the trust that allowed the merger of the two hospitals to come to fruition. At the same time, management was diligent in engaging all stakeholders in planning the new facilities, which allowed the various parties to know they had a part in the process of building the new entity.

In the midst of these negotiations, an attractive offer of land was made that was intended to encourage the relocation of all or part of the newly combined hospital to the suburbs. However, the leadership of Abbott Northwestern Hospital was committed to remaining in central Minneapolis, providing the opportunity to develop this institution as a privately owned, not-for-profit, central-city medical center.

Abbott Northwestern Hospital has developed into one of the most respected medical centers in Minnesota, one that deserves its national reputation for excellence. Many truly outstanding leaders at all levels have been involved over the years. Their skills in collaborating and anticipating the future have been a key factor in the institution's success. The rich history and traditions of the two institutions should be celebrated, and it should not be lost. Our thanks to Dr. Robert Scott and all those who contributed to this book. The stories of the evolution of the practice of medicine at these three remarkable hospitals, spanning three centuries, can now serve the community and the profession into the future.

Combining these two facilities continued a rich history – in Minneapolis and in the State of Minnesota – of providing cutting-edge leadership in health care.

Board members from both institutions were close friends on a professional and social level. These relationships were significant in building the trust that allowed the merger to come to fruition.

I was fortunate to have the opportunity to participate in the merger of the hospitals and the consolidation of the facilities, serving as the CEO of Abbott Northwestern Hospital for 25 years. I will forever be grateful for the opportunity to work with such a forward-thinking community, Board of Directors, medical staff, management team, and nursing staff.

—Gordon Sprenger

Part I

Abbott Northwestern Hospital Organizational History

Introduction
Robert H. Scott, M. D.

I joined the medical staffs of Abbott Hospital and Northwestern Hospital in July 1965, and was a member of those hospital staffs until 1970 when the two hospitals merged, at which time I became a member of the Abbott Northwestern medical staff. I retired from the practice of medicine in July 2006. Over those 41 years, I witnessed huge changes in each of these three hospitals and in the science of medicine. Having spent significant time on the Medical Boards as Chief-of-Staff and subsequently on the Board of Trustees of Abbott Northwestern Hospital, I have firsthand knowledge of many of the changes that resulted in the evolution of these institutions.

I had hoped for years that one of my former colleagues would write the history of these great institutions, but it didn't happen. In 2013, at a hospital event, Marna Fullerton, a long-standing Board member of Abbott Northwestern Hospital, asked if such a history existed. Neither Gordon Sprenger, former President and CEO of Abbott Northwestern Hospital, nor I knew of such a document. Since Abbott, Northwestern, and Abbott Northwestern hospitals had been delivering health care in Minneapolis for more than 100 years, I thought such a history was needed. After considering the project for a few weeks, its enormity became obvious.

I decided to break this history into two parts. Part I is a compelling history of the three organizations themselves and the administrative side of the story. It begins toward the end of the nineteenth century and concludes at the start of the twenty-first century.

Part II consists of chapters describing the changes in the science of medicine as practiced

The late twentieth century brought revolutionary changes to the delivery of health care in America, changes that many hospitals did not survive... How Abbott Northwestern Hospital became one of the survivors is one of the stories explored in this history.

at Abbott Northwestern Hospital, through the lenses of individual specialties, subspecialties, and professions.

I decided to take on the task of describing the roles of the founders, Boards of Trustees, and Administrators for Part I. It's a fascinating and complex story, both in terms of duration (more than 100 years) and in growth (evolving from six patient beds to more than 700 patient beds). As a result, Part I contains my perspective on this history, based in both research and personal experience. While other historians might have chosen to describe more about financial details or the personalities involved, I chose to focus on the larger forces that drove Abbott and Northwestern Hospitals to be started, subsequently merge, and to develop into a private medical center with a national reputation. It is an impressive story.

Historians Rosemary Steven (*In Sickness and Wealth*) and Paul Starr (*The Socialization of American Medicine*) detail in their books the scope of this enormous growth. Regardless of the funding source, hospitals mushroomed in the United States – from 178 in 1872 to more than 4,000 by 1910. World War I diverted attention and funding from the building of hospitals for a few years, but another surge of construction occurred in the 1920s. In the latter half of that decade, approximately $890 million was invested in hospitals and related structures. Development and expansion continues to this day. Abbott, Northwestern, and Abbott Northwestern hospitals were part of that history from the beginning into the present day.

The late twentieth century brought revolutionary changes to the delivery of health care in America, changes that many hospitals did not survive. Early in the twentieth century, there were 18 hospitals in Minneapolis. This history ends in the twenty-first century with the formation of Allina, one of the three health care systems in Minneapolis and St. Paul at the time of this writing (2015). How Abbott Northwestern Hospital became one of the survivors is one of the stories explored in this history.

In Part II, thirty-two of my colleagues – two nurses, two chaplains, two engineers, one librarian, and 25 physicians – describe the changes in their specialties and professions. Some specialties changed so dramatically that they virtually disappeared, while others were created and developed over these years. Without exception, these writers took on this daunting task with enthusiasm and dedication! I will forever be in their debt for contributing so significantly to this book. The story of these hospitals begins in the nineteenth century and extends into the twenty-first century. Two long-standing private hospitals in Minneapolis eventually merged to become one distinguished regional health center. This history ends there, with the changes that brought about the delivery of health care through complex, billion-dollar health care systems. Someone else gets to tell that story.

1

The History of Abbott Hospital
Part 1, 1902-1960

Dr. Amos Wilson Abbott

Any history of Abbott Hospital has to center on its founder, Dr. Amos Wilson Abbott. While the story begins in the nineteenth century, it has relevance in the twenty-first century as well. His parents, Amos Abbott and Anstice Wilson Abbott, were married in 1834 in Wilton, New Hampshire, and sailed for Bombay on May 23, 1834. They landed at Bombay, now called Mumbai, and lived about 120 miles east of Bombay in a village called Ahmednuggar (now named Amadnager). Mr. Abbott had studied at the Theological Seminary in Andover, Massachusetts, and had also studied medicine. In India, he worked as a medical missionary. Amos W. Abbott was born there on January 6, 1844. The family returned to the United States in 1847.

Amos W. Abbott attended Phillips Andover Academy from 1856 to 1859. During this time, he lived with his Aunt Eunice, his parents having returned to India. He was injured while working on a farm during the summer and was successfully cared for by his aunt. She then insisted that he return to the farm, but he refused. From the age of 15, he earned his own living, saving enough to enroll in Dartmouth College in 1859. He was working toward a law degree until August 1862, when he enlisted as a private in Company C, 16th Regiment, New Hampshire Volunteers to fight in the Civil War, where he served as a drummer boy. In 1863, he was captured and confined in a Confederate prison near New Orleans. With the help of a slave,

In 1877, Dr. Abbott rented a small house in Minneapolis to treat his patients... He also developed a relationship with Saint Barnabus, Saint Mary's, and Northwestern hospitals.

he managed to escape, and lived off the land until he reached the Union lines. He was quite debilitated and required hospitalization. While in the hospital, his physician encouraged him to go into medicine rather than law. He was discharged from active duty in August 1864 in a compromised health condition.

Though he was not on active duty, he nevertheless stayed in the Army working in the Pay Department in Washington D.C., where he also enrolled in Georgetown Medical College. He often took messages to the White House, delivering a number of them to President Lincoln personally. According to family papers at the Minnesota Historical Society, on April 14, 1865, Mr. Abbott was late in arriving at the Ford Theater for a performance of *Our American Cousin*. As he approached, he saw a man running from the theater. It was John Wilkes Booth, who had just assassinated President Lincoln.

In 1868, Abbott gave up his job in the Pay Department and went to New York City where he entered the College of Physicians and Surgeons, now the Medical School of Columbia University, colloquially known as P&S. He received his M.D. degree in 1869 and did an eighteen-month internship at the Colored Home Hospital of New York City on Ellis Island. Following his residency, he practiced medicine in Delhi, New York, 100 miles northwest of New York City. There he met Helen Griswold Wright, who was to become his wife. But Delhi was too small to meet his needs. He had a sister who was living and teaching in Minneapolis, and Dr. Abbott moved there in 1877. He and Helen Wright were married in 1880. They had one son (Wilson), two daughters. and lost two other children.

His medical office was in their home. Early on, he became friends with George Brackett, who owned land on Lake Minnetonka. Dr. Abbott was able to buy two acres from Mr. Brackett for $1.50 an acre. Thus he became an owner of part of Brackett's Point. Dr. Abbott would take the train 12 miles into Minneapolis in the morning, engage in the practice of medicine, and take the train back out to Lake Minnetonka for the evening.

In 1877, Dr. Abbott rented a small house in Minneapolis to treat his patients. This was at 121 10th Street N; it accommodated four patients. As his practice grew, he rented a six-bed house at Fourth Avenue near Bryant. In 1880, he moved to 18 West 14th Street where he could care for eight patients. In the late 1800s he also developed a relationship with Saint Barnabus, Saint Mary's, and Northwestern hospitals.

Dr. F. A. Dunsmoor was a colleague of Dr. Abbott's. Together they leased the Winslow House and organized the Minneapolis College Hospital in 1881. In 1885, they built their own building at Ninth Avenue and Fifth Street and changed the name to Minneapolis Hospital College, thus opening the first medical school in Minnesota. What was to become the University of Minnesota Medical School was just a state board of medical examiners at the time, whose main function was to certify physicians.

In 1888, the University of Minnesota Board of Examiners merged with the Minneapolis Hospital College and the St. Paul Medical College to become the University of Minnesota Medical School. Dr. Abbott was on the staff of the Medical School for twenty years, teaching anatomy and gynecology. He was emeritus professor at the time of his death in 1927 at the age of eighty-three. Dr. Dunsmoor went on to become the chair of Operative and Clinical Surgery.

In 1902, Abbott rented a yellow brick three-story house at 10 East 17th Street that had been The Stanley Hall School for Girls. This became Abbott Hospital – the city's first private, surgical hospital, which could serve up to 15 patients. Its resources were quite meager and the building inadequate. It had no elevator, so patients needed to be carried to and from the operating room on the second floor. This was often accomplished by an attendant, Jamey, who slung the patients over his shoulder. Otherwise, the patients were suspended in a blanket carried by Dr. Abbott's assistant and his anesthetist. The kitchen was in the basement, along with a dining room, laundry, and one large room that frequently functioned as an examining room. The building was not considered to be fireproof. Once Dr. Abbott's hospital was established, "he had his medical home," where he gathered about him "a distinguished family." This was the early beginning of medical specialization.

At the same time as Dr. Abbott's medical school training, Pasteur and Lister were in the experimental stages of their work on bacteria and asepsis. Dr. Abbott adopted the resulting sterile technique in his surgery and post-surgical care. The patient's preparation began the night before, when they were padded all night with boric acid. Just before surgery, the spot of incision was rubbed with ether. Dressings were steamed for 3 hours, left for 24 hours, and steamed

In 1902, Abbott rented a yellow brick three-story house at 10 East 17th Street...This became Abbott Hospital – the city's first private, surgical hospital, which could serve up to 15 patients. Its resources were quite meager and the building inadequate.

*[Abbott Hospital]
had no elevator,
so patients needed
to be carried
to and from
the operating
room on the
second floor.
This was often
accomplished
by an attendant,
Jamey, who slung
the patients over
his shoulder.*

again. All surgical specimens were examined under the microscope. Dr. Abbott became a leading pathologist before the American College of Surgeons required pathologic examination of all surgical specimens.

Advances were also being made in the administration of anesthesia. In 1905, 225 surgical cases were given anesthesia at Dr. Abbott's hospital. Ether was the main anesthetic, followed by nitrous oxide (laughing gas). Subsequently nitrous oxide was used initially and followed by ether and oxygen.

During his long career in medicine, Dr. Abbott established the Minnesota Pathological Society and held leadership positions in the Hennepin County Medical Society, Minnesota State Medical Society, the Academy of Medicine, and the Western Surgical Association. He was also the first delegate to the first House of Delegates of the American Medical Association, where he was a Fellow.

Dr. Abbott left a legacy as a surgeon as well. The pediatric surgical problem that most interested him was intussusception of the bowel. This is the telescoping of one section of the bowel into a contiguous section, thus causing constriction and/or obstruction. In December 1915, he presented a paper to the Western Surgical Association concerning his research into the problem in young children. His paper was entitled "Early Diagnosis of Intussusception in Children under Three Years of Age." Five operations had been performed by other surgeons, and seven cases had been diagnosed and treated by Dr. Abbott. Forty years previously, an eminent surgeon in London had diagnosed only five cases of intussusception among 40,000 sick children. In a children's hospital in an eastern city of the United States, only 27 cases were recognized in the previous seventeen years.

Of the 12 cases presented by Dr. Abbott, nine children were in their first year of life. In 10 of the cases, the diagnosis had been made or confirmed by Dr. J. P. Sedgwick, Professor of Pediatrics at the University of Minnesota or by his colleague, Dr. F. C. Rodda. And of the 12 cases, eight recovered.

Susan Holmes

Susan Holmes, the "Angel of Abbott," was born in Green Bay, Wisconsin. She trained at St. Luke's Hospital in Chicago where one of her sisters had also been trained. Another sister lived in Minneapolis, and Susan decided to join her. In 1903, she accepted Dr. Abbott's invitation to run the nursing school at Abbott Hospital. She stayed for 42 years, until 1945.

In 1927, after Dr. Abbott died, she suggested that a Ladies Auxiliary be formed. It would have strong ties to Westminster Church and would invite church members to join. The Auxiliary quickly became the backbone of Abbott Hospital. They raised money for equipment as well as for scholarships for nursing students. When the Wyman Wing of the hospital was built and opened in 1938, the Auxiliary provided the funds to furnish it. Mrs. Henry Doerr, whose son was born at Abbott Hospital and had been delivered by Dr. Abbott, was a member of the Auxiliary. Eventually, Mr. Doerr would become chair of the Board of Trustees of Abbott Northwestern Hospital.

The [Ladies] Auxiliary quickly became the backbone of Abbott Hospital. They raised money for equipment as well as for scholarships for nursing students.

Abbott Surgical Hospital and an Expanding Mission

At the turn of the century, Mrs. Kate Dunwoody, the wife of Mr. William Dunwoody, underwent a surgical procedure in Philadelphia that was not successful. Dr. Abbott became her physician in Minneapolis and was able to obtain a more successful surgical result. The Dunwoody's were very grateful.

To show their appreciation, Kate and William Dunwoody offered to build Dr. Abbott a new hospital at a cost of $100,000. Ground was broken for the Abbott Surgical Hospital in 1910 at 1717 First Avenue South. Completed the next year, it had 35 beds, 12 student nurses, and an apartment for Susan Holmes, the Superintendent. The hospital was built to be fireproof at Mr. Dunwoody's insistence. There was one operating room with a preoperative sterilization room, a doctor's dressing room, a cystoscopy room (for examination of the bladder), and a laboratory. The obstetrical department consisted of four rooms, and there was a four-bed pediatric section. The delivery of babies in a hospital was a relatively new concept.

The new Abbott Hospital was a state-of-the-art facility, and the small scale allowed Dr. Abbott to monitor all of the patients. Communal wards, with their lack of privacy and high potential for transmission of communicable disease, were banished and replaced by single- and double-occupancy rooms. The new

The new Abbott Hospital was a state-of-the-art facility, and the small scale allowed Dr. Abbott to monitor all of his patients. Communal wards, with their lack of privacy and high potential for transmission of communicable disease, were banished and replaced by single- and double-occupancy rooms.

structure had a wing named after Mr. Dunwoody, who had been a member of the Board of Trustees of Westminster Church for 37 years.

Mr. Dunwoody was an officer in the Washburn-Crosby Company, a company involved in the milling industry. In addition to building a hospital for Dr. Abbott, he also donated $100,000 to build the Minneapolis Institute of Arts. At the time of his death, he gave $1 million to the Institute for the purchase of works of art. He also left $100,000 to Westminster Church to be used to support Abbott Hospital.

In 1914, when Dr. Abbott was 70, a plan was devised so that, upon the death of Dr. Abbott, the hospital would become the property of Westminster Presbyterian Church, one of the largest Presbyterian congregations in the nation. Until then, the church had leased the property and equipment to Dr. Abbott, who continued to manage the operation, pay its taxes, assessments, and insurance. William Dunwoody's will specified that the church's Board of Trustees was to own and govern Abbott Surgical Hospital.

Since Dr. Abbott was on the teaching staff at the University of Minnesota Medical School, he was able to invite the best students to join the medical staff of Abbott Hospital. When Dr. Abbott died, the medical staff drew up a set of bylaws outlining qualifications for admission to the medical staff. The executive committee of the Medical Staff and the hospital committee of Westminster Church began to meet six times a year.

Setting Standards

The American College of Surgeons was created in 1912 in an attempt to standardize hospital practices. The organizing committee consisted of a dozen men, including Dr. William Mayo of Rochester, Minnesota. Many of the nation's most prominent surgeons were invited to Washington, D.C., in May 1913 for an initial meeting. Included in the list were Dr. Abbott and two other physicians from the Twin Cities: Dr. Archibald MacLaren from St. Paul and Dr. James E. Moore from Minneapolis.

An applicant to the College had to submit the medical records of 100 procedures he had performed "as evidence of his surgical judgment and technical ability." This quickly exposed the fact that many hospitals had inadequate record keeping and lacked adequate laboratories and X-ray departments, as well as other diagnostic and therapeutic facilities. After evaluating the best hospital practices, the College launched the Hospital Standardization program in 1918. This set minimum standards requiring each hospital to have an organized, competent, and ethical medical staff. Physicians would hold regular conferences to review clinical work, prohibit fee splitting, and maintain accurate and complete medical records on all treated patients, including adequate clinical, laboratory, and X-ray records.

In June 1919, Dr. Abbott reported to the Westminster Trustees that the demand for obstetric and pediatric beds had increased. "Certain parties" were interested in building a children's facility adjacent to the hospital. The new wing became a reality at the Westminster Church's Board of Trustees meeting in September 1919, when one of its members, Mr. Thomas B. Janney, announced that he would fund the new addition. Estimates of the size of his donation range from $200,000 to $330,000. Mr. Janney was a founder of the Janney, Semple, Hill Company, one of the largest wholesale hardware firms in the northwest. He had also been the president of the Farmers and Mechanics Savings Bank and a director of Northwestern National Bank.

When the new Janney Pavilion opened in 1920, Abbott Hospital had a capacity of 100 beds. It also attracted physicians who were practicing the new specialty of pediatrics. In the pediatric wing, examination rooms, reception areas, and private rooms were arranged so that children would not come in contact with each other. Isolation rooms were provided for those patients with communicable diseases. Every room had hot and cold water as well as bathtubs. This was a radical change from the typical hospital where sick children were crowded together in open wards, and the mortality rates from communicable infections were "disgracefully high." Special accommodations were also created to allow mothers to be with their children. In 1897, a state-supported hospital for children with physical abnormalities (now Gillette Hospital in St. Paul) had been built. However, the pediatric wing at Abbott Hospital was the first hospital built in the Twin Cities specifically dedicated to treating children with general illnesses; Children's Hospital in St. Paul wasn't built until 1923.

The previous administration of the hospital had not kept accurate business records, and there was no one skilled in business administration. In 1922, the

The pediatric wing at Abbott Hospital was the first hospital built in the Twin Cities specifically dedicated to treating children with general illnesses.

The next addition to Abbott Hospital was the Wyman addition, built in 1936... The hospital capacity rose to 160 beds, and the new addition included four operating rooms, an X-ray lab and other laboratories, as well as administrative and staff space, a new kitchen, and dining rooms for the entire hospital.

Westminster Hospital Committee installed a committee to provide a proper set of bookkeeping and administrative personnel and procedures. The management of the hospital was handed over to a committee of doctors and administrators. Dr. Abbott was named Chief of Staff in June 1925. He remained in that role until his death in February 1927 at the age of 83.

The next addition to Abbott Hospital was the Wyman addition, built in 1936. It was named after its major donor, Mr. Oliver C. Wyman, a neighbor of Mr. Janney. Mr. Wyman was president of a wholesale dry goods company, Wyman, Partridge and Company. He was also chair of the Board of Directors at Northwestern National Bank, as well as Vice President and Trustee at the Farmers and Mechanics Savings Bank. When he died in 1923, he left $500,000 to the Trustees of Westminster Church to be used at their discretion for the erection of a General Hospital to be connected to the current Abbott Hospital.

The original proposal was supposed to bring Abbott Hospital to a capacity of 200 to 250 beds by 1927. However, the hospital had financial difficulties in establishing the addition. At that time, there was an excess number of hospital beds in Minneapolis, which meant that Abbott Hospital was only half to two-thirds occupied with patients. The building of the addition was postponed. In 1928, the situation was reviewed and the estimated cost of the building was determined to be greater than the $500,000, so it was further delayed. By 1930, the building costs were down, but the Wyman heirs instituted a lawsuit to regain the $500,000. The Minnesota Supreme Court finally settled it in favor of the hospital in 1936.

New architectural plans were needed and would incur more costs. Fortunately, the original funds had grown to $638,000. The building was finally ready for occupancy in 1938. The hospital capacity rose to 160 beds, and the new addition included four operating rooms, an X-ray lab and other laboratories, as well as administrative and staff space, a new kitchen, and dining rooms for the entire hospital.

Hospital Insurance

A hospital insurance plan was first developed in New Jersey, but soon after one was established in St. Paul. The name "Blue Cross" was created in Minnesota in 1933, copyrighted, and loaned to the American Hospital Association for use by other states. Initially, Minnesota couldn't make it work. The company was about to fold when administrators from Abbott and Fairview Hospitals set up the plan on a non-profit basis.

While physicians were concerned that it would lead to socialized medicine, the Minneapolis Hospital Association recommended hospitalization insurance for employed people in December 1934. A weekly premium of 72 cents provided three weeks of hospitalization per year and a 25 percent discount on the hospital bills of all dependents. In February 1935, the Westminster Church Board of Trustees agreed to join the plan. By September, area hospitals could see the results, both in an increase in the number of patients and in an improved bottom line.

Nursing, and the Changes Brought by World War II

The first school of nursing in Minneapolis was opened by Northwestern Hospital in 1882. In 1898, nine Minneapolis and St. Paul nurses filed articles of incorporation, becoming the first official registry of nurses in the U.S. Abbott Hospital also provided for the training of nurses. In 1904, the first student completed her full two-year nursing training. When the hospital needed more nurses, they took in more students. Each woman graduated two years from the date she entered, after having passed an examination. By 1907, the Minnesota legislature had established a Board of Nurses' Examiners to determine qualifications for registered nurses – a three-year course in an approved school of nursing.

The Abbott School of Nursing was accredited in 1916. Once the Depression struck in the 1930s, hospital occupancy declined, and there was an excess of nurses. This ended dramatically on December 7, 1941. The armed forces called for nurses!

Thousands of nurses answered the call. In 1943, Congress formed the Cadet Nurse Corps. This doubled the number of high school graduates entering the nursing profession. From 1943 through 1945, 169,443 students enrolled in the Cadet Nurse Corps. After the war, the transition from a government-financed

In 1898, nine Minneapolis and St. Paul nurses filed articles of incorporation, becoming the first official registry of nurses in the U.S. Abbott Hospital also provided for the training of nurses.

By 1955, Abbott Hospital had established an association with Macalester College in St. Paul, in addition to previous associations with the nursing schools connected with St. Barnabas and Northwestern Hospitals... The Abbott School of Nursing had graduated approximately 1,600 nurses over the previous seven decades.

nursing program to a family-financed nursing program cut the number of new students to less than half of those needed.

One way of increasing the number of Abbott nursing students was to establish two $400 scholarships and a loan fund of $1,500, from which second- and third-year students could borrow as much as $200 to complete their training. The hospital also hired aides for non-professional hospital tasks such as scrubbing floors and cleaning.

By 1955, Abbott Hospital had established an association with Macalester College in St. Paul, in addition to previous associations with the nursing schools connected with Saint Barnabas and Northwestern hospitals. (The head minister of Westminster Presbyterian Church, Dr. Arnold H. Lowe, was the chair of the Macalester's Board of Directors.) The Abbott School of Nursing had graduated approximately 1,600 nurses over the previous seven decades. When combined with other schools, the number of graduates grew to 5,000.

One of the contributions to medicine during WWII was the discovery and use of antibiotics. In 1944, Abbott Hospital was approved as a civilian penicillin depot with an initial order of 10 million units. Another change during the war years occurred when all local hospitals signed their first contract with a labor union, though the first citywide strike did not occur until 1951.

Sister Kenny

Sister Elizabeth Kenny, a nurse from Australia, developed a new way to treat polio patients and eventually brought that treatment to the United States. She went first to Johns Hopkins Hospital to provide her services. However, they did not accept her. She then went to the Mayo Clinic and the University of Minnesota Hospitals, looking for an institution where she could apply her treatment principles. She came to the attention of Dr. John Pohl. Dr. Pohl, who was interested in pediatric orthopedics, had attended the University of Minnesota Medical School, graduating in 1929. He took the postgraduate training at Harvard's Postgraduate School of Orthopedics, and had his graduate residency at Massachusetts General Hospital and Children's Hospital in Boston from 1933 to 1935. He then practiced medicine at the University of Manchester Royal Infirmary Hospital in Manchester, England.

Dr. Pohl moved to Austria, where he practiced at the Vienna Clinic, before returning to Minneapolis. He was admitting patients to the Janney Children's Pavilion at Abbott Hospital, when, in 1940, he started to use Sister Kenny as his therapist, overcoming resistance by the medical staff. Sister Kenny demonstrated improvement in polio victims using her techniques. As a result, children came from all over the country to be treated by Sister Kenny. She eventually shifted her unit to Minneapolis General Hospital and then to the Sister Kenny Institute, before it merged with Northwestern Hospital. Ultimately, the Sister Kenny Institute became part of Abbott Northwestern Hospital.

Post-war Years

Following World War II, Dr. R.W. Koucky, a pathologist at Abbott Hospital, felt that the hospital had not been serving its patients well in administering blood transfusions. No one hospital could maintain a large enough blood bank to take care of all its needs. The only answer to this problem would be a citywide blood bank to serve all the private hospitals. Giving blood transfusions to surgical patients had not been common before World War II, but it was becoming increasingly common in the 1940s. As a result, much needed to be learned about blood types and the Rh factor.

The blood banks operated by the Red Cross during the war had stimulated public interest in blood transfusions. In 1941, the Hennepin County Medical Society realized the need for a blood bank. By 1945, the idea had progressed to the point that the Minneapolis Hospital Council appointed Mr. Anderson, the Abbott Hospital administrator, and Dr. Koucky to visit community blood banks throughout the nation. As a result of those visits, the two gentlemen approached the Junior Chamber of Commerce with a recommendation that a blood bank be created and dedicated as a memorial to those who had died in World War II. The Chamber raised $76,000, which allowed them to purchase and equip the needed building. They named the institution the "War Memorial Blood Bank." Within eight years, it had outgrown its original facility and was moved to larger quarters.

In 1954, a United Hospital Fund Drive in the metropolitan area raised $17 million. It was directed by George D. Dayton and subsequently Henry

Sister Kenny demonstrated improvement in polio victims using her techniques. As a result, children came from all over the country to be treated by Sister Kenny.

In 1941, Abbott Hospital had 175 employees and 42,000 patient days. By 1965, the hospital had grown to 350 beds, 647 employees, and 113,353 patient days.

Kingman. Abbott Hospital received a share of these funds and was also given $65,000 by the Ford Foundation. In addition, they secured a loan from Westminster Church that allowed the hospital to open the Stevens Wing, adding another 75 beds. A nursing home contiguous to Abbott Hospital was purchased in 1963 and named the Bushnell Building, after a former minister of Westminster Church.

In 1941, Abbott Hospital had 175 employees and 42,000 patient days. By 1965, the hospital had grown to 350 beds, 647 employees, and 113,353 patient days. Mr. Robert Millar, the CEO of Abbott Hospital, wrote to the Chair of the Board of Trustees, Mr. Conley Brooks, that it was becoming increasingly difficult for the medical staff to admit all of their patients to Abbott Hospital. On occasion, it was necessary to refer some of their patients to other hospitals around town. Mr. Millar was recommending that they stop the modernization of the hospital and instead increase the number of beds available.

At the same time, Northwestern Hospital had opened a new wing. During the construction of that wing, some of Northwestern's physicians admitted their patients to Abbott Hospital. Now those admissions would be shifted back to Northwestern. The two hospitals grew and eventually grew together, becoming Abbott Northwestern Hospital when they merged in 1970.

The history of this merger will be discussed in detail in Chapter 4 (*Two Great Hospitals Merge*).

2

The History of Northwestern Hospital
Part 1, 1882-1960

Harriet Granger Walker, the founder of Northwestern Hospital, was born on September 10, 1841. Her grandfather had played a distinguished role in the Revolutionary War at the battle of Bunker Hill. She attended Baldwin University, along with Thomas B. Walker, whom she married on December 19, 1863.

Thomas Walker was a traveling salesman impressed with the business opportunities in the West in general and Minneapolis in particular. He joined the government surveying party in northern and western Minnesota, which led to purchasing timberland and building a lumber mill. He eventually extended his lumber interests to California, becoming one of the largest individual owners of timber property in the United States.

Thomas Walker was active in virtually every movement promoting the welfare and growth of Minneapolis. He partnered with Mr. Levi Butler to form the Butler Brothers Company, a wholesale retail business. (Its original building still exists.) He was on the Board of Managers of the State Reform School, created the Minneapolis Public Library, and supported an art school as well as the YMCA. He was president of the Minnesota Academy of Science and developed the T. S. Walker Art Museum.

Harriet and Thomas Walker had six sons and two daughters. The last son was born in 1882

Mrs. Walker invited 44 socially prominent women living in Minneapolis to a "tea." They soon found out that the "tea" was actually a fundraising event. They were all introduced to the concept of starting a charity hospital to care for women, children, and the poor.

when Harriet was 42. That son, Archie, would play a role in the development of Northwestern Hospital and Abbott Northwestern Hospital for the rest of his life.

Archie Walker's birth was attended by Dr. Mary Hood. Dr. Hood had been trained at the Woman's Medical College of Pennsylvania. Shortly after the birth, Harriet Walker and Dr. Hood had a conversation about the poverty and disease that women and children faced every day. Following that conversation, Mrs. Walker invited 44 socially prominent women living in Minneapolis to a "tea." They soon found out that the "tea" was actually a fundraising event. They were all introduced to the concept of starting a charity hospital to care for women, children, and the poor.

Dr. Hood's colleague, Dr. Mary Whetstone, joined in the presentation. Finding the group to be receptive to the idea of creating a hospital, they formed a committee. The minutes of the first meeting on November 3,1882, report that they quickly agreed to become an organization, charitable in nature, to provide care for indigent women and children. This would also include the training of nurses. The first officers elected were President, Mrs. Harriet G. Walker; Vice Presidents, Mrs. Thomas Lowry, Mrs. Lindley, and Mrs. Wolff; Secretary, Mrs. Moses Marston; and Treasurer, Mrs. D. L. Kiehl. Harriet Walker was President from 1882 until 1917, the year of her death.

At that first meeting in 1882, 63 members and three honorary members were elected to the Board of Directors. After considerable discussion, they decided to name the new building "Northwestern Hospital for Women and Children." Within ten days, the House Committee had rented a house that could accommodate 10 patients on 25th Street and 4th Avenue for $25 per month. By the end of November, they had collected $120 to start furnishing the building. Early in December 1882, the hospital was open for business.

The staff consisted of Dr. Mary Hood and Dr. Mary Whetstone, along with two nurses and a house cleaner. The health care was patterned after the Woman's Medical College of Pennsylvania, of which Dr. Hood was an alumnus. The Board placed top priority on those patients who had little or no money to pay for their care. Of the first 97 patients, 74 were "free."

To support their charity work, Board members and others financed free beds by each paying $250 a year into the operating fund. In 1883, $167.17 was nearly enough to run the entire hospital for one month. Apparently, the financial existence of the hospital was a constant struggle. Their system seemed to be that, when faced with a deficit, the Board would either dip into their own pockets to satisfy their creditors or solicit their friends and even the tradespeople of the city, who would reduce their bills.

The original structure was quickly overwhelmed, and the hospital was moved in 1883 to a house on Clinton Avenue at a cost of $3,000. By 1884, the hospital had 50 beds and admitted 160 patients. This facility also quickly proved to be too limited in space, and they sought another solution. Mr. L. M. Stewart donated property on 27th Street and Chicago Avenue valued at $10,000. After months of struggling to raise the necessary funds, the building was renovated for $36,000. The Board had their first meeting in the new building on May 5, 1887, but the continuing need for more space required future additions. Electricity was added in 1900.

After World War I, the articles of incorporation were changed to admit both sexes as patients. This was necessary because of returning veterans who had been wounded and needed care. As a result, the hospital was renamed "Northwestern Hospital." Consistent with these changes, the all-woman Board of Trustees authorized the appointment of a Men's Advisory Committee in 1923. Up until that time, when the Board needed an opinion having to do with legal and/or financial matters, they would consult their husbands or confer with male business leaders. The members of the Men's Advisory Committee were appointed for a term of one year. The governing structure remained in place until 1967, when the Board of Trustees, in response to a request from the Medical Staff, voted to invite males onto the Board as full voting members.

At its 50th anniversary in 1932, many of the original founders were gone, but their daughters and daughters-in-law had followed the tradition of giving of their time, talents, and money. The progress that had been made was celebrated at the annual tea.

- Despite the Depression, Northwestern Hospital was worth a million dollars and could care for 200 or more patients at a time
- The staff of physicians numbered 30
- The Medical Staff included 81 student nurses and 16 graduate nurses

The Board placed top priority on those patients who had little or no money to pay for their care. Of the first 97 patients, 74 were "free."

...when the Board needed an opinion having to do with legal and/or financial matters, they would consult their husbands or confer with male business leaders... The governing structure remained in place until 1967, when the Board of Trustees, in response to a request from the Medical Staff, voted to invite males onto the Board as full voting members.

Overcrowding continued and in 1941 the Board raised $500,000 to erect the west wing and modernize the central pavilion. A thoroughly modern facility for the time, it actually cost $650,000, and had a capacity of 265 beds. By this time, the hospital could no longer be a charity hospital, and patients were asked to cover at least part of the cost of their care. The need to expand continued into the time when Stanley Nelson was hired as administrator of Northwestern Hospital in 1960.

After World War II, health care facilities received more attention because of the need to care for veterans. Government funds were allocated to ensure improved access. Technological advances were occurring in cardiovascular and pulmonary techniques, better diagnostic methods, and extended care for critically ill patients. In 1953, Northwestern Hospital completed the Memorial Pavilion, which included a post-anesthesia recovery room, expanded physical therapy facilities, a new classroom, and an electrocardiograph machine. The next year, because of a severe shortage of hospital beds in the Minneapolis-St. Paul area, a United Hospital Fund Drive was organized and raised $17 million, a portion of which went to Northwestern Hospital.

Woman's Auxiliary Northwestern Hospital

The Woman's Auxiliary was formed at Northwestern Hospital beginning in 1955. Its purpose was three-fold: Give service to Northwestern Hospital through volunteer work, raise money, and promote good public relations. Initially, there were 50 members, but as reported by Jean Krogness, President of the Auxiliary in 1966 and 1967, it grew to 150 members. These volunteers had multiple responsibilities. They staffed the information desk at the entrance to the hospital every day except Saturday. They greeted patients and/or their families, answered the telephone, sorted and delivered mail and flowers, took patients to their rooms, oversaw children in the lobby, and answered general questions. They ran the gift shop five days a week and thus raised $10,355 in 1966. One of the volunteers became the Pediatric Play Lady assisting in the recovery of children. They provided special services to patients such as distributing books to patients via the library cart, providing diaper services, and taking pictures of babies. In 1966 the latter service earned $1,205 for the hospital. These women also assisted in surgical suites, physical therapy, and the laboratory. They also developed the Candy Stripe Program, which consisted of teenage girls assisting patients. There were 85 candy stripers working in two shifts in the hospital in 12 different areas. This was the first such program in Minneapolis. The Auxiliary also put on a Candle Light Ball at the Sheraton Ritz yearly. In 1966 they raised $8,846. The total amount of money that the Auxiliary raised in 1966 was $20,416. This was donated to the Medical Education Fund. They also donated $600 to the Student Nurses Scholarship Fund. They were successful in promoting good relations between themselves, the medical staff, administration, board of trustees, nurses, and the public.

3

Principals and Principles
Visionary Administrators
Stanley Nelson

The history of Northwestern Hospital, Abbott Hospital, and eventually Abbott Northwestern Hospital, involves the role of innovative administrators after World War II. The first of these remarkable individuals was Stanley Nelson. After earning a Master's of Hospital Administration degree at the University of Minnesota in 1954, he became the administrator of a hospital in Fort Wayne, Indiana, at the age of 28. In 1961, he was hired as the administrator of Northwestern Hospital, and the next year, he hired Scott Parker as an Assistant Administrator. Mr. Parker left Northwestern Hospital in 1967 to serve as the CEO of hospitals in Arizona and California, prior to becoming the CEO of Intermountain Health Care in Utah. Mr. Nelson then hired Gordon Sprenger as Assistant Administrator. He, like Stan Nelson and Scott Parker, had also earned a Master's of Hospital Administration degree at the University of Minnesota.

Once Stanley Nelson was on board, he began a building program that took five years to complete. The older part of the hospital was renovated, and the entire hospital was air-conditioned. This was accomplished without any adverse effect on the bottom line or the delivery of health care. In 1962, he petitioned the City of Minneapolis to close part of Elliot Avenue to allow Northwestern Hospital to expand. Once the re-zoning was allowed, the Board

Northwestern Hospital was developing its medical staff with increasing specialization in the 1960s. As a result, it was perceived that the hospital should develop an educational program and research facilities.

of Trustees gave him the right to purchase the homes on the nearby avenues, i.e., Elliot, Chicago, and Tenth, as they became available. Eventually this would cost the hospital $500,000.

With the establishment of an on-campus nursing school being planned, there was a need for a new nurses' residence. The funds – $750,000 – were approved in 1962. This satisfied the needs of the hospital until the proposed merger with Sister Kenny Institute in 1975.

Northwestern Hospital was developing its medical staff with increasing specialization in the 1960s. As a result, it was perceived that the hospital should develop an educational program and research facilities. In a meeting of the Board of Trustees in March 1961, Board member Anne Hull (Mrs. Hadlai Hull) reported on an article in *Consumer Reports* from February 1961, concerning the quality of care administered in hospitals.

"One can go beyond the numerous accreditations in judging the quality of a hospital by asking a second question: Does it have a formal program for the training of medical personnel? The higher the level of teaching, the more likely the hospital is to provide good medical service. The best indication of a good teaching program is having an affiliation with a medical school. Hospitals with such affiliation are likely to have the services of qualified family doctors and specialists in all available fields as needed. They often have full-time physicians in charge of key departments. As a result they attract many of the best young physicians who want residency training in the specialties. Such surroundings also are likely to bring out the best in practicing family doctors currently affiliated with that hospital. Only 229 hospitals in the entire country have such affiliations, however, and they are concentrated near the 85 medical schools currently in existence. Consequently, most consumers do not have access to such a hospital. But the consumers can get somewhat similar benefits from a hospital approved for residency training in at least the four major specialties fields: Obstetrics and Gynecology, Internal Medicine, Surgery, and Pediatrics."

In 1962-63, Northwestern Hospital had participated in the Matching Program in an attempt to obtain medical school graduates to serve as interns and residents. In this system, graduates ranked the hospitals where they had applied for further training in the order in which they valued them. Similarly, the hospitals listed the candidates they had interviewed in the order of preference. However, Northwestern Hospital had not received any candidates that year, which meant that in 1962, the hospital would have only two residents and one intern. As a result, Dr. Mark Hanson stressed the need to establish a relationship with a medical school.

Stan Nelson contacted 12 medical schools in an attempt to understand just how such a program would work. Dr. David Hickok and Virginia Piper visited Evanston Hospital in Chicago to see how their program with Northwestern University Medical School was working. They realized that a research facility would cost $200,000. A full-scale medical education program would cost $50,000 in 1964, $100,000 in 1965, and $137,000 in 1966.

In order to have a relationship with the University of Minnesota Medical School, the Hospital was required to fund a Professorial Chair at the Medical School. This professor would spend all of his or her time at Northwestern Hospital. The financial commitment for funding the Chair was $500,000.

In July 1964, Archie Walker pledged $250,000 as an initial step to fund such a Chair. In making this pledge, Mr. Walker requested that the Hospital contribute a matching amount. This was accomplished and duly reported to Mr. Walker in August 1965. Virginia Piper and the Board, along with one member of the Men's Advisory Committee and a member of the Medical Staff, called on potential donors. They raised three million dollars to endow the educational program. Mr. and Mrs. Archie Walker gave an additional $250,000.

The Medical Education Program would cost $300,000 annually. To meet those costs, $100,000 would come from annual giving, $100,000 from the hospital operating funds, and $100,000 from the endowment income. (The Medical Education and Research Facility, initially estimated to cost $200,000, actually cost $850,000.)

In May 1963, the hospital began seeking a full-time Medical Director. Dr. Cecil J. Watson, the Chief of Medicine at the University of Minnesota Medical School, was scheduled to retire and was interested in the new professor position

Virginia Piper and the Board, along with one member of the Men's Advisory Committee and a member of the Medical Staff, called on potential donors. They raised three million dollars to endow the educational program.

The program was scheduled to have six medical internships and six residents in Internal Medicine. The goal was to provide a teaching program that included continuous medical education for medical students, house staff, and practicing specialists.

at Northwestern Hospital. The University of Minnesota Medical School also needed additional hospitals to which to send their medical students for further training.

The Board of Regents at the University of Minnesota voted in January 1965 to approve the affiliation of Northwestern Hospital and the U of M Medical School. As a result, Dr. Watson was hired in July as Medical Director at Northwestern Hospital at a salary of $35,000. He established the teaching program on July 1, 1966. In addition to Dr. Watson, a Chief Resident, Dr. Vince Fromke, as well as an assistant and a secretary were hired, and the program began.

The program was scheduled to have six medical internships and six residents in Internal Medicine. The goal was to provide a teaching program that included continuous medical education for medical students, house staff, and practicing specialists. This required a free bed unit of 30 medical and 20 surgical beds plus outpatient facilities. In addition, the Hospital planned an educational facility with office space for 20 faculty members, a seminar room for 25 people, an auditorium seating 250 people, laboratory space, a library, and a meeting room for in-service education.

Dr. Watson, who had a national and international reputation in Internal Medicine, gained initial accreditation for the new internship/residency program from the American Medical Association. The full story of the residency program is told in Part II (Medical Education Program).

An indication of the foresight of Stan Nelson is encapsulated in an annual report Nelson gave to the Board of Trustees in April 1966. He warned the Board that, "in a growing, dynamic industry such as ours, one is never done. Change is the only constant factor.... We are no longer an autonomous, independent organization. Rather, we are now a hospital which is to become a system." The national Medicare program was to begin in July 1966. Those who were responsible for running health care facilities had to consider what changes were needed in response. Mr. Nelson went on to summarize an article authored by Dr. Ward Daley and published in the April 18, 1966 issue of the *Journal of the American Medical Association*. In the article, Dr. Daley predicted imminent changes in the health care system to include increasing knowledge, specialization, and institutionalization, as well as complexities in data processing and communication. In addition, demand for services, and their costs, was on the rise, and there was a shortage of personnel to address all of these changes.

Up to that time, many Americans had enjoyed discounts in health care, with the prime example being the Salk vaccine for preventing poliomyelitis. Contracting polio meant years of physical therapy, as well as varying degrees of disability. The Salk vaccine eliminated a significant medical cost to society. Stanley Nelson predicted that in the future the advances in medicine were going to come at a tremendous cost and would benefit relatively few. He thought this trend would drive hospitals together in order to accomplish those things of which they were most capable. He further stated that "the nature of hospital economics is much like a vice, where the pressure of increased costs through the demand for new and improved services and more equitable pay for our employees comes against the ability of the hospital to provide added income."

In closing, Mr. Nelson noted that, "The hospital had made significant progress toward meeting their goals in medical education. Continuing down that path was going to be demanding and expensive and not without problems." He also predicted that expanding the Medical Education program at Northwestern Hospital "was rewarding and worth the price."

In the Minneapolis/St. Paul area, philanthropic giving to health care was not very prominent or successful at that time. At the Board meeting in April 1966, Mr. Nelson thanked Virginia Piper, Chairman of the Board of Trustees, and her husband Harry C. Piper, Jr., for leading the effort to dramatically improve the endowment of the hospital. He reported that, "The amount of endowment funds raised this past year exceeded the total of endowment funds raised in the previous 80 years!"

After successfully managing the merger between Abbott and Northwestern hospitals in 1970, Stan Nelson resigned as CEO of Abbott Northwestern Hospital to become the CEO of the Henry Ford Hospital in Detroit, Michigan. While in that position, he created the Henry Ford Health System, one of the first vertically integrated health care systems in the nation. He founded and directed the Voluntary Hospitals of America from 1977 to 1981. The hospital members as a group were able to bargain for and purchase capital equipment in a more efficient and less costly manner than had been possible previously. He was named Chairman of the American Hospital Association in 1982.

"...in a growing, dynamic industry such as ours, one is never done. Change is the only constant factor.... We are no longer an autonomous, independent organization. Rather, we are now a hospital which is to become a system."
—Stan Nelson

Mr. Sprenger was instrumental in bringing some of the techniques being used in the Intermountain Health Care System to Abbott Northwestern Hospital. This allowed and encouraged physicians to better evaluate the process and results of treatment programs, demonstrating the impact on outcomes and costs.

Scott Parker

Scott Parker, after serving as Assistant Administrator at Northwestern Hospital, was the CEO of Intermountain Health Care centered in Salt Lake City, Utah, where he also developed a vertically integrated health care system. His system was particularly innovative in improving the efficiency in data processing. Mr. Parker invited Gordon Sprenger to join his Board of Trustees.

As a result, Mr. Sprenger was instrumental in bringing some of the techniques being used in the Intermountain Health Care System to Abbott Northwestern Hospital. This allowed and encouraged physicians to better evaluate the process and results of treatment programs, demonstrating the impact on outcomes and costs. Having been part of that experience, I recall how painful that process was since it demonstrated both our strengths and our weaknesses in delivering care to our patients. Mr. Parker was also named as Chairman of the American Hospital Association in 1986, and subsequently Chairman of the International Hospital Federation.

Gordon Sprenger

Gordon Sprenger earned a Master's of Hospital Administration degree at the University of Minnesota in 1961. He had a hospital residency in Milwaukee, Wisconsin, and served three years in hospital administration while in the U.S. Air Force. He was hired by Stanley Nelson as Assistant Administrator of Northwestern Hospital in 1967, and served as President and CEO of Abbott Northwestern Hospital from 1971 to 1995.

At an Abbott Northwestern Board of Trustees meeting on November 30, 1972, the administrative team, under the leadership of Mr. Sprenger, made a presentation concerning their views of the future of health care. The independence of institutions involved in the health care industry was going to be diluted as government health care planning agencies assumed regulatory roles. At this time, 96 percent of the Medical Staff were practicing in specialties, which meant Abbott Northwestern Hospital was taking on the role of a regional health care center. It was possible that Abbott Northwestern would become the only private sector regional health care center in Hennepin County. The public sector health care centers were Hennepin County General Hospital and the University of Minnesota Hospital.

During the previous 10 years, the traditional metropolitan community health care system had been under attack. Some of the forces causing the health care delivery system to change were:

- Consumer participation
- Government intervention
- High cost of health care
- Comprehensiveness of care
- Increasing use of outpatient care
- Neighborhood health care
- Over-bedding in the center city
- Inaccessibility of doctors and hospitals due to population growth and expansion of suburbs
- Growth and sophistication of public hospitals and medical practice in general
- An expanded definition of health, and health care perceived as a right
- Quality of health care review
- Changes in reimbursement
- The growth of regulatory bodies

There were two basic alternatives for dealing with these forces: the community hospital system and the regional medical center.

The community hospital system, for example, Fairview Hospitals, consists of a network of related, geographically dispersed community hospitals. In the case of the Fairview system, it includes several suburban hospitals providing a variety of family-oriented services to the local community and a downtown hospital providing a moderate range of specialty services, as well as general services to the center city population.

Alternatively, the regional medical center would provide a full range of highly specialized medical, surgical, and rehabilitative services. Its medical staff would include specialty and subspecialty care. Frequently, members of the

Mr. Sprenger believed that Abbott Northwestern Hospital could not continue operating only as a community hospital in the center city of Minneapolis for the next 10-20 years.

medical staff of the regional medical center hold appointments on a medical school faculty. The regional medical center would have several of its own full-time physicians engaged in research. These research programs would be externally funded. The referral sources to such a center would be both regional and national.

Mr. Sprenger believed that Abbott Northwestern Hospital could not continue operating only as a community hospital in the center city of Minneapolis for the next 10-20 years. The difficulty of remaining a community hospital in the center city included the fact that primary care physicians needed to go to where the patients were, and the facilities in the center city were older and less modern compared to suburban hospitals. Finally, there were too many community hospitals in center city Minneapolis. If Abbott Northwestern Hospital was to remain a community hospital, it would have to relocate some of its assets to the suburbs, thus serving more than one geographic area. Abbott Northwestern would also have to recruit more primary care physicians rather than specialists. This would represent a change in the priorities of Abbott Northwestern Hospital.

The implications of becoming a regional medical center included:
- Developing financial resources other than patient income
- Emphasizing programs, equipment, education, and research
- Placing more full-time physicians on the house staff
- Developing clinics, as well as outstate and suburban hospitals, as resources for referral
- Operating without a major suburban hospital setting, due to lack of resources
- Developing a patient mix characterized by both more free care and more expensive care
- Risking alienating some physicians

The advantages of becoming a regional medical center included:
- Building existing medical staff
- Gaining partners nearby who could assist through their subspecialty expertise

- Developing a Board of Directors that would raise funds

- Acquiring a relationship with the University of Minnesota through specialists on staff at Abbott Northwestern who also held appointments at the University

- Channeling of future funding to Abbott Northwestern as a regional medical center

Once management decided to direct their efforts toward developing Abbott Northwestern as a regional medical center, their priorities would be to develop an effective organization that would permit Abbott Northwestern, Minneapolis Children's Hospital, and Sister Kenny Institute to become that regional medical center. Sister Kenny Institute had merged with the Abbott Northwestern Hospital Corporation and moved to the Northwestern campus in 1976. Abbott Northwestern had supported Minneapolis Children's Hospital for many years by providing food service, heat, and operating rooms.

The roles of the Abbott and Northwestern Divisions would have to be clarified. For the Abbott Division, the major priorities would include the development of general medical-surgical programs with an emphasis on community service, the development of the community mental health center, and community clinics in concert with the Minneapolis Age and Opportunity Center. This would focus on the development of services to senior citizens.

The Northwestern Division's priorities would include the development of general medical-surgical services with an emphasis on increasing specialization in certain areas, growth in medical education and research, the development of a center for alcoholic rehabilitation, and the development of an obstetrics high-risk unit to retain the corporation's obstetrical component. This would also include the development of a high-risk neonatal unit.

According to the minutes from the November 1972 meeting where these ideas were discussed, Board members were quite positive and even excited about the plans for the future. Some members of the medical staffs were more reserved and cautious.

Malpractice Insurance

At the Abbott Northwestern Hospital Board of Directors meeting on December 29, 1975, the issue of the hospital's malpractice insurance coverage was raised. The hospital had been covered by the Argonaut Insurance Company up to that time. However, malpractice insurance coverage for hospitals and physicians was becoming increasingly expensive and less available nationally. For typical coverage, Abbott Northwestern Hospital paid a premium of $88,000 in 1974. While the experience of the hospital in regard to medical malpractice had not changed, the insurance premium for 1975 rose to $425,000. The Hospital received notice that the premium to be paid in 1976 was increasing to $1,127,000!

The premium being requested had no relationship to Abbott Northwestern's actual experience. Having anticipated this, Mr. Sprenger explored the possibility of developing a captive insurance company. He had a sense of who the administrators of the well-run hospitals in the nation were. He invited Alan Hicks, an administrator in charge of a hospital in Indianapolis, to address the Abbott Northwestern Board. As a result of this presentation, Abbott Northwestern Hospital joined 34 other hospitals to form an insurance company called Multi-Hospital Mutual Insurance Company (MMI). To avoid restrictive – to the point of punitive – insurance industry regulations, the company was registered offshore in Bermuda.

Physicians practicing medicine in member hospitals were sometimes unable to obtain malpractice insurance coverage of any kind, thus leaving those hospitals with excessive risk. As a result, MMI eventually developed coverage for individual physicians. For political reasons, Bermuda did not want to have both components of MMI registered there, so the physician's coverage sector went to Grand Cayman.

Again, in response to restrictive policies the insurance industry lobbied to pass in the United States, offshore funds were invested through Lloyd's of London. MMI was in business "off shore" for at least 10 years. Eventually MMI purchased an insurance company in the United States and was able to operate onshore. At that point, the physician's insurance portion of the company was sold to the hospital portion of the company. Approximately 85 percent of the premium dollars that the physicians had paid for their malpractice insurance was returned to them. The hospital had had a similarly positive financial experience with MMI.

Physical Merger and Improvements
to the Abbott Northwestern Campus

Abbott and Northwestern hospitals had been merged into one corporation since 1970. The next step in the process was to join the two hospitals on one campus. This was accomplished a decade later when Abbott Hospital moved its operations to the Northwestern Hospital campus. The story of that process is told in Part 1, The Physical Merger of Abbott and Northwestern hospitals.

Once Abbott Northwestern merged onto one campus, it was time to address other problems. The area along Chicago Avenue had become a crime and drug scene. Absentee landlords, who paid little attention to their properties or the occupants, owned many of the houses along the west side of Chicago Avenue. With the consent of the Board of Trustees, the hospital purchased a number of those houses and sold them to owners who occupied the properties. The down payment was refunded if the owner lived in the house for seven years. The Honeywell Corporation, located in the same neighborhood, followed a similar strategy. Soon, the Wasie Center, an economy hotel that provided rooms to families receiving health care at the hospital, was built on the south end of the campus. Finally, a parking ramp was built to replace the surface lot.

Minneapolis Children's Hospital

Fundraising for Minneapolis Children's Hospital began in 1953. At the urging of the Minneapolis Junior League, the intention to build a children's hospital gained momentum. Many of the women behind this effort were the daughters of women who had participated on the Board of Trustees at Northwestern Hospital. Dr. Arnold Anderson, a pediatrician, was the first medical director. He was hired in 1967 as the CEO of Children's Hospital before the hospital was actually built. Dr. Anderson insisted on spending half of his time serving neighborhood children whose families couldn't afford health care and half of his time on administration. Ground was finally broken in 1969. Gordon Sprenger convinced the Board of Directors at Abbott Northwestern to close their pediatric services at both hospitals in February 1973. This made a

At the urging of the Minneapolis Junior League, the intention to build a children's hospital gained momentum. Many of the women behind this effort were the daughters of women who had participated on the Board of Trustees at Northwestern Hospital.

significant impact on Abbott Northwestern's bottom line but was crucial to the success of Children's Hospital. (Other hospitals in the community implied that they, too, would close their pediatric services, but it didn't happen.)

The hospital was built on the block just north of Northwestern Hospital. Abbott Northwestern Hospital continued to be supportive of Minneapolis Children's Hospital, supplying heat from the heating plant for 25 years and providing the food service. In the opinion of Gordon Sprenger, Northwestern Hospital wasn't "losing" their pediatric unit; it was just moving one block north.

Virginia Piper Cancer Institute

In October 1988, long-time Board member Virginia Piper died of pancreatic cancer. Gordon Sprenger discussed with her husband, Harry C. Piper Jr., the idea of a cancer institute at Abbott Northwestern Hospital to be called the Virginia Piper Cancer Institute (VPCI). Mr. Piper led the fundraising drive in 1989 and 1990, which was also the year of his death. He was assisted by Newell Weed and Bill George. Groundbreaking for VPCI was in 1992. (See Part II, Cancer Care.)

Growth and Expansion

Fulfilling Stanley Nelson's prediction in 1965, Mr. Sprenger continued the process of developing a hospital system built around Abbott Northwestern Hospital. He became President/CEO of LifeSpan in 1982, while serving simultaneously as President of Abbott Northwestern Hospital. Lifespan consisted of Abbott Northwestern Hospital, Eitel Hospital, and Sister Kenny Institute, and its mission was to develop a new regional health care center. This led to the creation of Healthspan in 1992. Healthspan was the merger of Lifespan and Health One, which had combined United Hospital in St. Paul, Unity Hospital in Fridley, and Mercy Hospital in Coon Rapids. Allina Health System was formed in 1994, the result of the merger of Healthspan and Medica, a health insurance company. At the time of its creation, Allina consisted of 12 hospitals and 69 clinics. Mr. Sprenger was President/CEO of Allina until 2002. He was named Chair of the American Hospital Association in 1996.

Robert Spinner

Robert Spinner succeeded Gordon Sprenger as President of Northwestern Hospital in 1984 and held that position for a decade. He had earned his Master's of Hospital Administration degree at the University of Minnesota and was hired as Assistant Administrator at Northwestern Hospital in 1968. He became Administrator of Abbott Northwestern Hospital in 1980, when George Adamovich was simultaneously named Administrator of Abbott Hospital. He retired as president of Allina Hospitals and Clinics in 2001.

While many of the policies, such as becoming a health system and increasing the specialization of the medical staff had already been determined, the execution fell to Mr. Spinner. The Abbott Northwestern campus needed to be enlarged, which meant that the remaining homes in the surrounding area needed to be purchased. This proved to be difficult since a number of the homeowners were reluctant to sell. Patience and diplomacy were required! The resulting additions included the Wasie building addition in 1982, the heliport in 1984, and the ambulatory center at the corner of 10th Avenue and 26th street. This center included an outpatient treatment center and day surgery center. In 1992, the Virginia Piper Cancer Institute was built above this structure. In 1994, more surgical suites were constructed in the basement level. In addition, the process of purchasing expensive technology was never-ending. Equipment such as the linear accelerator, which is used to treat cancer, continued to be purchased. The increasing demand for outpatient surgery, made possible by advancements in anesthesia, also required new facilities.

The talents of the administrators of Abbott Northwestern Hospital throughout its history have been crucial to its mission. Each made inventive and forward-thinking decisions. And each was able to communicate both the risks and benefits associated with making groundbreaking choices. Thus our administrators, along with the Boards of Trustees and the Medical Staff, moved Abbott Northwestern Hospital into the future.

4

Abbott Northwestern Hospital
Two Great Hospitals Merge
1960-1970

The 1960s brought a variety of discussions among hospitals in Minneapolis. Some were driven by an attempt to share the expenses involved in running a hospital, which opened the possibility of affiliations or mergers. Abbott Hospital explored affiliations with St. Barnabus and Swedish hospitals. These two facilities then merged and became the Metropolitan Medical Center (MMC). Prior to its closing, Mount Sinai Hospital, which opened in 1951, also became part of MMC. Finally MMC closed in 1991 and became part of Hennepin County Medical Center.

Minneapolis General Hospital became Hennepin County General Hospital in 1964 before becoming Hennepin County Medical Center in 1974. The Minneapolis Medical Center was formed in 1976, composed of Northwestern Hospital and Sister Kenny Institute. This entity also had limited affiliations with Lutheran Deaconess and Mount Sinai hospitals. Abbott also explored a relationship with St. Mary's Hospital, which eventually became associated with Fairview.

The ever-changing population pattern and the changing locations of physicians' offices in the metropolitan area drove the need for center-city hospitals to take advantage of clinical

The ever-changing population pattern and the changing locations of physicians' offices in the metropolitan area drove the need for center-city hospitals to take advantage of clinical service consolidation whenever possible.

service consolidation whenever possible. From 1958 to 1968 the number of physicians' offices being maintained in downtown Minneapolis had decreased from 485 to 430. During that same time, the number of physician offices in just the southern suburbs had grown from 194 to 397 — it more than doubled. The increase was significant, and identical, in the northern and western suburbs, from 102 physicians' offices in 1958 to 167 in 1968. In total, the increase of physicians moving their offices to the suburbs over the decade was 188 percent.

Prior to the merger of Abbott and Northwestern hospitals, the number of obstetrical deliveries at Abbott and Northwestern had decreased by approximately 50 percent. By consolidating the obstetrical services of the two hospitals, there could be better utilization of medical and nursing skills so important in maintaining high-quality service. Consolidation of services such as obstetrics, pediatrics, otolaryngology, psychiatry, ophthalmology, and orthopedics offered the best solution to assure quality care and preserve these services. In addition, consolidation of services would mean very significant economic savings.

Throughout the 1960s, Abbott and Northwestern hospitals met intermittently to discuss the possibilities. The two hospitals began to share expenses in running their laundries, in data collection (in its infancy by today's standards), as well as in purchasing departments. By November 1968, Abbott's medical staff included 182 active senior and associate members. Of these 182 physicians, 112 held appointments on the Northwestern Hospital staff. Of the 175 regular and associate members of Northwestern's medical staff, 102 physicians held a similar appointment at Abbott Hospital. In keeping with the remarkable comments by Stan Nelson to the Northwestern Hospital Board of Trustees in 1965 concerning the future of health care (see Principals and Principles), Abbott and Northwestern hospitals began in earnest to discuss the possibility of a merger. Initially this was to be a corporate merger as compared to a physical merger.

Robert Millar, President of Abbott Hospital, remarked that in the future a hospital with only 300 beds would not be able to afford the new equipment and technology that was coming on line. As discussions between Abbott and Northwestern hospitals progressed, this principle became more widely accepted. According to Gordon Sprenger, who eventually served as President and CEO of

Abbott Northwestern Hospital, the reason Abbott and Northwestern hospitals merged was due to the increasing sophistication of health care personnel.

Not everyone agreed with the concept of consolidating the two hospitals. However, it was not going to be possible to stay alive and well in the health care industry by maintaining small hospitals. Abbott Hospital had 321 beds while Northwestern Hospital had 400 beds and was in the process of adding 80 more. From time to time, some members of the Abbott Hospital medical staff tried to admit patients to other downtown hospitals and were not always able to do so because of their high occupancy.

Similarities in the composition of the Boards of Directors and medical staff, as well as similar management philosophies and organizational objectives increased the potential to combine the two hospitals. In November 1968, the Abbott Hospital Board of Directors authorized CEO and President Robert Millar to continue these exploratory discussions with Northwestern Hospital. The following is the record of the steps leading to the merger of the two hospitals:

1. February 22-April 2, 1969: Continued discussions by administrators and the chairs of the two respective Boards of Trustees.

2. May 3, 1969: First meeting of the Liaison Committee, members of the Boards of Trustees appointed to the Committee by the two hospitals, and including John Holden, Tom Crosby, Robert Brooks, Phillip Harris, Conley Brooks, and Robert Reeves. Also included was Robert Millar of Abbott Hospital, Mr. and Mrs. Harry C. Piper, Jr., Charles Bellows, Henry Doerr, and Thomas Reeves, as well as Stanley Nelson, the Chief Northwestern Hospital Administrator.

3. May 12, 1969: The second meeting of the Liaison Committee, which now included Drs. John Pewter, Ray Scallen, O. J. Campbell, and Bill Petersen from the Abbott Hospital medical staff, plus Drs. Dan Moos, Richard Tudor, Morris Rothnem, and William Stromme from the Northwestern Hospital medical staff.

4. May 13, 1969: Approval of the proposed merger by the Northwestern Medical Staff.

5. May 27, 1969: Approval of the proposed merger by the Abbott Hospital Board of Trustees.

6. May 29, 1969: Approval of the proposed merger by the Northwestern Hospital Board of Trustees.

7. June 3, 1969: Approval of the proposed merger by the Abbott Hospital Medical Staff.

8. October 23, 1969: Approval of the proposed merger by the Northwestern Hospital Corporation.

9. October 27, 1969: Approval of the proposed merger by the Abbott Hospital Corporation.

10. January 7, 1970: Agreement of the consolidation filed with the Minnesota Secretary of State.

The name of the new hospital and corporation was an issue. Virginia Piper described the possibilities as:

1. Abbott Northwestern because "A" came first in the alphabet.

2. Northwestern Abbott because Northwestern Hospital was the larger of the two.

The alphabet argument won out.

The new Abbott Northwestern Hospital Board included the President and immediate Past President of each medical staff. Conley Brooks was named Chairman of the new Board of Trustees, and Harry C. Piper, Jr. was named Chairman of the Executive Committee. Following a private discussion by Stan Nelson and Robert Millar, Stan Nelson was named President and Chief Executive Officer of the new Abbott Northwestern Hospital, while Robert Millar was named Executive Vice President and Associate Chief Executive Officer.

The initial Board of Directors was to be the combined Boards of the two hospitals. Each hospital would have an equal number of corporate members, board members, and principal officers. Since the entire congregation of Westminster Church were officially corporate members of Abbott Hospital, the church needed to make appropriate reductions in numbers to match the number of corporate members on the Northwestern Hospital side. This arrangement would create an unwieldy Board of Trustees of 76 members. It was further agreed that attrition would be permitted and necessary to achieve a workable board size, and as a result, an Executive Committee was elected consisting of 10 members from each hospital. After the first year, no attention would be paid to the hospital of origin in selecting people to serve as corporate or board members or in any other capacity in the corporation.

What were the forces driving these two institutions to a merger? The memo presented to the Board of Directors on January 30, 1969 included the following points. It was essential that:

1. Neither Abbott nor Northwestern would be required to abandon any of their existing programs or services.

2. The current expansion plans of each institution would be pursued with diligence. This included expanded parking and a doctors' office building on the Chicago Avenue site. It also included the possibility of a proposed satellite hospital in the western suburbs. At the time of the merger there was a proposal by Curt Carlson to proceed with the construction of a new community health center in the western suburbs to include a general hospital and medical office building. Mr. Carlson was to donate 10 acres of land and the hospital would purchase an additional 15 acres.

3. The jobs of personnel at all levels within each hospital would not be jeopardized.

What were the advantages?

1. Greater strength from the increased community representation, as well as increased resources at the Board level.

2. Greater strength and resources at the medical staff level from the increase in the number of physicians.

3. Greater strength at the management level.

4. Added financial resources for both hospitals. In 1969, the net worth of Abbott was $6 million and the net worth of Northwestern was $11 million. The combined resources would increase debt service capabilities.

5. Increased scope of service through access to the suburbs and an entrée for Abbott Hospital to the Minneapolis Medical Center.

...the entire congregation of Westminster Church were officially corporate members of Abbott Hospital... This arrangement would create an unwieldy Board of Trustees of 76 members.

Because the buildings and endowments had been given to the church and thus secondarily to the hospital, the courts needed to make a judgment to separate the hospital from the church.

6. Increased opportunities for Abbott Hospital through the undergraduate and graduate medical education at Northwestern Hospital.

7. Greater teaching and clinical resources for Northwestern Hospital's medical education program.

8. Greater efficiency managing operating costs through the opportunity to coordinate and consolidate existing as well as future clinical services.

9. More effective use of increasingly scarce medical personnel in health care.

10. Greater opportunity to introduce new clinical and support services.

11. Increased opportunity to coordinate and consolidate existing education programs for para-medical groups.

12. Opportunity to consolidate and coordinate department heads and supervisory functions.

13. Improved chances to qualify for federal and foundation funds for a wide variety of medical purposes.

There was an additional legal issue in that the Westminster Presbyterian Church owned Abbott Hospital. Because the buildings and endowments had been given to the church and thus secondarily to the hospital, the courts needed to make a judgment to separate the hospital from the church. A number of the Trustees of the church were also on the Board of Directors of Abbott Hospital. The church had come to the conclusion that this separation was needed and advisable so that the resources of the church would not be susceptible to a lawsuit involving the hospital. The courts resolved the issue within six months.

In the end, the vote was to merge the two hospitals into one corporation. There was serious consideration given to developing a hospital in the western suburbs because of the generous offer made by Mr. Carlson. However, there was not a great appetite on the part of the medical staffs to expand their medical practices to the suburbs. In their minds, they had enough patients to care for in the heart of Minneapolis and did not like the idea of the commute to the suburbs. As a result, the consideration of the suburban site was rejected. It was many decades later before Abbott Northwestern Hospital established a site in the western suburbs in the form of WestHealth, a part of the Allina Health System.

5

Abbott Northwestern Hospital
The Physical Merger
1974-1980

Dean McNeal, Chairman of the Abbott Northwestern Hospital Board of Trustees, wrote the Executive Committee on July 31, 1974 to ask, that while Abbott and Northwestern hospitals had merged as a corporation 3½ years previously, what of the future? There were new pressures on hospitals and doctors in the form of financial regulation from various levels of government. As a result, the Joint Medical Staff Board had asked the Hospital Board to re-examine the existing financial, physical, and medical configuration of the two hospitals to determine what changes, if any, were advisable.

The eight-member ad hoc committee consisted of Conley Brooks as Chairman, Virginia Piper as Vice-Chair, Henry Doerr, Herb Bissell, Dr. Craig Freeman, and Dr. Frank Johnson. Each of the physicians also selected one other physician to serve on the committee. The administrators – Bob Millar, Gordon Sprenger, and George Adamovich – were to bring the report from the ad hoc committee to the Executive Committee. Dr. Robert Blomberg would report to the Joint Medical Staff Board, no later than November 1974, about changes recommended by

There were new pressures on hospitals and doctors in the form of financial regulation... As a result, the Joint Medical Staff Board had asked the Hospital Board to re-examine the existing financial, physical, and medical configuration of the two hospitals to determine what changes, if any, were advisable.

the Executive Committee. The Executive Committee's recommendations would go to the full Board by January 1975.

The external priorities and problems, according to the minutes, were perceived as:

- Developing relationships between Abbott Northwestern, Children's Hospital, Sister Kenny Institute, and other health care providers

- Surviving with excellence under government dominance over decisions, which had previously been left up to the individual institutions

- Developing a formal interdependence between hospitals and doctors as the new format for medical practice

- Determining the future of the Abbott Hospital facilities

- Determining the future of Northwestern Hospital facilities

Bob Millar, Chief Executive Officer of Abbott Northwestern, would present his plan to respond to the external priorities listed above to the ad hoc committee. Gordon Sprenger was relieved of all other duties and became responsible for reporting his evaluation of the following alternatives. Only one of the four alternatives proposed a physical merger of the hospitals.

1. Support both Abbott and Northwestern as strong, high-quality, acute-care hospitals.

2. Transfer Abbott's medical-surgical strengths to the Chicago Avenue complex (Northwestern Hospital). Also transfer Northwestern's clinical services such as chemical dependency, mental health, and chronic and extended care services to Abbott.

3. Expand Abbott's role as a pioneer provider of comprehensive health care for senior citizens.

4. Transfer Abbott's strengths to the Chicago Avenue complex or, in part, to a new suburban health care facility. Dispose of a major part, or all, of Abbott's present facilities.

The Board members – who otherwise were businesspersons, lawyers, or other professionals – and the administrators met with the physicians on the medical staffs of Abbott and Northwestern. At the time I was Chief of Staff at

Northwestern, and it is interesting to recall that the medical staffs were still identified as belonging to either Abbott or Northwestern despite the merger four years earlier and the commonalities of the two staffs. Abbott's medical staff was described as being a relatively close-knit group who enjoyed being together in a sort of club-like atmosphere. In the four years since the merger, the Abbott staff felt that more resources had gone to Northwestern than to Abbott. The Abbott doctors felt there was more backbiting and less cohesion among the Northwestern physicians. However, the Northwestern medical staff viewed itself as being more professional and less of an old boys' club. These differences made a physical merger both more difficult and took longer to accomplish than planned.

Throughout 1974, Abbott Northwestern held a series of conversations with the leadership of Eitel Hospital, which was getting involved in a Health Maintenance Organization (H.M.O.) as a way of funding health care. As a result, Eitel was in need of more hospital beds. Eitel was primarily a hospital for general practitioners, as compared to Abbott and Northwestern hospitals, which were increasingly specialized. The concept of Eitel Hospital being an H.M.O. arm of Abbott Northwestern Hospital or of Metropolitan Medical Center Incorporated was entertained. In the end, Eitel Hospital's view of the future was to continue with its current identity and autonomy, whereas Abbott Northwestern's view of the future was to become part of a larger system.

After discussing the options open to Abbott Northwestern for nine months, on December 17, 1974, the following facts were agreed upon by the ad hoc committee:

- The long-term use of Abbott Hospital as a non-acute facility did not appear feasible.
- There did not appear to be enough patients in specific disease groups to allocate specific acute services between the two facilities.
- Regulatory bodies were going to make it very difficult to spend money on equipment and/or facilities that constituted duplication in two hospitals owned by the same corporation in relatively close proximity.
- The polarity between the two hospital groups, both in regard to the Medical Staff and the Board of Trustees was so deep and so emotionally

charged that a relatively high degree of separate existence, or else complete union in one facility, was needed.

- The needs of the Abbott medical staff, in their judgment, had not been adequately met during the years since the merger.

- A regional medical center, as described to the committee, would not likely be possible if the Abbott Northwestern facilities remained separate.

- Obstetrics would best be removed from both Abbott and Northwestern facilities and located at Minneapolis Children's Hospital. Alternatively, a high-risk obstetric unit would be placed at the Abbott Northwestern Hospital campus on Chicago Avenue in order to be adjacent to Children's Hospital's neonatal intensive care unit.

- A move to the suburbs was not feasible at that time. Decisions would be made irrespective of plans for a suburban hospital in the future.

- Abbott Northwestern should keep a foot in the suburban door and stake out or retain a claim in the western suburbs. At an appropriate time in the future, some form of family health clinic that could be a feeder to the downtown facilities would be developed.

In 1975, Abbott Northwestern engaged the James A. Hamilton Associates, Hospital Consultants, to conduct a facility analysis and physical development study. The hospital consultants recognized that this was a tremendous challenge for the Abbott Northwestern family. They had to analyze the current space, special needs for the immediate future in a consolidated facility, a consolidated site plan, and its capital costs. They had to determine staffing needs, the reaction of the medical staffs to using a consolidated facility, and their reaction to building a suburban unit. In essence, they were instructed to determine the spatial needs in a new, consolidated facility. These needs would be based on the volume of work, which in turn would be based on how many physicians would use the consolidated facility.

Each facility was evaluated separately and significant needs and deficiencies identified. Recommendations were initially presented to the ad hoc committee on December 9, 1975, and to the Executive Committee on January 26,

1976. While some of the structures on the Abbott site could be expanded vertically, there was not adequate space for horizontal expansion. In order to accommodate the Abbott patients at the Northwestern site on Chicago Avenue, significant expansion would be required.

The Northwestern site allowed both horizontal and vertical expansion. Most of the buildings had been designed anticipating future need for additional space. The Northwestern site consisted of two square blocks totaling just less than 1.6 acres. The hospital did not own every lot on the two blocks, but it did own most of them. Others could be purchased, and the hospital would likely be allowed to further close Elliot Avenue to increase consolidation of its property. The expansion at the Northwestern site would accommodate the 485 beds currently existing, plus the 337 beds being utilized at the Abbott site. In addition, 32 beds were being utilized at Sister Kenny Institute, bringing to the proposed facility a total of 854 beds. An additional recommendation was to increase the private room status from 18 percent to 40 percent.

The attempt to determine how many physicians would use the consolidated site was interesting. When the Abbott medical staff spoke as a group, there was significant opposition to moving to the Northwestern Hospital's Chicago Avenue site. However, when 106 Abbott doctors were interviewed individually, very few physicians said they would not use a consolidated facility. The medical staff most critical of a consolidated facility was the primary care physicians. The specialists would follow their referring doctors. A significant number were waiting to see if the consolidated facility was being properly developed, so they could give their patients the same quality of care. Good communications had to be achieved and the whole process handled well, but if that was accomplished, 90-95 percent of the Abbott medical staff said they would move to the Chicago Avenue site. (It turned out to be closer to 99 percent.) Another pertinent observation by the interviewers was that all doctors were strongly supportive of the facility they were currently using, whether it was Abbott or Northwestern. That degree of support by the physicians was quite unusual, in the opinion of the interviewers.

To make this consolidation successful, the Hamilton consultants had established seven primary criteria:

Good communications had to be achieved and the whole process handled well, but if that was accomplished, 90-95 percent of the Abbott medical staff said they would move to the Chicago Avenue site.

1. Develop a first-class facility.

2. Facilitate the way in which physicians would be able to find patients in the larger space and reorganized hospital.

3. Allow for the facility to expand in the future, i.e., beyond 1985.

4. Be fiscally responsible. This meant that the Northwestern Hospital structure should not be gutted or changed unless economically viable.

5. Develop the space to recognize the patient as a human being. The space should try to humanize the medical experience of the patient and the patient's family.

6. Scale units down in size, wherever possible.

7. Develop the support space, including dietary, materials, and diagnostic areas, so it can be used by all the inpatient and outpatient activities of the hospital.

While Hamilton Associates made recommendations concerning the medical staff and the new construction, Booz, Allen, and Hamilton Consulting made recommendations concerning the cost and affordability of the project. The recommendations of the Ad Hoc Committee were made initially to the Executive Committee, and then to the Board of Directors. The latter meeting was held January 27, 1976. The suggestion was to accept and implement the recommendations of the Hamilton Associates study and build the consolidated facility at the Chicago Avenue site at a cost not to exceed $24 million dollars.

On March 4, 1976, the Board of Trustees recommended a petition to the District Court for approval to consolidate facilities. A committee submitted a Certificate of Need to the Metropolitan Health Board to allow the building of a specific number of hospital beds. The State Board of Health gave final approval of the Certificate of Need on August 12, 1976. Ground breaking was tentatively scheduled for April 1977. The actual final transfer of patients from the Abbott facility to the new Abbott Northwestern Hospital was completed several years later on a cold day in January 1980.

6

The Changing Landscape
The Abbott Northwestern Hospital Campus
Gene Torrey and Daryl Schroeder

Time-lapse photography of the eight-block area in the Phillips Neighborhood of Minneapolis that comprises the Abbott Northwestern Hospital campus, Children's Hospitals & Clinics in Minneapolis, and several related medical office buildings would reveal a radically changed landscape between 1960 and 2016. The eight-block area stretches from 25th Street on the north to the railroad tracks south of 28th Street and is bounded by Chicago Avenue on the west and 10th Avenue S on the east.

Three facility leaders—Dick Waltz, Gene Torrey, and Daryl Schroeder—helped shape the campus to accommodate rapid changes in care delivery models, driven by the innovative, cutting-edge physicians who practiced there. There was rarely a year when major construction would not disrupt our main mission, but the creativity of our hospital staff and facility leaders found ways to keep the patients' needs a first priority.

Northwestern Hospital in 1960 was a six-story hospital that included east and west wings joined by a central six-story pavilion. A remodeled boiler plant was located on the former site of the beautiful Harriet Walker Nurses Residence, built in 1912. The boiler plant remodeling

Time-lapse photography of the eight-block area in the Phillips Neighborhood of Minneapolis that comprises the Abbott Northwestern Hospital campus, Children's Hospitals & Clinics in Minneapolis, and several related medical office buildings would reveal a radically changed landscape between 1960 and 2016.

in 1958 was the first of more than 20 significant projects that Mortenson Construction built at Abbott Northwestern.

Below is a chronology of growth and change to the Chicago Avenue campus that supported the innovative patient care within.

1962—An addition to Northwestern Hospital designed by Ellerbe & Company of Minneapolis includes two patient floors north of and connected to the existing patient care areas. The basement construction includes mechanical rooms that are sized for future vertical expansion of the added patient areas (Stations 24 and 34 on the west and Stations 25 and 35 on the east). A new kitchen, still in use in 2016, is added on the first floor. Lab and X-Ray areas are also added.

1969—Three additional circular patient floors are added (Stations 55, 64, and 65).

1970—On January 1, 1970, Abbott Hospital and Northwestern Hospital merge into one corporation.
- The second Harriet Walker Nurses Residence is built at the corner of Chicago Avenue and 26th Street. Today it's known as the Harriet Walker Building.
- The Massie-Moos Education Building is built just to the east of the Harriet Walker Building.

1973—On January 31, 1973, Children's Hospital opens for business at the north end of the eight-block area. A pedestrian tunnel connects Northwestern Hospital, Children's Hospital, and a three-story medical office building located just north of 26th Street that serves both hospitals. Northwestern Hospital's boiler plant is expanded to provide for the added load of heating Children's Hospital.
- Construction starts on Parking Ramp 1, located south of 27th Street and along 10th Avenue. Up until this time, only surface parking existed.

1974—Construction begins on an addition to the Medical Office Building.
- On April 16, 1974 ground is broken for the construction of the initial

two-story Sister Kenny Institute Building. The Sister Kenny building is designed by Bergsted, Wahlberg, Bergquist & Rohkohl Architects and is the first of many projects the firm designed on the hospital campus.

1975—Sister Kenny Institute merges with Abbott Northwestern Hospital on May 21, 1975. Construction is completed on the two-story Sister Kenny Institute Building, along with the Wasie Therapeutic Pool, located to the south of the building. The construction connects Northwestern and Sister Kenny with a skyway over 27th Street. (The street was still open at that time, though it was closed in 1977.)

1976—The Certificate of Need for the physical merger of Abbott and Northwestern hospitals is approved on August 12, 1976. Henningson, Durham & Richardson Architects, as well as engineers from Omaha, Nebraska, are chosen to design an addition. Mortenson Construction leads the construction work.

1977—Groundbreaking and construction starts on the addition for the consolidated Abbott Northwestern Hospital. The addition includes:
- Two patient floors with four nursing stations (Stations 30, 31, 40, and 41).
- Horizontal connections to the existing Stations 35 and 45.
- Expanded Laboratory and Radiology areas on the first floor.
- Expanded Pharmacy and Central Supply Resource in the lower level.
- Skyway connection from the new addition to the parking ramp.
- New entrance with a larger lobby.
- A chapel near the new lobby.
- Two patient floors added to the Sister Kenny Institute building with five nursing stations.
- A first-floor connection from the existing Northwestern Hospital to the Sister Kenny Institute Building, with escalators to the lower level of the building and a new cafeteria and conference rooms. This addition closed 27th Street.

1979—Construction starts on Parking Ramp 2, located north of 26th Street and along Elliot Avenue. The parking ramp serves Children's Hospital and the Medical Office Building.

1980—On January 26, 1980, the physical consolidation of Abbott Northwestern Hospital culminates on a cold winter day, when the remaining 32 patients are moved from Abbott Hospital to the former Northwestern Hospital campus and the new facilities.

1982—Groundbreaking and construction starts on the addition to the Wasie Building at the corner of 28th Street and Chicago Avenue and the adjacent Wasie Center and Gymnasium Building.

1984—Construction starts on a rooftop heliport located above Station 41 to serve both Abbott Northwestern Hospital and Children's Hospital via the pedestrian tunnel.

1986—Groundbreaking and construction starts on the Ambulatory Care Center at the corner of 26th Street and 10th Avenue. The Center includes outpatient treatment areas on the first floor and day surgery operating rooms on the lower level.

1987—Groundbreaking and construction starts on the Cardiovascular Care ICU building along 10th Avenue.
- Construction starts on Parking Ramp 5, located north of 26th Street and along 10th Avenue S.

1989—An additional circular patient floor is added (Station 75) for Perinatal patient care.

1990—Groundbreaking and construction starts on the McDonald's restaurant addition, connected to the west side of the first floor connection from the hospital building to the Sister Kenny Institute Building. This partnership was needed to help the hospital accommodate the demand for meals beyond the traditional retail cafeteria model. Little did we know that this McDonald's relationship would become the hospital's number-one negative image issue. The hospital ended that relationship in 2016.

1992—Construction starts on the six-story Piper Building above the Ambulatory Care Center. The Virginia Piper Cancer Institute, the Institute for Low Back Care, and a new Medical ICU were included in the building, along with medical office space.

1994—Groundbreaking and construction starts on the addition of six underground operating rooms developed under the area between the Education Building and the Piper Building. The operating rooms are directly connected to the existing operating rooms in the main hospital, as well as to the operating rooms of the Ambulatory Care Center. Once the construction is completed, the roadway between the buildings is restored. This operating room upgrade gave the hospital 35 operating rooms.

In 1994, the formation of Allina led the campus into a whole new direction. Allina began to create integrated solutions for programs and services for Abbott Northwestern Hospital and others. The years to follow justify a second book all in itself to capture this growth and the changes to the Abbott Northwestern campus after it became part of Allina.

In 1994, the formation of Allina led the campus into a whole new direction. Allina began to create integrated solutions for programs and services for Abbott Northwestern Hospital and others.

ABBOTT
HOSPITAL
·1902~1911·

Dr. Amos Abbott.

In 1902, Dr. Amos Abbott rented a yellow brick three-story house at 10 East 17th Street that had been The Stanley Hall School for Girls. This became Abbott Hospital – the city's first private, surgical hospital, which could serve up to 15 patients. Its resources were quite meager and the building inadequate.

Abbott Hospital in 1917 at 1717 First Avenue South.
Staff (primarily student nurses) display a banner honoring graduates serving in the First World War.

The Abbott Surgical Hospital was completed in 1911 at 1717 First Avenue South. The hospital had 35 beds, 12 student nurses, and an apartment for Susan Holmes, the Superintendent. There was one operating room with a preoperative sterilization room, a doctors' dressing room, a cystoscopy room (for examination of the bladder), and a laboratory. The obstetrical department consisted of four rooms, and there was a four-bed pediatric section. The delivery of babies in a hospital was a relatively new concept.

It was a wintry November day in 1882 when Harriet Walker summoned 44 women to lay plans for what would become Northwestern Hospital for Women and Children. Opened in a small rented house one month later as a charity hospital, Northwestern Hospital dedicated the first structure built specifically for hospital use on June 10, 1887, at the corner of Chicago Avenue and 27th Street in Minneapolis.

Harriet Walker.

*Northwestern Hospital
Nursing School Class of 1897.*

"In the very early days of the life of this school, and when it was the only one in the city, we were hesitating about enlarging the number of pupils from two to four, for fear of overstocking the market. An elderly and somewhat old-fashioned physician, even for those times, remarked, 'You are spoiling them – utterly spoiling them. You are teaching them to use the thermometer, and to know the nature and effects of medicine, and to understand a patient's symptoms as well as a physician. All a nurse needs to know is how to make a bed, fill a hot water bottle, and wait for the doctor. That is all I want my nurses to know.' The times have certainly changed."

—Harriet Walker, addressing the graduates
of the Nursing School of 1915

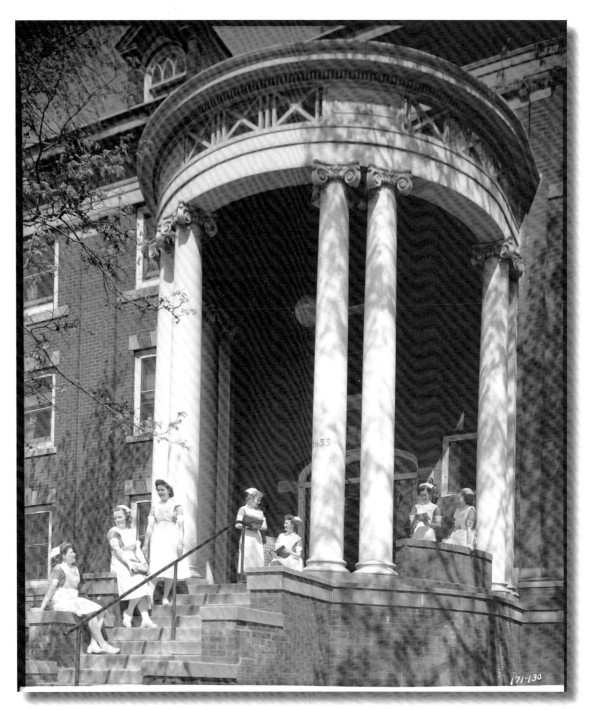

Harriet Walker Home for Nurses (circa 1925).

Northwestern Hospital, 1914.

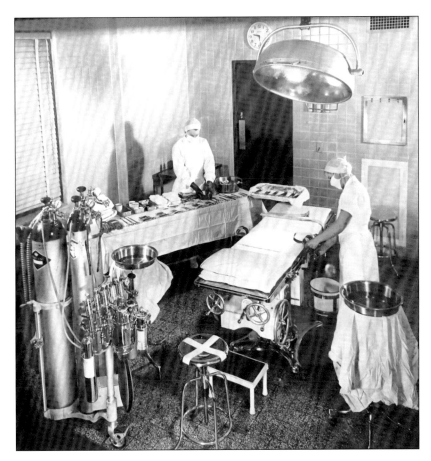

Operating Room.

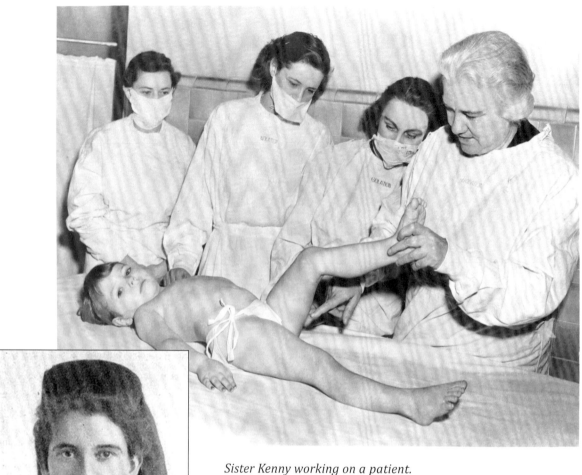

Sister Kenny working on a patient.

Sister Elizabeth Kenny, 1915.

Australia native Sister Elizabeth Kenny (nurses were called "sister") brought her brash dedication to treating polio patients to Abbott Hospital in the summer of 1940.

Sister Kenny Institute polio patients help Sister Kenny celebrate the institute's first birthday.

Some physicians were put off by her style, but the volume of patients and people wanting to be trained in her methods quickly outstripped the capabilities of the hospital. So Sister Kenny took her pioneering rehabilitation efforts to the old Lymanhurst School, six blocks north of Northwestern Hospital in Minneapolis. It was here that the original Sister Kenny Institute was dedicated in 1942. In 2013, Sister Kenny Institute merged with Courage Center to become Courage Kenny Rehabilitation Institute.

The Healing Spirit.
Sculpture by Georgette Sosin.

Mt. Sinai Hospital was built in 1951. This was necessary because of antisemitism, both locally and nationally. As a result, Jewish doctors were not always able to get admitting privileges at many of the metropolitan hospitals. The hospital consisted of seven stories and 192 beds. About thirty years later there was a contest to select a work of art that would be identified with Mt. Sinai Hospital. As a result, Georgette Sosin was selected to design the piece of art. She chose a sculpture that was to be hung on an external wall. It was called "The Healing Spirit."

Mt. Sinai Hospital, like other hospitals at that time, was exploring possible mergers because hospitals of that size were having difficulty surviving. It formed the Metropolitan Medical Center along with Hennepin County General Hospital. However, this relationship was short-lived, lasting only a year. While the sculpture had been part of Mt. Sinai, there were plans to move it to General Hospital. However, with the dissolution of the Metropolitan Medical Center, those plans were never realized. Shortly thereafter, many of the Mt. Sinai medical staff joined the medical staff of Abbott Northwestern Hospital. As a sign of solidarity, the "Healing Spirit" was placed on the southern wall of the entrance of Abbott Northwestern Hospital and it is still there today.

The sculpture is derived from the letters of Jeremiah 30:17 and the Hebrew blessing Refu Schlema, which means "perfect healing of mind, body and spirit." The Hebrew letter "shin" is an extended W and represents the presence of God. It is found at the base or bottom of the sculpture and balances all the abstract forms of the sculpture. The coming together of the parts to form a whole is much like the process of spiritual as well as physical healing. It is a delicate balance.

Virginia Piper.

Virginia Piper, a well-known member of the community, died of pancreatic cancer in 1988. She had been a devoted supporter of Abbott Northwestern Hospital for many decades. Virginia ("Ginny") was actually born at Northwestern Hospital. She joined the hospital's all-female board in 1961 and served as its chair from 1964-69. Under her leadership, men were added to the board in 1967. Then, when Abbott and Northwestern hospitals merged in 1970, she became chair of the Abbott Northwestern Hospital Board. The physical facilities merged in 1980. She provided many more years of service after the merger, retiring from the board in 1986. Known as a gifted leader of integrity who could inspire others, patients and their families were her primary concern.

After her death, memorials poured in, directed to Abbott Northwestern Hospital. Gordon Sprenger, then president and CEO of Lifespan, talked with her husband Harry (Bobby) Piper about developing a cancer institute as a memorial to Ginny.

The Minneapolis Tribune

FRIDAY

Cold

THURSDAY'S TEMPERATURES

Details Page 21

Vol. CIII—No. 146   Copyright 1969 Minneapolis Star and Tribune Company   MINNEAPOLIS, MINN., FRIDAY, OCTOBER 17, 1969   ★★★   Single Copy Price 10c   Lower Price for Carrier Delivery

---

SOME RETAILERS SAY

Bad Check Rate Bouncing Upward

By DENNIS CASSANO
Minneapolis Tribune Staff Writer

If you've been having trouble cashing checks in the Twin Cities area retail stores lately, it's because merchants are concerned over an apparent increase in bouncing checks.

While not all retailers have noticed an increase, others say there may be as much as a 40-percent increase in the number of checks that come back from the banks marked "insufficient funds."

A PART of the problem is attributed to careless addition and subtraction by customers trying to balance their checkbooks. But merchants say there is also an increase in deliberate fraud — forgery, writing checks on closed accounts or opening a checking account with a small deposit and then writing large checks.

Whether purposeful or accidental, many retailers are imposing more strict requirements for allowing customers to cash checks.

Their problem is to tread the line between protecting themselves from bad check writers and, on the other hand, not be so restrictive as to lose their good customers.

"IT'S BEEN getting worse and worse," one credit manager said. His stores have instituted "tough procedures to get a check cashed. We've been turning down more checks than ever before."

His stores, which have lost $15,000 so far this year from bad checks, have started taking photographs of every person who cashes a check.

"This scares away the people who write bad checks on purpose," he said, "but people don't seem to worry about bouncing a check."

PEOPLE WHO allow their checks to bounce, however, do have cause for worry. The Retail Credit Association, which keeps tabs on the credit ratings of area merchants' customers, gives persons a bad rating if they bounce more than one check a year.

Another merchant said he is "demanding a little more of our customers" when they attempt to cash a check. He said he goes into great detail in getting information on the customer. He may call the customer's employer and make other telephone calls to verify the information given him by customers.

That helps reduce the overnight fraud, he said, but there is little he can do to protect himself from a customer with a good credit rating who allows his checks to bounce.

THE COMPUTER also has caught up with the people who make a habit of cashing a check they don't have funds to cover.

Checks
Continued on Page Five

Stocks Soar in Busy Day

NEW YORK, N.Y. (UPI) —Hopes for peace and an early downturn in interest rates buoyed stocks to their highest level since mid-July Thursday.

The price advance was not quite as sharp, however, as Monday and Tuesday. Volume was very strong at 19.5 million shares, and the Dow Jones average of 30 industrial blue chips advanced 8.71.

(STOCK TABLE—Page 10.)

Two City Hospitals May Merge

Northwestern, Abbott Boards Agree on Plan

By DAVID KUHN
Minneapolis Tribune Staff Writer

The Boards of Trustees of Northwestern and Abbott Hospitals have reached a preliminary agreement to merge, it was disclosed Thursday.

The consolidation is subject to the approval of members of each of the two non-profit corporations that operate the Minneapolis hospitals.

MEMBERS of Northwestern, a privately operated and nonsectarian institution at 810 E. 27th St., will vote next Thursday on the merger.

Members of Westminster Presbyterian Church, who also constitute the membership of Abbott Hospital, 110 E. 18th St., will vote Oct. 27.

The consolidation would put Abbott's 320 beds and Northwestern's 400 beds under one administration. The combination would provide operating economies and enable Northwestern's teaching program for interns to be expanded to Abbott, said Charles S. Bellows, vice-chairman of Northwestern's board.

THERE IS "tremendous duplication" of general hospital facilities in the Twin Cities, Bellows said, and the merger would be a step toward making health care more efficient.

Some 60 percent of the medical staff members involved already practice at both hospitals and they favor the merger, he said.

Both hospitals operate nursing schools.

In a letter to Westminster members, Rev. C. John L. Bates said:

"Despite the fact that Northwestern is a somewhat larger hospital, the steps toward consolidation have been taking place in complete parity, and the plans are built on equality in representation, governance and administration."

IN 1965 Abbott was given a 10-acre site in Minnetonka near the intersection of Hwy. 12 and Interstate Hwy 94 for a new hospital.

Bellows said a thorough

Hospitals
Continued on Page Five

PITCHER JERRY KOOSMAN CATCHER JERRY GROTE DID VICTORY DANCE
World champions cavorted on the infield after final out of the Series

Associated Press

Ombudsmen to Replace Police's Little City Halls

By DAN WASCOE JR.
Minneapolis Tribune Staff Writer

Police ombudsmen will replace the "Little City Halls" program of the Minneapolis Police Department, Chief Basil Lutz announced Thursday.

"Little City Halls" was the name of a community relations program begun last December by Lutz's predecessor, Donald Dwyer. They were established at four locations, which were changed when some members of the black community complained that the police were using the facilities to spy on them. At one location, the patrolmen were forcibly ejected.

THE OMBUDSMEN, plainclothes beat patrolmen, will seek out residents' complaints about city services, from garbage collection to housing codes, and will previously had been critical of the program because it had announced who Dwyer became chief last winter with little groundwork to assure community support.

WILSON SAID the new ombudsman approach, which originated in a proposal by planners in Minneapolis Model City program, has been tried during the past 17 months in an unpublicized experiment.

The experiment, which had Patrolman Rodney Tchida trying to help Indians in south Minneapolis, has been so successful, Wilson said, that it will be put into effect citywide. The program will expand to north Minneapolis in the next few weeks, he said.

The 28-year-old Tchida, who has been with the police force for about 11 years, is

Lutz   Wilson
Discussed program

sonally carry those complaints to the appropriate city departments.

They then will follow up the complaints to see that they are resolved, according to Deputy Chief Eugene Wilson, who explained the program during an interview yesterday.

People have a tendency not to come to the Little City Halls," Wilson said. He pre-

---

Nixon Draft Plan Clears House Panel

Attempt to End Student Deferments in Lottery Defeated

From The Tribune's Wire Services

WASHINGTON, D.C. — President Nixon's lottery plan to limit the draft to 19-year-olds was approved Thursday by the House Armed Services Committee and sent toward the House floor for action late next week.

The speedy action on a surprising 31 to 6 vote indicated the chances the House approval are good and that the Senate might take up the bill before the end of the year.

The Senate Armed Services Committee chairman, John Stennis, D-Miss., has said his committee may take up the President's proposal this year if it passes the House.

THE HOUSE committee refused even to consider eliminating draft deferments for college students.

Such a proposal, by Rep. Richard H. Ichord, D-Mo., was ruled out of order on a 21 to 10 roll call.

The draft lottery approval was recommended unanimously by a special subcommittee that was highly critical of the plan during four days of hearings this month.

The subcommittee, headed by Rep. F. Edward Hebert, D-La., said in its report that it was not persuaded that Mr. Nixon's plan "would provide any greater equity in the selection process than is provided by the present oldest-first system.

"HOWEVER, in view of the strong recommendation of the President in this regard, urging the Congress to permit him to modify the existing system of selection, the subcommittee believes that this request of the commander-in-chief of our armed forces should be honored."

The committee, one senior member acknowledged privately, was attempting "to put the monkey on the back of the administration and the Senate Armed Services Committee."

With its present legislative workload, it was doubtful that the Senate committee would get around to acting on the lottery proposal this year.

Furthermore, if it went to the Senate with a simple lot-

MIRACLE METS WIN

World Champion Losers Now World Champions!

By DWAYNE NETLAND
Minneapolis Tribune Staff Writer

NEW YORK, N.Y. — A swarm of jubilant Mets fans swirled onto the Shea Stadium playing field as the New York Mets completed one of the most astonishing feats in baseball history Thursday.

over in smaller corner of the World Series championship clubhouse, Jerry Koosman, the farm boy from Minnesota, was unusual in happy enclosed with Jerry Payson, the New York lefty who won the Mets.

Mrs. Payson phoned...moved Koosman's cap and

"YOU'VE GOT to expect McNally to pitch in that situation," Koosman said. "I was surprised when he swung and a hook was hit, most surprised when I saw the ball sailing over the fence.

"I tried a little harder after what McNally had done to me," he admitted. "Moment of the World.

Article about the Hospital Merger, October 17, 1969.

74

Consolidation endorsed for Abbott-Northwestern

By GORDON SLOVUT
Minneapolis Star Staff Writer

A $38-million proposal to consolidate Northwestern and Abbott Hospitals was endorsed 12 to 3 by the Metropolitan Health Board last night after a 4-hour public hearing.

The plan, which ultimately must be approved by the Minnesota Board of Health to meet the requirements of the state certificate of need law, is to:

EXPAND the existing Northwestern Hospital campus at 27th St. and Chicago Av. S. to 838 beds, including those of the connected Sister Kenny Institute, by 1980.

CLOSE the existing 337-bed Abbott Hospital, 1¼ miles away at 110 E. 18th St.

CALL THE expanded hospital Abbott-Northwestern and make up part of the additional cost by getting along with 180 fewer employees, a savings Abbott-Northwestern consultants estimate at $4 million a year.

Dr. Raymond Scallen, a Minneapolis physician and opponent of the consolidation, pointed out that Abbott-Northwestern got some of its advice from the same consultants who vastly underestimated the construction cost and number of employes needed for the new Hennepin County Medical Center.

The Abbott and Northwestern organizations were merged in 1970 under a 77-member board which, after lengthy deliberations, decided it would be unwise to spend the estimated $11 million needed for improvements at the separate Abbott and Northwestern campuses when for $38 million—$24 million of it for basic construction costs—the organization could get what its consultants describe as the efficiencies of a single campus arangement.

The proposal originally had strong opposition from doctors on the staff of Abbott. They voted unanimously last year to oppose the closing of the hospital.

The opposition apparently has weakened because the entire job of challenging the proposal before the metropolitan board fell last night on Scallen, a busy 50-year-old heart specialist who served as Abbott chief of staff for three years and is currently the part-time unpaid head of the coronary care unit at the hospital.

Scallen argued that the cost of the consolidation — which would mean either seven fewer hospital beds or 77 fewer, dependent on who did the counting — would fall on the public through unnecessarily higher hospital rates.

Scallen said that Abbott now offers a high quality of care, at least partly because it is not a huge, impersonal institution but a comfortable, 337-bed hospital. Furthermore, he said, the Abbott-Northwestern representatives have not been able to show clearly how they will have 180 fewer employees.

He emphasized that the large new institution would offer no new health services. The project, he said, will simply add $28 a day to a patient's hospital bill in return for treatment given in "a new pile of bricks."

Gordon Sprenger, president of Abbott-Northwestern, said that the cost will go up even if the consolidation doesn't go through because the $11 million will have to be spent for improvements such as a new boiler and new food preparation facilities, and the saving of having 180 fewer employees will be lost.

George Adamovich, administrator of the Abbott unit for the past seven years, said that Abbott is too small to indefinitely support the current level of services. Only a fairly large expansion would make the volume large enough, he said.

Dr. William Petersen, president of the joint 462-physician Abbott-Northwestern medical staff, said he originally opposed the consolidation, but now he had decided it is the only thing to do.

Scallen said he isn't giving up. He said he is going to go to the Metropolitan Council, parent agency of the health board, and urge that body to recommend that the state health board refuse to grant a certificate of need for the project.

Star Photos by Tom Sweeney

DR. RAYMOND SCALLEN BEFORE HEALTH BOARD
Opposed $38-million hospital project

SCALLEN AWAITING THE HEALTH BOARD VOTE
Then heard the board endorse proposal 12-3

Whites protected too, judge decides

By GWENYTH JONES
Minneapolis Star Staff Writer

The Minnesota Human Rights Act prohibits racial discrimination against whites as well as minorities, Hennepin District Judge Stanley D. Kane ruled today.

Kane denied a motion by Dayton Hudson Corp. to dismiss a suit in which a white man charges that a Dayton's store fired him and hired a black man in his place.

The plaintiff, Daniel J. McCrary, 3140 Chowen Av. S., alleged that Dayton's wanted to show blacks in areas of "high visibility" in the store.

ATTORNEYS for Dayton's did not deny that McCrary was replaced by a black man but said he was dismissed for economic reasons. They argued that even if he had been discriminated against, he was not protected by the human rights act because it was intended to protect minorities.

Kane rejected this argument.

He said that even though there has been no Minnesota Supreme Court interpretation of the state law with regard to discrimination against whites, the June 25 decision of the U.S. Supreme Court concerning the federal law was binding.

That decision held that the federal law banned discrimination against whites as well as minorities.

Kane said the decision was supported by "essential logic and reasonableness."

HE SAID it was "repugnant to (his) instincts of fairness and common sense that (the law) means something other than what it plainly states."

The law makes it an unfair employment practice for an employer to fire anyone because of "race, color, creed, religion, national origin, sex, marital status, status with regard to public assistance or disability."

Kane said he was not deciding whether there actually was racial discrimination against McCrary, only whether McCrary had a right under the law to sue for racial discrimination.

Jim Klobuchar

The Hilton hotel dynasty is alive and flourishing in Minnesota. They sold the St. Paul Hilton, but the family succession appears secure. Conrad Hilton III is mopping hotel floors for $3 an hour in Plymouth.

He is also a candidate bellhop and has been promised consideration when an opening develops.

I bring you this information to dispell any suspicions that a Hilton emerges from the lobby palm fronds as an instant and fully grown magnate.

NEW BELLHOP IN TOWN NAMED CONRAD HILTON

Conrad III is 16, the grandson of the empire-creating Hilton and the son of the late Conrad "Nicky" Hilton. His mother, Patricia Nicholson Hilton Jr., married Minneapolis attorney Charles Bart Faegre in Florida a month ago, and the family now lives in Wayzata.

To nobody's shock, young Hilton decided a few years ago on a career in hotel management. His intention is to enroll at Cornell University, which maintains a world-recognized school in hotel management, and from there to acquire some professional art in Switzerland. The Swiss did not invent hotels. But they are the only people on earth who can run them consistently without plunging them into bankruptcy or flames. Here and there you will find successful American hotel managers. They have been made in Peoria but they almost certainly have been polished in Geneva.

CONRAD HILTON III
He also mops floors

As an adolescent, Conrad Hilton III asked his elders where to launch his career.

They suggested the kitchen.

THE YOUNG man was willing. He also displayed early versatility, a hallmark of the Hilton clan, by being able to run the dishwasher and put up food orders with equal verve. He performed most of his apprenticeship in the Hilton operations in Boston.

He moved here with his mother late in the spring, intending to put in his application for work at the Hilton in St. Paul.

"Who," he then asked, "is Radisson?"

Radisson, of course, was an old French explorer whose nominal descendant is Curt Carlson. Carlson builds and buys hotels and calls them Radisson. One of the hotels Carlson bought recently was the St. Paul Hilton.

So we had here a situation of wrenching poignancy: a Conrad Hilton marooned in a strange city without a Hilton hotel.

Hiltons do not build hotels on seven continents without being bold, lucky and on friendly terms with the banker. Being qualified on all counts, the young man walked up to the personnel manager of the new Radisson in St. Paul and asked whether there was any work in the hotel. He identified himself as Conrad Hilton III. The manager said he would be surprised if they didn't have an opening, possibly in the kitchen.

It turned out to be the restrooms, which—young Hilton noted with approval—was an advancement.

He has now been transferred to the Japanese Radisson Inn Plymouth, where he is regarded as one of the promising wall-washers and floor-moppers in the system.

HE IS a mannerly and well-adjusted young man who accepts these accolades sincerely. "I also," he said, "think I do a pretty good job of putting the linen away."

Neither his mother, an heiress of the McClintock oil family in Oklahoma, nor young Hilton III had experienced much of Minnesota before. They have decided they are enchanted. Hilton III plays tennis. He is also an occasional fisherman. Marlin and swordfish are notably absent on Minnetonka, but the lake does compensate with fierce-fighting crappies.

"Your lakes," he said, "are great. I was always a little more comfortable with westerners and easterners, and I feel I understand the people here a little better. I have to explain something. I lived in Los Angeles for a while and I would die rather than give up being a Los Angeles Rams' fan."

The conversion process here, it was explained, is normally less painful than that. But it may require one or two sessions with the St. Louis Park shish-ka-bob irregulars in the Kansas City lot at the Met this fall.

A few days ago they supplied Conrad with a bellboy's uniform. Guests seeing their luggage hefted by a bellhop with the nameplate "Conrad Hilton III," gasped.

"Can you imagine their quandary," an employee observed, "when it came time to figure out a tip?"

THE MINNEAPOLIS STAR

thur., july 15, 1976 • 1B

INSURANCE FRAUD

Complaints name 4 as arson suspects

By DEAN FOSDICK
Minneapolis Star Staff Writer

Criminal complaints have been issued against four men in the setting of two residential fires in the Twin Cities area.

Named in complaints filed yesterday by the Hennepin County attorney's office were James Peterson, 7816 Shingle Creek Dr., Brooklyn Park, Charles Rasmussen, Chisago City, James Jones, 8528 5th Av. S., Bloomington, and Duane Albert Flick, 655 E. Old Shakopee Rd., Bloomington.

The men, being sought by Hennepin County sheriff's deputies and Minneapolis Fire Department arson squad investigators, have been charged with intent to defraud an insurer and attempted theft by trick in connection with fires at 2801 26th Av. S. and 256 Irving Av. N. in October 1973. The men also are listed as suspects in the setting of about 20 other fires, officials said.

Thomas E. Bauer, assistant county attorney, said he expects more charges.

"The arrests will end a six-month-long investigation by the Hennepin County attorney's office and the Minneapolis Fire Department's arson squad," Bauer said.

A source said that although the individuals named in the complaints are being charged with only the two fires, "apprehension of the men will close 20 files" for the fire department.

Two informants, according to the complaints, told fire department arson squad investigators that Peterson hired Jones and Rasmussen to hold ownership to the two properties.

Peterson agreed to pay more money to Jones and Rasmussen after the property burned down, the complaint said.

Then Peterson hired Flick to set fire to the properties, which the complaint alleges he did Oct. 12 and Oct. 18, 1973.

When an insurance estimator decided that the building at 2801 26th Av. S. hadn't been destroyed by the Oct. 12 fire, a second blaze occurred one week later which did that, the complaint said.

All the fires were blamed on incendiaries by the arson squad.

DESPITE THOSE findings, the complaint said one insurance company paid Jones, the owner of record for the northside residence, $7,895.31 in damages.

Loss claims on the south Minneapolis building that burned twice were not paid, the complaint said.

Bauer said Peterson will be charged with two counts of defrauding an insurer and all but Jones will be charged with attempted theft by trick in addition to defrauding an insurer.

The theft by trick violation arose, Bauer said, when Peterson and Rasmussen allegedly overvalued the south Minneapolis property when taking out insurance on it.

Then, after the building burned down, the pair tried to collect an inflated amount of money in damages, Bauer said.

Conviction on charges of defrauding an insurer carries maximum penalties of three years in prison, a $3,000 fine, or both.

Maximum penalties for attempted theft by trick could result in five years imprisonment, a $5,000 fine, or both.

Emergency action urged to save elms

Minneapolis should use $100,000 of its emergency fund to aid in the trimming and removal of diseased elm trees, the city's two Independent-Republican aldermen said yesterday in a joint statement.

Aldermen Walter Rockenstein, 11th Ward, and Charlee Hoyt, 13th Ward, said they will ask the council's ways and means committee at its next meeting to recommend appropriation of the funds.

"One of Minneapolis' most valuable assets, its trees, is facing virtual extinction. Ninety percent of our shade trees are elms. The spread of Dutch elm disease threatens to destroy 75 percent of these trees by 1985 and a staggering 90 percent by 1987," the aldermen's statement said.

They said the key to slowing the spread of the disease is a vigorous trimming and removal program. The Minneapolis Park Board has had to transfer its trimming crews to the task of removing dead trees due to the spread of the disease and limited funding.

"The city's contingency fund is set aside for emergency situations. The threat to our city's trees is indeed an emergency," they said.

The funds would be used to trim trees only on city property.

State use of gasoline for 6 months is record

By JOE BLADE
Minneapolis Star Staff Writer

Gasoline consumption in Minnesota reached new highs in the first six months of 1976 after two years of conservation had cut usage in the state.

The amount of gasoline sold through June was 2 percent above previous record levels in 1973 and 6 percent above last year, according to Dixie Diehl, director of local services for the Minnesota Energy Agency.

A particular problem is developing with unleaded gasoline, used by almost all new cars, Ms. Diehl said. Consumption has risen to 15 percent of all gasoline, compared with 9 percent during 1975.

To avoid contaminating unleaded gasoline, special refinery equipment, trucks and storage tanks must be used.

In another five days, the energy agency will know whether supplies of unleaded gasoline will be adequate for August when tourism is high, she said.

The supply of gasoline is adequate, she added, but extra supplies that would allow independent dealers to cut prices are not available.

Greater-than-expected auto sales, particularly of middle-sized cars, have increased usage of leaded gasoline above earlier estimates, Ms. Diehl said.

Gasoline usage is rising because consumers no longer are trying to conserve, she said. There also is more long-distance auto travel this year and people are leaving buses and car pools.

AREA NEWS

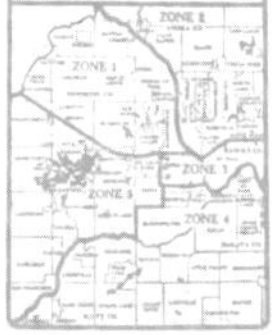

Luverne boy drowns in unused city pool

LUVERNE, Minn. (UPI) — James Johnson, 8, son of Edith Johnson of Luverne, drowned in an unused municipal swimming pool yesterday.

Police said the boy apparently climbed over a fence and fell into an area of the pool that had about 5 feet of seepage water in it.

Stanley Nelson (L) and Bob Spinner (R).

Scott Parker.

Gordon Springer and his wife Dee.

Former Administrators

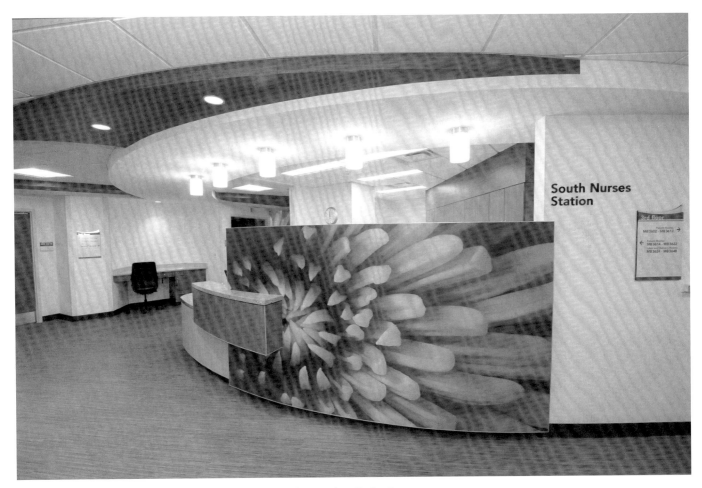

The Mother Baby Center.

Allina Health and Children's Hospitals & Clinics of Minnesota formed The Mother Baby Center. After years of planning, the center opened in 2013 with a new facility.

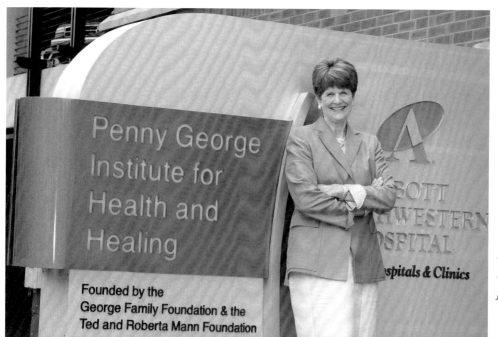

Penny George at the Penny George Institute for Health and Healing.

A celebration to mark the long-awaited Magnet® designation in early 2009.

Abbott Northwestern Hospital Campus, 2016.

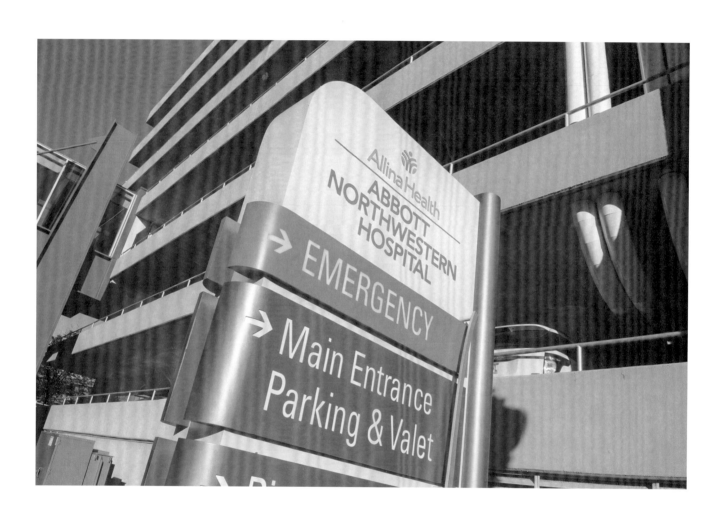

Part II

The Practice of Medicine
at Abbott Northwestern Hospital

Introduction

Robert H. Scott, M. D.

The post-World War II years saw a dramatic growth in the scale of American medicine. The United States built an immense medical research establishment, and enlarged and equipped the most scientifically advanced hospitals in the world. Between 1950 and 1970, medical personnel increased from 1.2 to 3.9 million people. During this period, national health care annual expenditures grew from $12.7 billion to $71.6 billion (4.5 to 7.3 percent of the GNP). Health care had become the largest industry in the country.

Americans now gave science unprecedented recognition as a national asset. During World War II, the research that produced radar, the atom bomb, and penicillin convinced even the skeptics that support of science was vital to national security. At the War's end, an advisory board on medical research reported that penicillin and the sulfonamides, the insecticide DDT, better vaccines, and improved hygienic measures had all but conquered yellow fever, dysentery, typhus, tetanus, pneumonia, meningitis, and malaria in this country. Disability from venereal disease had been radically reduced. Dramatic progress in surgery had been aided by the increased availability of blood and plasma for transfusions.

After World War II, prosperity gave Americans the opportunity to worry about their health. From the beginning of the twentieth century, the chief factors affecting mortality had been shifting from infectious disease to chronic disease. The Depression and World War II had diverted attention to more urgent needs. Now the nation began to face its medical problems. Scientists and the public became more concerned about cancer, heart disease, and conditions

There are multiple examples of physicians at Abbott Northwestern cooperating to improve outcomes and improve their departments, rather than viewing their colleagues as competitors. This spirit was rather unusual both in the community as well as in the profession.

such as obesity and diabetes, conditions that only an affluent society can afford to dwell on.

Abbott Northwestern Hospital was able to attract a talented group of physicians to join the medical staff partly because of its history as well as its reputation. There are multiple examples of physicians at Abbott Northwestern cooperating to improve outcomes and improve their departments, rather than viewing their colleagues as competitors. This spirit was rather unusual both in the community as well as in the profession.

In addition to the talents of the medical staff, revolutionary changes occurred in the science of medicine with the development of new products and equipment such as the artificial lens to replace the cataract and radiological equipment, including the CT scan and MRI. Some of these changes led to the development of new specialties, such as interventional neuroradiology. Some of the specialties were dramatically changed to the point of disappearing, while others thrived through the development of revolutionary new techniques. In many cases, the Medical Staff at Abbott Northwestern led the way, pioneering and excelling in a remarkable number of these developments in treatment and prevention.

 Part II brings you the stories of these changes as told by 30 individuals associated with Abbott Northwestern, including 25 physicians, two nurses, two chaplains, and a librarian. I am indebted to them for their research, expertise, and insight in describing the practice of medicine at Abbott Northwestern Hospital.

The changes in medical technology continue to race forward. The period of time described here relates more to the practitioners describing them than to any other marker of change. In fact, the evolution of medical science is proceeding at a more rapid pace than ever. This is the nature of medicine in the modern world.

Enjoy these stories and their portrayal of the practice of medicine from the 1960s to the 21st century. I think you'll agree that Abbott Northwestern Hospital's reputation for excellence is well-deserved, and that those who contributed to and strive to continue this legacy have much about which to be proud.

1

Anatomic Pathology

1980-2015

Dr. John W. Jones

Anatomic pathology is the examination of organs and tissues as a diagnostic tool. The practice of anatomic pathology at Abbott Northwestern Hospital has undergone extraordinary change in the past 35 years. These changes include a major expansion of the pathology staff, development of subspecialty expertise, and the addition of an ever-expanding scope of ancillary testing.

In the early 1980s, the Abbott Northwestern Pathology Department was staffed by seven general pathologists, all of whom provided surgical pathology, cytopathology (cell pathology), and autopsy services. Ancillary testing was limited to various histochemical stains (trichrome, elastic, Congo red, etc., along with gram, acid-fast, and fungal stains for suspected infectious cases). Subspecialization in surgical pathology did not exist. Following the merger of Abbott and Northwestern hospitals in 1970, Dr. Craig Freeman provided initial leadership. Dr. Mark Arnesen became laboratory director after Dr. Freeman retired in 1983. Dr. Arnesen initiated subspecialization in Anatomic Pathology with the recruitment of Dr. Charles Horwitz, a highly respected Minneapolis pathologist who became director of Cytopathology Services.

An early development was the acquisition of an electron microscope in 1980 to assist with tumor diagnosis. Electron microscopy, however, turned out to be beneficial in only a handful of cases and was soon made obsolete with the advent of immunohistochemistry, the cellular chemistry of the immune system. Immunoperoxidase stains (a technique to detect enzymatic antigens in tissues) proved to be less expensive, less labor-intensive, and far more practical for the characterization of the vast majority of neoplasms (tumors) encountered in our practice. Electron microscopy today is primarily restricted to specialized laboratories for evaluation of medical, renal, and neuromuscular biopsies, as well as used as a research tool. Our electron microscope was finally wheeled out of the laboratory in 1990.

We remained a group of general pathologists through the 1980s into the early 1990s. A dramatic change occurred in 1995, when the formation of Allina led to the merger of the Abbott Northwestern pathology staff with those of United, Mercy, and Unity Hospitals. We suddenly grew from nine to 18 pathologists to ensure that all Allina pathologists would have staff privileges at the four major Twin Cities hospitals. This expansion permitted the development of subspecialization in surgical pathology, initially spearheaded by the recruitment of Dr. Kenneth Batts from Rochester Mayo Clinic. Dr. Batts, a nationally acclaimed expert in hepatobiliary (the liver and bile system) and gastrointestinal pathology, developed a subgroup of gastrointestinal pathologists at Abbott Northwestern.

Other subspecialty groups were gradually developed and currently include breast, gynecology, genitourinary, pulmonary, hematopathology, neuropathology, and dermatopathology. With subspecialization came initiatives to standardize pathology reports, along with the inclusion of staging parameters for the great majority of new malignancies. Subspecialization has allowed us to work effectively with our clinical colleagues at the Virginia Piper Cancer Institute. The hospital-wide "Tumor Conference" of the 1980s has long since been abandoned. Instead, numerous subspecialty tumor conferences, all of which include participation by a pathologist, are now held.

The number of staff pathologists credentialed at Abbott Northwestern Hospital has continued to expand to accommodate an ever-increasing workload. The surgical pathology caseload not only includes tissue specimens from the major Allina hospitals, but also from an expanding number of outpatient

Allina medical clinics and Allina-affiliated hospitals. We currently provide pathology services in Cambridge, Buffalo, Northfield, Hastings, Monticello, Faribault, Owatonna, Shakopee, and Hutchinson in Minnesota, as well as in Grantsburg and River Falls in Wisconsin.

The histology laboratory was eventually centralized at the Tenth Avenue facility in 2011, and all tissue processing in the Allina system is now performed in the new central laboratory.

Resident training in anatomic pathology has been an important part of our activity.

Pathologist Assistants

We recruited our first pathologist assistant (PA) to Abbott Northwestern Hospital in the late 1980s. Prior to the Allina merger, we worked with a single PA at Abbott Northwestern. After 1995, our reliance on PAs increased substantially as our workload expanded. We now partner with a talented group of ten PAs who assist the pathology staff by receiving, examining, and dissecting surgical pathology specimens with minimal pathologist supervision. In addition, the PAs submit tissue, as appropriate, for frozen section and permanent microscopic examination.

This group also contributes to pathology resident training at the "bench" and assists with research protocols requiring fresh tissue from surgery. Other duties include gross specimen photography and submitting samples for special studies such as immunofluorescence, flow cytometry, cytogenetics, microbiology, and molecular diagnostics. Our PA colleagues contribute to the overall efficiency of the department and free up valuable time for the pathologists.

Ancillary Testing

The expansion of ancillary testing in surgical pathology that began with immunohistochemistry in the 1980s continued to expand under the direction of Dr. Tamara Lillemoe. Our immunoperoxidase laboratory now includes approximately 200 separate antigenic (tissue) markers and is invaluable in tumor diagnosis. In addition, this laboratory performs in situ hybridization (ISH) testing, which places markers on chromosomes. One important application of ISH testing is its use to provide prognostic information for high-risk human papilloma

Dr. Lillemoe's laboratory has also developed an image analysis technique for measuring estrogen and progesterone receptor activity for carcinoma of the breast.

virus (HPV) for squamous cell carcinoma of the head and neck. Dr. Lillemoe's laboratory has also developed an image analysis technique for measuring estrogen and progesterone receptor activity for carcinoma of the breast.

Flow Cytometry

The Flow Cytometry laboratory under the direction of Dr. Stan McCormick is routinely utilized for characterization and sub classification of most lymphoid neoplasms (cancers) via lymphocyte immunophenotyping. This is a process used to identify cells based on the type of antigens or markers on the surface of the cell. The data provided by this laboratory includes important prognostic information as well.

Molecular Diagnostics

The Molecular Diagnostics laboratory under the direction of Dr. John Reinartz and Dr. John Mendiola made major contributions to lymphoma diagnosis and classification. This involved the use of polymerase chain reaction (PCR), a technique that makes multiple copies of DNA. In addition, Southern blot technologies are used to detect B and T cell gene rearrangements to diagnose T-cell lymphoma. These techniques are particularly useful when tissue is limited and flow cytometry is not available. PCR technology is also being used to detect other tumor markers such as EGFR and KRAS mutations in patients with lung cancer (stage IV pulmonary adenocarcinoma) and BRAF mutations in patients with metastatic melanoma. These tests have valuable therapeutic and prognostic implications.

Cytogenetics

The Cytogenetics laboratory directed by Dr. Rodney Higgins and Dr. Sue Kang has been useful for characterization of hematologic neoplasms (cancers of the blood), using both classic cytogenetic analysis as well as the technique of fluorescent in situ hybridization (FISH). Fluorescent in situ hybridization involves placing fluorescent markers on parts of chromosomes within a cell. It can detect the presence or absence of specific DNA sequences on tumor chromosomes. The FISH test for HER-2/neu is important for breast cancer patients. The over expression of this oncoprotein is associated with a high risk of early relapse and poor prognosis. (An oncoprotein is coded by an oncogene, which is a gene that transforms a cell into a tumor cell.)

Resident Training Program

Throughout this period, resident training in anatomic pathology has been an important part of our activity. Dr. Nikola Kostich gained approval in 1981 from the American Board of Pathology for an independent pathology residency at Abbott Northwestern Hospital. Our program was subsequently incorporated into a combined residency with Hennepin County Medical Center. Residency training for pathologists in Minneapolis has continued to evolve. We currently participate in a city-wide training program that includes the University of Minnesota, Minneapolis VA Medical Center, and Hennepin County Medical Center.

Our involvement in the pathology residency at Abbott Northwestern is limited to anatomic pathology, with residents participating in surgical pathology, cytopathology, and autopsies. Many outstanding pathology residents have rotated through Abbott Northwestern Hospital over the years, nine of whom are currently members of our pathology staff.

Autopsy Service

One area that has not been expanding is the autopsy service, with autopsy numbers dropping from greater than 250 in 1980 to fewer than 50 in 2013. However the autopsy retains its value, not only as a teaching tool for our residents, but also as a means of providing diagnostic feedback to the clinical staff. The importance of the autopsy should not be underestimated. Unexpected findings, occasionally major in nature, continue to be identified. One casualty in the decline of the autopsy has been the elimination of a monthly Cardiac Pathology conference initially staffed by Dr. Jesse Edwards and subsequently by Dr. Jack Titus from the Jesse E. Edwards Registry of Cardiovascular Pathology. This

conference was well received and attracted both Clinical Cardiology and Pathology staff. The elimination of this popular conference was a direct result of the decline in autopsy numbers.

Summary

In summary, the Pathology Department at Abbott Northwestern Hospital has grown from seven general pathologists in 1980 to 35 pathologists in 2014. As a result, we are able to provide subspecialty expertise in surgical pathology and incorporate an ever-expanding variety of ancillary testing. Particular recognition should be given to Dr. Mark Arnesen and Dr. John Strickler for their valuable leadership in overseeing this expansion. Pathology at Abbott Northwestern is in the capable hands of its current director, Dr. William McDonald, who is the first board-certified neuropathologist to join our staff. We look to the future with optimism and remain committed to providing state-of-the-art pathology services to the hospitals and physicians we are privileged to serve.

2

Anesthesia
1964-2014
Dr. Bryce C. Beverlin

In the early1960s, Abbott Hospital and Northwestern Hospital were separate entities with their own administration and staff, sharing some of the physician staff. Surgical cases were growing both in number and complexity due to the baby-boomer demographics post WWII. Close ties between staff and other institutions like the University of Minnesota, University of Wisconsin, and the Mayo Clinic assured that anesthesia practice would keep pace with the latest advances in the field. Social, economic, safety, and scientific advances were the driving forces that would mold anesthesia private practice throughout the country and at Abbott Northwestern.

In 1960, locations for administering anesthesia consisted of a few operating rooms in Northwestern Hospital and a few at Abbott Hospital. With expansion in the 1970s, the number of operating rooms at Abbott Northwestern increased to nearly twenty. Obstetrics opened an additional two operating rooms in the new facility. Anesthesia was also delivered in the mental health area for ECT (shock therapy). Occasionally, Radiology would request an anesthesia team for certain procedures like CT scans and fluoroscopy. As more heart surgeons came to Abbott Northwestern, so did anesthesiologists who specialized in the growing field of cardiac surgery. Heart surgeries included coronary bypass, heart valve replacements/repair, transplants, and

Social, economic, safety, and scientific advances were the driving forces that would mold anesthesia private practice throughout the country and at Abbott Northwestern.

artificial heart mechanisms like the Jarvik Heart. Six rooms were remodeled to make them suitable for the expanding caseload.

In 1970, Ford and Reed opened their first freestanding Surgicenter® in Arizona. Hospitals began to perform outpatient surgeries. The American Association of Anesthesiologists approved guidelines for safe administration of anesthesia in outpatient surgery centers in 1973. Medicare and other insurers approved increasing numbers of procedures in the outpatient setting. The hurdles for anesthesia were shorter recovery times with adequate pain relief and lowering post-operative side effects like nausea – the reasons a patient might not be able to be discharged to home after surgery.

By the early 1980s, select cases were admitted as same-day admission and some as outpatient surgery. By the middle of the 1980s, ten new rooms were opened and dedicated to outpatient surgery, including three for ophthalmology. By 1987, ophthalmology moved off campus to the Phillips Eye Institute, but outpatient surgery was growing and other types of cases filled those rooms.

Construction of the new Virginia Piper Building allowed for the creation of six new rooms and a new Preoperative Care Center. With all of these new operating rooms came increased ENT, Gynecologic, Orthopedic, Plastic, and Urologic caseloads. During the 1990s, the top floor of the Virginia Piper Institute would become the Minimally Invasive Care Center, adding three more operating locations. After 2000, three more anesthetizing locations were added for operative endoscopy.

Between 1980 and 2000, Cardiology increased the number of cases in the catheterization labs. These were the early days of coronary artery dilations/stents, ablations for rhythm disturbances, and complicated pacemaker/defibrillator procedures. In 2005, the Heart Hospital opened on campus, attached to the main hospital. Heart surgeries and the catheterization labs moved there, and some anesthesia personnel followed to provide services. Old cath labs and previous heart surgery rooms were then remodeled to accommodate the latest DaVinci robotic laparoscopic surgery. The Department of Anesthesiology grew accordingly to meet the needs of these expanding requests.

In addition to the growth of the operating suites, obstetrical anesthesia grew dramatically during these years due to the increasing demand for epidural anesthesia for labor. In addition, HealthPartners obstetrical patients were served by Abbott Northwestern, which increased the referral of complex obstetrical cases due to the proximity of Children's Hospital, which was providing neonatal care. More recently, The Mother Baby Center was constructed with a skyway link to Abbott Northwestern. Anesthesia again followed!

Yet another area of growth outside of the operating suites was Radiology. General anesthesia was provided for Magnetic Resonance Imaging (MRI), fluoroscopy, Radiation Oncology, and Interventional Radiology. This included catheterization for coiling or shunting of aneurysms in the brain, clot extraction for strokes, arteriovenous malformation treatment in the brain, CT scan ablation techniques, hepatic vein shunting and others.

With all of this growth, operations grew to well over 100 per day. The number of operating rooms had nearly tripled. The total number of "anesthetizing locations" had increased four-fold. Outpatient Surgery numbers increased steadily, as a part of this growth. Some estimates put outpatient surgery today at 65 percent of all surgeries. The Anesthesia Department grew proportionately to accommodate the increasing needs of the main operating suite of rooms, Heart Hospital, obstetrical, and radiology demands. Not only was there a growth in the number of anesthesia providers but also these providers needed to keep abreast of the latest scientific developments and techniques. Credentialing made sure that every provider was ready to offer cutting-edge anesthesia for patients at Abbott Northwestern Hospital.

The hurdles for anesthesia were shorter recovery times with adequate pain relief and lowering post-operative side effects like nausea – the reasons a patient might not be able to be discharged to home after surgery.

Techniques and Pharmacology

Flash back to the Sixties. The typical general anesthetic in 1960 included sedation with a pre-operative barbiturate, intravenous sodium pentothal to induce sleep, muscle relaxation with curare or succinylcholine, then maintenance with a non-flammable, inhaled agent like Halothane vaporized in a copper kettle or Vernitrol using a nitrous oxide/oxygen mixture for gas flow. Muscle relaxant drugs were "reversed" before wake-up. Morphine was used mostly for post-operative pain relief. Gas machines consisted of pressure regulators from tanks of oxygen and nitrous oxide flowing through metered columns. The gas mixture was then directed through the vaporizer to a semi-closed circle of delivery tubes using a soda-lime carbon dioxide absorber. Knowledge of respiratory

With all of this growth, operations grew to well over 100 per day. The number of operating rooms had nearly tripled. The total number of "anesthetizing locations" had increased four-fold.

physiology and methods of ventilation had substantially improved after the polio epidemic a few years earlier. Mechanical ventilation could now be used during and after the operation as needed.

Monitoring included a blood pressure cuff, a precordial or esophageal stethoscope, and direct observation of skin color and temperature. Vital signs and other observations were charted along with the administered agents as a permanent record to review later. Most surgical patients were admitted to the hospital the night before surgery for work-up, and the operation was performed in the operating room. Afterward, the patient would go to a dedicated recovery room prior to returning to their hospital room. It was common for patients to remain in the hospital many days before discharge home.

This was all about to change.

Techniques and knowledge in many fields of medicine advanced over the next 50 years. Surgeons devised new methods of operating that would cause patients less trauma, quicker recovery, and shorter hospital stays. Some procedures were transferred to outpatient surgery. Laparoscopic surgery was among these important techniques. Surgeries that more than likely were performed as outpatient were ophthalmology, otolaryngology (ENT) procedures, laparoscopic cholecystectomy (removal of the gall bladder), hernia repair, lumpectomies, many urologic procedures, laparoscopic gynecologic procedures including hysterectomy. Many orthopedic procedures and some herniated disc procedures were performed on an outpatient basis.

Without scientific advances and improvements to the quality of anesthesia, outpatient surgery would not have been possible. The knowledge of pharmacology, cardiac, and respiratory physiology grew, and research and development at major pharmaceutical companies mirrored this growth. Drugs were being developed that did impact the practice of anesthesia dramatically. A given drug might, however, be developed in one year but not make it to clinical practice at Abbott Northwestern for a decade or more, depending on trials and Food and Drug Administration approval. Information about a new drug prior to its release was disseminated through journals and conferences prior to its use in private practice. As an example of this lag, Etomidate (used to induce sleep) was developed in 1964 but not released until 1972 in Europe and 1983 in the United States.

There was a continual quest to find the best anesthetic. The best anesthetic might be defined as one with the following properties: anxiolytic (without stress), analgesic (without pain), amnesic (without memory), and anesthetic (without sensation), plus rapid onset and recovery, fewest side effects, easily administered, non-flammable, and least expensive. The work of Woodbridge in 1957 formulated general anesthesia into four components: (1) sleep or unconsciousness (2) blockade of undesirable reflexes (3) motor blockade and (4) sensory blockade. This can be accomplished with one drug or a combination of several different drugs each in smaller quantities to give a "balanced anesthetic" that would have fewer side effects overall.

Between 1960 and 2010, there were many developments toward achieving these four elements of general anesthesia. Most of these changes were made to increase safety, improve recovery time, and decrease the side effects of the anesthetic. This, of course, would play into the needs for outpatient surgery or at least a decreased length of hospital stay.

Credentialing made sure that every provider was ready to offer cutting-edge anesthesia for patients at Abbott Northwestern Hospital.

Sedation

Preoperative sedation with barbiturates was replaced with the use of drugs like Valium and Versed. In the 1960s, a class of drugs was developed including Haldol, Valium, Librium, and Droperidol. Droperidol was one of the first used to attempt to replace the preoperative barbiturate. Innovar was the combination of Droperidol and a newly developed synthetic narcotic, Fentanyl, producing what has been known as "neurolept-anesthesia." Unfortunately, this led to a panic state in some patients, resulting in the cancellation of surgery, and it fell into disfavor.

Versed was introduced in the late 1970s and has been an important sedative, allaying anxiety and providing some amnesia about surgical events both during general anesthesia and what's known as "Monitored Anesthesia Care" (MAC). MAC with sedation is accomplished when local anesthesia is administered for sensation/pain relief, and the anesthesia provider, who makes sure the vital signs are kept stable, also gives sedation. It has stood the test of time, and is used widely for many minor operations. It is so effective that many patients swear that they have had a general anesthetic.

Versed was introduced in the late 1970s and has been an important sedative, allaying anxiety and providing some amnesia about surgical events both during general anesthesia and what's known as "Monitored Anesthesia Care" (MAC).

Sodium pentothal, given intravenously, was crowned "king" in 1934 for inducing sleep during a general anesthetic, when Ralph Waters at the University of Wisconsin first used it clinically. It was replaced in the late 1960s by new drugs. Ketamine was introduced as a "dissociative anesthetic" first administered in 1970 to soldiers in the Vietnam War because of its ease of use in the field. It had a rapid onset of action and did not depress the heart or respiration. It was also a profound analgesic. However, because of its potential to create psychosis during recovery, it fell out of favor as an anesthetic in and of itself, though the postoperative effects could be lessened with lower doses and when used in combination with other agents. Ketamine is used in smaller doses today, along with other maintenance drugs or in an infusion as an adjuvant for pain relief in opiod-tolerant individuals.

Etomidate was developed in 1964 but not released here until 1983. It did not have the cardiac depression that was an undesirable side effect of Pentothal. Yet it had its own undesirable side effects that did not allow it to take the throne. After many years of development, the new king of induction agents came along, namely Propofol, released for clinical use in 1986. This drug has replaced sodium pentothal for intravenous induction of anesthesia. The properties of rapid onset, rapid recovery, "clear head on arousal," and anti-nausea make it a near-perfect drug for induction of anesthesia. It can also be infused constantly with a pump for maintenance of general or MAC anesthesia. The combination of Versed and Propofol basically won over the kingdom!

Blocking agents

Drugs to block muscle movements started with curare a long time ago. Because of its potentially deadly side effects (no breathing with relaxed patient), it was used only when necessary to place a breathing tube or to relax the operative field for closure. Various drugs had been discovered, which could "reverse" the effects but sometimes incompletely, leading to respiratory failure in recovery. Many deaths were attributed to just this complication.

Pancuronium was marketed in 1964 as a non-depolarizing, long-acting, amino steroid muscle relaxant with fewer side effects and more completely reversible. Vecuronium and Atracurium are two muscle relaxants introduced into practice in the 1980s. Both were shorter acting than previous relaxants and had fewer side effects. Their mechanisms of elimination make them unique and useful for certain patients with kidney or liver disease and even less likely to cause respiratory failure in recovery. In 1994, Rocuronium was introduced. Its properties made it a faster onset than Vecuronium and shorter acting, making it more controllable, particularly because it could be titrated using an infusion pump.

We were coming closer to the ideal muscle relaxant.

As for inhaled anesthetics prior to the 1960s, empiricism ruled both practice and research. Little could be measured accurately. Clinical experience rather than evidence-based medicine drove anesthesia administration. Edmond Eger's research in 1963 defined minimal alveolar concentration (a different "MAC") more clearly. Temperature-compensated vaporizers improved along with these new agents to allow more scientifically precise methods of administration of these new volatile anesthetics. Now, there was a "measuring stick" with which to compare these inhaled anesthetics and any new ones that might be developed.

More fluorinated inhalation agents were being developed. Halothane was still being used, but incidents of liver failure in adults occurred after repeated exposure. Although a large study somewhat vindicated the drug, it was not the perfect inhalation agent. The quest was on, and the volatile anesthetic Methoxyflurane (Penthrane) was released in 1960. It was used clinically until the late 1970s, when it was discontinued due to its potential kidney toxicity with metabolic release of inorganic fluoride.

Next came Enflurane, first used in 1966. It had a degree of heart toxicity and lowered the seizure threshold. Even so, it started to replace Halothane in adults by the 1970s. Enflurane's pungent odor did not make it suitable for children for inhalation induction (the common method), so Halothane hung on until something better came along.

In 1981, Isoflurane, an isomer of Enflurane was finally released. With shorter onset, little cardiac effects, and no seizure potential, this agent would replace Enflurane in adults. In 1987, Desflurane was released. It gained popularity because of its more rapid onset and recovery, compared to Isoflurane, but it has potential to cause rapid heart rate and still had a pungent odor. In 1993,

Sevoflurane was released as the latest inhalation anesthetic. Low solubility makes it a very rapid onset and a rapid recovery drug, therefore making it more "controllable." It has less pungency, making it more useful than other drugs for pediatric cases and even some adult cases using mask induction. (There is a potential for it to be metabolized to a deleterious Compound A in the presence of moist carbon dioxide absorber chemicals like soda lime. This may be avoided by limiting its concentration/time usage.)

We have progressed greatly toward the best inhalation anesthetic, but we are not there yet. Some have said that Xenon, the noble gas, may be the next. Stay tuned!

Pain Relief

Fentanyl was the first of several synthetic narcotics to be developed in the 1960s. It has properties of rapid action, high potency, short duration, and has fewer side effects than morphine. Today Fentanyl is being used widely for its ability to provide pain relief in all phases of anesthesia. It can be given preoperatively, throughout surgery with either general or MAC, and as a postoperative bridge to longer-acting narcotics. Patient-controlled analgesia was made possible by sophisticated pumps that could administer a continuous dose and patient-initiated boluses (large single doses) as needed. These pumps are able to provide lock-out times to avoid over dosage.

In the late 1970s, Sufentanil was released and had application mostly as an intraoperative analgesic. Its potency is 5-10 times that of Fentanyl. Remifentanil, released in 1996, is the latest of the synthetic narcotics. Its potency is twice that of Fentanyl. The drug has an ultra-short duration due to its ester hydrolysis. This lends itself nicely to infusion controllability like some of the other desirable anesthetic drugs. This one is very close to the ideal narcotic for anesthesia but is still somewhat pricey.

Non-Steroidal Anti-Inflammatory Drugs like Keterolac have contributed to pain relief as I mentioned earlier. The discovery of the μ (Mu) opioid receptors in the spinal dorsal horn cells made central opioid analgesia possible. This is accomplished with spinal or epidural application of narcotics that act on these receptors. This technique has gained some popularity over the last few years.

As an adjunct to pain relief, we see the resurgence of Regional Anesthesia. In 1885, Dr. William S. Halsted recognized that direct application of cocaine to nerves in a region of the body could supply transient relief of pain post operatively. In 1965, Dr. Alon P. Winnie revitalized the concept with longer-acting drugs like bupivicaine applied to the regional plexus of nerves in the upper and lower body with certain percutaneous (needle through the skin) techniques. In the last ten years, more sophisticated ultrasound techniques, better catheters, and controlled administration apparatuses allowed anesthesia to provide improved pain control post operatively.

Nausea

Nausea and vomiting went hand-in-hand with general anesthesia in the early days. This was especially true with ether. After extensive research, we understand that nausea has a multifaceted cause. Everything from genetics to gender and hydration to body habitus may play a role. Nervous system triggers may occur with medications, smells, motion, and other sensory inputs. Several drugs have helped to decrease the incidence of nausea but not abolish it. Propofol seems to have its own anti-nausea effect. Metoclopramide (Reglan) helps in some by emptying the stomach. Droperidol in small doses is known to decrease nausea. Probably the greatest breakthrough occurred with the discovery of the 5-HT3 (serotonin) receptor around 1985. In 1991, the FDA approved Odansetron (Zofran) a potent 5-HT3 receptor antagonist. Although Droperidol and Odansetron have potential cardiac complications, they are the best we have to curb post-operative nausea/vomiting. I'm sure more will need to be accomplished in this area.

Additional Developments

As an alternative to general anesthesia, neuraxial anesthesia with local anesthetics of varying durations can be used. Spinal anesthesia has been available for lower body procedures like urology, gynecology, and orthopedics. Epidural

Patient-controlled analgesia was made possible by sophisticated pumps that could administer a continuous dose and patient-initiated boluses (large single doses) as needed. These pumps are able to provide lock-out times to avoid over dosage.

anesthesia was in its infancy in the 1960s but used in labor and delivery mostly in its "caudal" method. Lumbar epidural for labor pain relief was being perfected in the 1960s but very few would choose to use it in those early years. Reliable epidural catheters for repeat dosage were not available until the 1970s. This route requires less use of drugs, results in fewer drops in blood pressure, and the block can be extended for a cesarean section if necessary. The epidural could now be administered earlier in labor rather than just before delivery.

More compact and reliable pumps became available in the 1980s for continuous administration. Some now even allow patient control (PCEA). Longer-acting local anesthetics like Bupivicaine were developed in the mid-1960s but found to have some cardiac toxicity in higher concentrations. In the 1980s, opioids like Fentanyl were added to the mix to allow even less local anesthetic and decrease in epidural side effects. Ropivicaine with less toxicity was developed in 1996 and has replaced the use of Bupivicaine completely for epidurals. During the 1990s, a technique of combined spinal/epidural became popular. The spinal would act very quickly to relieve pain, and the epidural could be administered continuously. The use of epidural analgesia in labor is as high as 80 percent in some hospitals.

Fiber optics has improved placement of breathing tubes. Initially used in endoscopies, thoracic, and ENT surgeries, many other fields of medicine, including anesthesia, quickly adopted them. From difficult intubations to placement of double-lumen tubes for single lung technique used in thoracic surgery, the fiber optic scope has been indispensible. Fiber optic laryngoscopes using video have recently made their way to the provider's armamentarium. Another item in the tools of the trade is the Laryngeal Mask Airway. Developed in the 1980s in Europe as an alternative to a breathing tube, it made its way "across the pond" quickly. This device is used in select patients, especially those in certain outpatient surgeries. It has also made its way to the algorithm during difficult intubation.

Improvement in monitoring over the last 50 years is one of the main reasons safety has been a driving force in anesthesia. Increased knowledge of body fluid and acid-base homeostasis made it possible to readily test the acid-base status with newly devised electrodes for oxygen, carbon dioxide, and pH of blood. One could detect and correct the inadequacies in respiration and blood flow in the surgical patient. "Third spacing" of fluids with the trauma of surgery was better understood so that appropriate salt-water solutions could be administered. The Swan-Ganz catheter (1970s) allowed the practitioner to administer fluid and blood, and to adjust anesthetics to keep the system as steady as possible.

We were even learning to conserve blood components by detecting just what component was needed. The use of autologous transfusion of the patient's own blood, taken a few days before a planned surgery, became a good method for conservation of blood. "Cell saving" was also devised to collect blood from the field of certain surgeries, wash, and return the patient's own red blood cells. Trans Esophageal Echo, developed in 1976, has become the preferred method of detecting heart function and is used extensively today.

Monitoring the agents delivered and exhaled by a patient has been in the works over many years with various techniques, including mass spectrometry and, later, less-expensive infrared methods. The more knowledge of "real time" events is possible, the more controlled and safer the anesthetic. Inhaled agent monitoring would mean better management and possibly lower the cost of the anesthetic.

In 1986, the Harvard Monitoring Standards were published in response to studies that showed at least 4 percent of critical incidents in anesthesia were caused by human error. These incidents were preventable with certain strategies such as better training, supervision, ergonomics, and monitoring. They recommended continual presence of a provider, blood pressure, and pulse (EKG and pulse oximetry) to be charted every five minutes, continuous monitoring of ventilation and circulation by alarm-capable oxygen delivery analysis, breathing circuit disconnect alarms, end-tidal carbon dioxide detection for breathing tube placement, and continuous temperature measurement. These recommendations were adopted by the ASA (American Society of Anesthesiologists) and AANA (American Association of Nurse Anesthetists) immediately. With these new monitors on every case, the cost of anesthesia rose, but the number of critical incidents and malpractice suits declined dramatically. Mortality from anesthesia in 1930 was almost 1 in 1,000, but by 2010 the rate had dropped to less than 1 in 200,000.

Social, economic, scientific, and safety factors will continue to drive the

The more knowledge of "real time" events is possible, the more controlled and safer the anesthetic. Inhaled agent monitoring would mean better management and possibly lower the cost of the anesthetic.

practice of anesthesia to become better. We have come a long way in seeking the "best anesthetic," but are not quite there yet. As long as there is a desire to keep looking, anesthesia at Abbott Northwestern will continue to draw on a rich tradition of academics applied to clinical practice.

3

Cancer Care
1800-2014
Dr. Thomas P. Flynn

The evolution of cancer care at Abbott Northwestern Hospital has mirrored the evolution of cancer care in history. The three major components of cancer treatment – surgery, radiation, and chemotherapy – came into existence in that order. Cancer care, of course, encompasses far more than treatment. The elements of prevention, screening and early detection, survivorship care, palliative care, and hospice are each critical in their own right, and will be addressed briefly in this history, recognizing that each could fill many pages on its own.

Surgery

Surgical treatment of cancer dates back to prehistoric times. The oldest known surgical texts were written in Egypt 3500 years ago. The work of Vesalius on anatomic dissections in the sixteenth century brought to Europe a whole new understanding of the field. Then with the advent of anesthesia in the mid-nineteenth century, using ether and chloroform, much more invasive procedures became possible. To this day, surgery remains the foundation of treatment for many cancers that fall into the category of "solid" tumors.

Cancer care, of course, encompasses far more than treatment. The elements of prevention, screening and early detection, survivorship care, palliative care, and hospice are each critical in their own right.

Initial concepts focused on "getting it all." In the early days of cancer surgery, if a tumor couldn't be removed in its entirety, or was considered "inoperable," there was little else to offer. The patient could anticipate that their cancer would progress and lead to death. For decades, the thinking was that if surgery could remove more tissue around the tumor, the patient's chance for cure would be improved. In the late 1800s, Dr. William Halstead at Johns Hopkins Hospital was a proponent of increasingly radical surgery for breast cancer. He was in favor of taking more and more tissue, removing not only the chest wall muscles (pectoralis major and pectoralis minor), but also dissecting lymph nodes in the supraclavicular, infraclavicular, and mediastinal locations in addition to the nodes in the axillary region. Despite the "Halstead radical" mastectomy procedure, many patients suffered recurrence of their cancer both locally and in distant sites. Out of this experience, concepts of cancer biology and micro-metastatic disease eventually evolved. As a result, the approaches of postoperative adjuvant chemotherapy and postoperative radiation therapy were developed for many malignancies.

Subsequent to the merger of Abbott and Northwestern hospitals in 1970, surgeons caring for cancer patients included Drs. David Hickok, Leonard Schultz, and later Jack Graber. Dr. Bill Stephens joined that group in the latter part of his career. Others included:

- Dr. Henry Sosin and Dr. Michael Schwartz had another surgical practice and were involved in cancer surgery, as were a group of surgeons made up of Drs. John Parrot, John O'Leary, and Ernie Lampe.

- Dr. Dan Dunn joined the staff in 1985 and established the surgical residency program with residents rotating from Hennepin County Medical Center. Dr. Dunn left to practice medicine in Texas in 1994, but returned in 1996.

- Dr. Margit Bretzke was recruited to join the group in the early 1990s. She brought a strong interest and expertise in breast cancer.

- Dr. Robert Harrie practiced general surgery at Abbott Northwestern Hospital for several years before moving to the Southwest U.S.

In the early 1990s, discussions began around the development of a breast cancer center. (See section on the Virginia Piper Breast Cancer Institute.) Oncologic surgery at Abbott Northwestern saw steady advancement and innovation in many areas beyond the outstanding work of the Piper Breast Center. Building on the multidisciplinary approach, programs for the treatment of a number of malignancies have evolved. Dr. Dan Dunn and Dr. Eric Johnson developed robotic surgical techniques for resection of esophageal cancers and have presented their experience and results at national meetings. Dr. Peter Dahlberg came later from River Falls, Wisconsin, to join that team.

The colorectal surgery group, led by Dr. Stanley Goldberg and, more recently by Dr. Ann Lowry, has provided surgical expertise for cancers of the colon and rectum for decades. Currently there is a multidisciplinary approach, particularly for rectal cancer. Dr. Charles Finne employed radiation within the cavity of the rectum for early rectal cancers for many years. (See Radiation Therapy below.) General surgeons have been performing resections for colon cancer as well.

Surgical Specialists (Drs. Dan Dunn, Margit Bretzke et al) brought in a formally trained surgical oncologist, Dr. Cassandra Anderson. Dr. Anderson provided additional expertise, particularly in the areas of sarcomas and melanomas, along with the specialized technique of hyperthermic intraperitoneal chemotherapy. She also became involved with management of cancers of the esophagus and gastric (stomach) pouch. Most recently, in 2015, another surgical oncologist, Dr. Natasha Rueth, joined the medical staff with that group.

Radiation Therapy

Radiation therapy has been in use for the treatment of cancer for more than one hundred years. The discovery of X-rays by the German physicist Wilhelm Roentgen in 1895 was followed soon after by the application of X-rays in the treatment of cancer. Dr. Emil Grubb of Chicago was probably the first American physician to use X-rays to treat cancer (1896). Marie Curie discovered radium, which later led to cobalt therapy. She also discovered cesium, which was used to treat cancer beginning in the mid-1900s. Cobalt remained the mainstay of radiation therapy into the 1980s in much of the world, and it is still used in the developing world. Modern equipment to deliver high-energy radiation came into use some time after the development of linear accelerators in the late

Oncologic surgery at Abbott Northwestern saw steady advancement and innovation in many areas beyond the outstanding work of the Piper Breast Center.

1940s. This allowed for more focused delivery of higher doses of radiation to a tumor site, while at the same time limiting the amount of radiation delivered to the normal surrounding tissues.

In the 1930s, a Swiss radiologist, Dr. Renee Gilbert, had shown that radiation could temporarily shrink lymph nodes involved with Hodgkin's lymphoma. However, the disease typically recurred, often in lymph nodes surrounding the treated ones. A Canadian surgeon named Dr. Vera Peters broadened the radiation field to include an entire region of lymph nodes. Her retrospective data seemed to indicate results better than treating only the enlarged node. In the 1950s, Dr. Henry Kaplan at Stanford University used the high-energy radiation from a linear accelerator to treat early-stage Hodgkin's lymphoma, ultimately performing seminal trials using a randomized prospective design. By the 1960s, this demonstrated that extended field radiation could be a curative therapy for those with lymph node involvement of limited extent.

At Northwestern Hospital, Dr. Cyrus O. Hanson provided radiation therapy in the early days. He was a radiologist, using what is now considered low energy radiation from 250 kV orthovoltage equipment. In 1963, Dr. Donn Mosser came to Northwestern Hospital from the University of Minnesota, establishing a more formal department of therapeutic radiology. Dr. Mosser was one of the first radiation specialists to use cobalt therapy in Minnesota as well as in the U.S. The first rotational cobalt machine at the hospital was installed at that time. Bertha Walker, wife of Archie Walker, the youngest child of Harriet Walker, who had started Northwestern Hospital donated the funds to make this possible. Grace Dayton, of the family-owned Dayton's department store, provided funds for a research effort.

Dr. Mosser was the first formally trained, full-time Radiation Therapist at Northwestern and subsequently at Abbott Northwestern Hospital. This position is now designated as Radiation Oncologist. In 1963, Dr. John Kelly came to the department to work with Dr. Mosser. They formed their own group in 1969 after initially being part of a radiology group. Dr. Tom Fallon joined the practice, and subsequently moved his practice to Willmar. Dr. Kelly continued in the department until the early 1990s. Later, Dr. Larry Past was part of the department for several years.

In 1979, an X-ray simulator was added. The first linear accelerator, a

Siemens 10 MV machine, was installed. Thomas Payne, Ph.D., joined the department as a medical physicist. His specialized expertise was needed to provide oversight and quality control for the new, more powerful equipment. In 1985, in cooperation with Dr. Charles Finne of colorectal surgery, a 50 kv Phillips endocavitary therapy modality was added specifically for the treatment of early stage rectal cancer. This allowed radiation to be delivered from inside the rectal cavity.

1990 was a year of significant change. Dr. Mosser retired after running the department for 27 years. As he liked to joke, he was the highest-paid parking attendant at Abbott Northwestern Hospital, making sure that only radiation patients could park in the designated spots just outside the radiation department. A new Siemans linear accelerator was installed in 1990, along with a multileaf collimator to control dosages. This technology made it possible to focus radiation on the cancerous areas while limiting the amount of radiation going to normal tissues, without having to use lead blocks carved specifically for each patient.

Dr. Tae Kim came to the department as Medical Director of Radiation Oncology in 1990. He distinguished himself on the University of Minnesota Medical School faculty with a particular expertise in pediatric cancers. In addition, he developed the use of total body radiation in bone marrow transplantation. Dr. Kim established a new practice group, Minnesota Radiation Oncology, P.A. In 1991, a Nucletron High Dose Rate Brachytherapy machine was installed, providing the capability to deliver very high doses of radiation to very localized areas in a relatively short time. (Brachytherapy places seeds or other sources of high radiation near a tumor.)

Dr. David Monyak joined the group as a full-time radiation oncologist from the faculty of the University of Minnesota Medical School. The first linear-accelerator cone rotational arc frame-based radiosurgery was administered in 1992. Used for brain cancer, this treatment involved attaching a metal frame to the patient's skull in order to deliver highly focused radiation to a precise location in the brain.

The last rotational Cobalt machine was retired in 1994 with the addition of a new Siemans linear accelerator and a mutileaf collimator. Special software (Philips Pinnacle) was added in 1999 to provide three-dimensional, conformal

In 1991, a Nucletron High Dose Rate Brachytherapy machine was installed, providing the capability to deliver very high doses of radiation to very localized areas in a relatively short time.

radiation therapy planning. In 2002, software (Corvus) was deployed to make it possible to deliver intensity-modulated radiation therapy (IMRT), making Abbott Northwestern the first institution in the Twin Cities with that capability. With IMRT it is possible to further refine the treatment field to focus on the cancer and minimize radiation exposure of normal tissues. Along those lines, the department also instituted image-guided radiation using a special ultrasound unit known as BAT (B-mode acquisition and targeting). This was used, for example, to treat prostate cancer. The image guidance is important since the prostate's position in the pelvis can vary from day to day and one needs to deliver high doses of radiation to a small area, without damaging the bladder or rectum, in order to achieve a cure.

Over the next several years a number of additions and changes occurred. In 2003, Richard Giese, Ph.D., became head of medical physics. Dr. Margaret Winters and Dr. David Pence provided additional part-time professional services. Dr. Patsa Sullivan joined the group as a full-time radiation oncologist in 2005. That year, radioembolization treatments were started using SIR-Spheres. These are tiny packages of radioactivity injected directly into the liver. The department began providing Zevalin® radioimmunotherapy. The latter is a radioactive isotope attached to a monoclonal antibody that delivers the radioactivity specifically to certain lymphoma cells – a "smart bomb" of sorts. Dr. Kim retired in 2006, and Dr. Carol Grabowski became medical director of Radiation Oncology. The department acquired its first Varian Trilogy linear accelerator, which brought further technical capabilities for the delivery of radiation treatments. With the availability of this new technology, the kV superficial radiation machine was retired.

Advancements continued unabated thereafter, with the addition of respiratory gating in 2007. This allowed for the radiation delivery to be coordinated with the movements of the patient's breathing. Stereotactic ablative body radiotherapy (SABR) made it possible to deliver focused, high doses of radiation to a small area virtually anywhere in the body. Initial use of this technique included the treatment of small lung cancers in patients who were not candidates for surgery.

Dr. Laura Willson joined the group as a full-time radiation oncologist in 2008. In 2009, the high-dose-rate brachytherapy suite was remodeled with the addition of a Simulex cone beam-CT simulator. Late 2009 saw the addition of a second Varian Trilogy linear accelerator. In early 2010, the department began using "Rapid Arc" IMRT delivery, which helped shorten the length of time to deliver each treatment. Dr. Sally Lee took over as head of medical physics in April 2010. Dr. Grabowski left the group in 2012 to pursue other interests, including palliative care.

In 2013, the department achieved accreditation by the American College of Radiology, the only department in the Twin Cities to do so voluntarily. (The Minneapolis Veteran's Administration health care system is required to maintain this accreditation as a federal facility.) Such accreditation speaks to the high quality of care and technical expertise that the department at Abbott Northwestern maintains. The same year, the physicians of Minnesota Radiation Oncology, P.A. became employees of Allina Health. On the technology side, while the Phillips endocavitary therapy machine for rectal cancer was retired, a new modality was added. This was the radium 223 radioisotope (Xofigo®) treatment that was used for bone metastases.

In 2015, Vision RT surface mapping technology was installed to allow for patient position monitoring so that stereotactic radiosurgery and radiation therapy can be delivered without rigid immobilization of the patient. As of mid-2015, the department is delivering 55-60 treatments per day on two Varian Trilogy linear accelerators with a GE wide-bore CT simulator for treatment planning. The department provides 80-90 HDR brachytherapy treatments per year. Vision RT surface mapping of patient positioning in real time for image guidance of treatments is now available. Additional capabilities include Yttrium 90 radio-embolization for liver lesions, Novoste beta cath for delivery of radiation into the coronary arteries of the heart, and administration of radio-isotopes Sumarium 153 and Radium 223.

Throughout the consistent pursuit of the best equipment and technology detailed above, the department focused as well on attracting the highest-quality professionals to deliver the best possible care for patients. Radiation Oncologists, physicists, dosimetrists, therapists, and nurses, along with support personnel, have worked as a team to achieve the most technologically advanced treatment capabilities. This has been achieved while never losing sight of the importance

As of mid-2015, the department is delivering 55-60 treatments per day on two Varian Trilogy linear accelerators with a GE wide-bore CT simulator for treatment planning.

of patient service and the patient experience. Patients who have received care in the department consistently speak to the wonderful care they have received.

Medical Oncology

Chemotherapy had its origins far more recently than surgery or radiation therapy. Its story only goes back several decades. In 1942, World War II military investigations of mustard compounds, initially used as agents of warfare, led to the discovery of their anti-tumor effects. A study published in 1946 reported the effectiveness of nitrogen mustard in the treatment of lymphoma, marking the beginning of cancer chemotherapy. Also in the mid-1940s, Dr. Sidney Farber and his colleagues in Boston, after finding that folate supplements promoted the growth of leukemia and lymphoma in children, studied the effects of anti-folates in these patients. In 1948, he reported the induction of complete remissions in childhood leukemia using such agents. For the first time, there was the potential to cure cancer with chemotherapy.

Many new and more effective chemotherapy agents have been developed since that time. These agents have been used both in treating advanced cancer as well as in the surgical adjuvant setting, i.e., after the tumor and adjacent lymph nodes have been removed. This technique has been used to reduce the risk of cancer recurrence and improve cure rates. We have also seen the evolution of and improvements in supportive care, with drugs to prevent and treat the nausea and vomiting associated with chemotherapy. Blood cell growth factors to address low white counts and anemia have come into use.

Medical Oncology has been a designated subspecialty of internal medicine only since 1972. Dr. B. J. Kennedy of the University of Minnesota Masonic Cancer Center, often called the "father of medical oncology," led the achievement of such designation. The professional society for medical oncology, the American Society of Clinical Oncology (ASCO), was established in 1964 as the result of efforts spearheaded by Dr. Arnoldus Goudsmit, then of Rochester, New York, and later on staff at the Minneapolis VA Hospital. ASCO was formed to create a forum for clinical research in oncology.

In 1964, one of B.J. Kennedy's first trainees in oncology, Dr. John Brown, ventured out as the first formally trained medical oncologist to enter communi-

Throughout the consistent pursuit of the best equipment and technology... the department focused as well on attracting the highest-quality professionals to deliver the best possible care for patients.

ty practice in Minnesota. Dr. Brown came to Minnesota after medical school at Washington University in St. Louis. Initially a part of the St. Louis Park Clinic (now Park Nicollet/HealthPartners), he joined the Abbott Northwestern medical staff in 1965. He and Dr. Bud Green provided oncology consultations and care at Abbott Northwestern. Dr. Charles Murray was also on staff. Dr. Lee Newcomer (now Senior Vice President for Oncology at United Health Care) was part of that practice for a few years. Dr. Brown established the first chemotherapy clinic at Abbott Northwestern with just himself and Ann Nelson, RN, seeing the patients, as well as mixing and administering chemotherapy in a very small space.

Also in the 1960s, Dr. James "Seamus" McKenna came to Minnesota after a hematology fellowship at the Medical College of Wisconsin to join Minneapolis Internal Medicine Associates. He recruited Dr. P.J. Flynn, who trained in hematology/oncology at the University of Minnesota, into the practice in 1981. Aware of the growing need for oncology services and seeing the vision of subspecialty practice extending into the future, Dr. Brown left St. Louis Park Clinic and established Oncologic Consultants, P.A. (OC) in 1982 in partnership with Dr. Ignatio Fortuny from the University of Minnesota Medical School. Shortly after, Dr. Burton Schwartz joined them. The practice, initially focused at Abbott Northwestern, Metropolitan Medical Center, and Mount Sinai Hospital, grew steadily in the next several years. Dr. Mark Sborov and Dr. Margaret MacRae left their internal medicine groups to join OC in 1985. Their practice was based at Fairview Southdale Hospital but also covered Abbott Northwestern Hospital. Dr. P. J. Flynn left his internal medicine group to join OC in 1986.

In 1987, Dr. Tom Flynn came from St. Paul Ramsey Medical Center to join the group, practicing primarily at Abbott Northwestern. Dr. McKenna came to OC in 1990, transitioning from his prior Abbott Northwestern-based internal medicine group. He retired from practice in 1998 and worked as a medical director at Allina Hospice. In the 1980s and 1990s, Dr. Neil Hoffman also provided oncology care at Abbott Northwestern as part of his internal medicine practice, later returning to general internal medicine. Dr. Barbara Bowers, who completed her internal medicine residency at Abbott Northwestern and medical oncology fellowship at the University of Minnesota, practiced at Abbott

Northwestern in the 1980s and 1990s both independently and as part of OC. She then moved her practice to Fairview Southdale Hospital.

Dr. Burt Schwartz provided the vision and leadership to develop a group of oncologists and hematologists that spanned the Twin Cities, bringing together three groups in 1995. These included Oncologic Consultants; St. Paul Internal Medicine, led by Dr. Irving Lerner (also a B.J. Kennedy-trained oncologist); and St. Paul Hematology and Oncology, led by Dr. F. Bruce Lewis. This group became Minnesota Oncology Hematology, P.A., which is now known as Minnesota Oncology (MNO).

With the establishment of this subspecialty practice spanning the metropolitan area, the ability to attract additional high-quality physicians was enhanced. This was certainly the case for the portion of the practice based at Abbott Northwestern, given the reputation of the hospital as a tertiary-level facility that was among the best hospitals in the state. Dr. Paul Zander, who trained at the Mayo Clinic, came on board in 1996. Dr. John Seng, who trained at the University of Minnesota, joined the practice in 1998. Dr. Fortuny retired in 1995. Drs. Candy Corey, Gretchen Ibele, and Carol Weitz came to MNO from HealthPartners in 1995, ultimately returning to HealthPartners a few years later. In 2001, Dr. M. Obinna Nwaneri was added to the staff as a hematologist/oncologist. Originally from Nigeria, where he attended medical school, Dr. Nwaneri did his internal medicine residency at Abbott Northwestern and then had his fellowship in oncology at the University of Iowa. Dr. Nwaneri moved to Texas in 2008 to take a research position.

In 2006, Dr. Dean Gesme, who had been a fellow in medical oncology at the University of Minnesota, came back to Minnesota after many years of practice in Cedar Rapids, Iowa, to practice at Abbott Northwestern. Dr. Stuart Bloom, with a particular interest in breast and urologic malignancies, came to Abbott Northwestern from the Humphrey Cancer Institute at North Memorial Hospital in 2008. Also coming from North Memorial, Dr. Tim Larson joined the practice in 2010. Shortly before, Dr. Joe Leach came on staff after several years at Park Nicollet and St. Francis Hospital in Shakopee. In 2010, Dr. Shou-Ching Tang, an established researcher in breast cancer, was jointly recruited by MNO and the Virginia Piper Cancer Institute (VPCI) as the first Stimpson

Chair in Breast Oncology. Dr. Tang left that role to pursue other interests in 2012.

Growth in the medical oncology staff continued with Dr. Michaela Tsai coming on board in 2012 from Park Nicollet to occupy the Stimpson Chair in Breast Oncology at the VPCI. Dr. Vinay Gupta, after a fellowship at the Mayo Clinic, joined the Abbott Northwestern staff in 2014, followed by Dr. Samith Kochuparambil, who also trained at Mayo. At the Abbott Northwestern Hospital WestHealth facility, Dr. Nicole Hartung, who moved over from the east metro part of MNO in 2012, established medical oncology services. Dr. Burt Schwartz also provided care part-time at that site in its initial phase. Dr. Kiran Lassi was added to the staff in 2014. She had previously practiced with Fairview Oncology. Dr. Gesme moved his clinic practice to that site in 2015, and Dr. Uzma Ali, based at Unity Hospital, has been there one day per week since 2014.

Just as the staff in medical oncology expanded dramatically in the decades since the 1960s, so too have the available therapies. When Dr. Brown and Ann Nelson started the clinic in the early 1960s, there were only a handful of chemotherapy agents in use. In addition, chemotherapy was often given in the hospital until the 1980s, when anti-nausea medications were developed that were dramatically more effective. In the early days of chemotherapy, nausea and vomiting were difficult to control. Patients had to spend days in the hospital to receive intravenous hydration. The medications then in use to control the nausea were also very sedating. For some protocols, such as those containing cisplatinum or nitrogen mustard, patients were often "snowed" with drugs such as secobarbital to make the nausea more tolerable. With better anti-emetics and supportive care measures, it became possible to administer most chemotherapy as an outpatient treatment. Over time, most treatment came to be administered in the oncologist's office.

In the early years at Abbott Northwestern, the inpatient medical oncology care was focused on Station 41 in the old part of the hospital. Around 1980, the current unit was established at Station 30 in the newer section of the hospital. The nursing staff, with special focus, education, and experience in oncology provides outstanding, compassionate care for these patients. Before the newer anti-emetic medications were available, more patients were hospitalized to receive chemotherapy. Since the 1990s, patients have required inpatient

The nursing staff, with special focus, education, and experience in oncology provides outstanding, compassionate care for these patients.

care primarily for complications of treatment such as febrile episodes with low white blood cell counts, infections. and dehydration. Chemotherapy regimens requiring infusions still require inpatient administration, and acute leukemia patients are treated in the hospital with stays of four to six weeks.

New and more effective chemotherapy agents have become available for many tumors. More effective adjuvant therapies, which were given to reduce recurrence rates after surgery, were developed first for breast cancer, beginning in 1975. Such therapies in later years were similarly developed for colorectal cancer and most recently for lung cancer.

In 1974, Lawrence Einhorn, a young oncologist at the University of Indiana, developed a combination chemotherapy regimen of cisplatinum, bleomycin, and vinblastine. He began to see dramatic responses in patients with widespread metastases. Those responses were durable, with many patients being cured of their advanced cancer. This represented the first cure of an advanced solid tumor using chemotherapy.

Other treatments have been developed, such as monoclonal antibodies that block angiogenesis, which is the growth of new blood vessels. These new blood vessels are necessary for tumors to grow and metastasize. These treatments block receptors on the cancer cell – inhibiting its growth. Trastuzumab (Herceptin®), in certain breast and gastro-esophageal cancers, performs this function.

In recent decades there has been an explosion in the understanding of cancer at the molecular level. Mutations in the malignant cells of many tumors have been identified. This has led to the development of agents that can block the intracellular mechanisms associated with these mutations. The first of these was imatinib (Gleevec®). This is an agent for the treatment of chronic myelogenous leukemia. This drug has transformed the treatment of this leukemia from a condition with short survival, for which the only cure was a bone marrow transplant, into a chronic disease controlled for many years by taking a pill once a day.

With the identification of all these molecular targets, many of which are found in malignant cells of various tissue origins, we may eventually move to an era where cancer treatment is determined by the molecular targets found in the cells, rather than on the tissue of origin (breast, lung, colon, prostate, etc.).

Many other drugs of this type have become available at an increasingly rapid rate for a variety of malignancies. In 2015, the FDA approved a new agent every few weeks.

The most recent development in medical oncology has been the field of immunotherapy. Harnessing the immune system to treat cancer has been studied since the mid-1900s. Only very recently have drugs been developed that are significantly effective. Central to this development has been the discovery of so-called "checkpoint inhibitors" that signal immune cells, specifically T-cell lymphocytes, not to recognize cancer cells as foreign. There are now agents available that can block these receptors (e.g., PD-1) or their ligands (PDL-1) and unleash the patient's immune system to attack the cancer cells. Ipilumumab and nivolumab are two examples on the market in 2015. These drugs, used alone or in combination in various malignancies such as melanoma, lung cancer, and Hodgkin's lymphoma, are producing responses in many patients. Some of these responses have been prolonged. Because these drugs work in a unique way, they have their own unique set of side effects. Instead of the nausea and vomiting common to cytotoxic chemotherapy, these agents can lead to autoimmune activity manifested in phenomena such as severe colitis. Management of these patients requires new knowledge and expertise.

Given the plethora of new agents and the unique nature of many of them, medical oncology is changing rapidly. It is increasingly difficult to be a general oncologist as was possible in the days when Dr. John Brown started out. The cancer specialists at Abbott Northwestern have kept pace with these changes and are using all the available new agents. What is also changing is a move toward subspecialization, where each oncologist focuses on a small number of tumor types in order to maintain expertise and have adequate experience in managing certain tumor types.

What is also changing is a move toward subspecialization, where each oncologist focuses on a small number of tumor types in order to maintain expertise and have adequate experience in managing certain tumor types.

Piper Breast Center

In the early 1990s, radiologist Dr. Beverly Trombley became interested in a new technique for doing biopsies of breast lesions. Up to that time, breast lesions were typically biopsied by incisional or excisional surgical procedures. Needle localization of the tumor by radiology was used when necessary.

Nearly 20 breast cancer survivors from all walks of life came to meet with [those] involved in planning the breast center... The patient stories told in these focus groups shaped the vision for the breast center as a multidisciplinary clinic that would provide the highest level of patient care, using a coordinated approach for the best possible patient experience.

The new technique was called a stereotactic biopsy. Radiologists used breast images to locate the suspicious area to be biopsied with a core needle. Dr. Trombley wanted support from the surgeons on staff to determine that this was an effective approach before proceeding with more definitive treatment. A study was undertaken where the patient had a stereotactic biopsy followed immediately by a surgical biopsy of the same area. The original plan was to do this on one hundred patients. However, the results after just thirty patients showed excellent correlation of the pathology results for the two techniques, and so the study was concluded at that point.

Dr. Trombley presented the new technique at a grand rounds attended by the medical oncologist, Dr. John Brown. Dr. Brown talked with Dr. Trombley afterward to tell her he had a group of breast cancer patients who would support the development of a breast center if it was developed as a patient-focused program. These advocates from the community, including Anita Kunin and Martha Atwater, were included as advisors on the development of the breast center. Christine Norton, co-founder of the Minnesota Breast Cancer Coalition, assisted in organizing a breast cancer survivor focus group that provided invaluable input and advice on making the breast center a patient-focused facility and program.

The first of these was on a December evening when it was feared no one would show up because there was a blizzard. Nearly 20 breast cancer survivors from all walks of life came to meet with Dr. Tamera Lillemoe, Carol Bergen, RN, and others involved in planning the breast center. This was a pivotal meeting for the design of the center and program. The patient stories told in these focus groups shaped the vision for the breast center as a multidisciplinary clinic that would provide the highest level of patient care, using a coordinated approach for the best possible patient experience. It would prove to be a model for groups of patients receiving treatment for other kinds of malignancies.

A planning committee began to meet that included Drs. John Brown, Margit Bretzke, Dan Dunn, Michael Schwartz, Beverly Trombley, Deborah Day, Tamera Lillemoe, Marty Oken, along with Carol Bergen, the nurse manager on the inpatient oncology unit, Station 30. This group included medical oncologists, surgeons, radiologists, nurses, and pathologists. Dr. Tae Kim, Director of Radiation Oncology, was also involved. Dr. Deborah Day had joined Consulting Radiology with Dr. Trombley to focus their practice on breast imaging.

With the patient focus group's input, the vision for the center was unique at the time – to have breast imaging and clinical services in one location. Drs. Day and Trombley were able to convince their group to allow them to focus their practices on breast imaging at the new center, which would be a money loser, knowing that the improvement in patient care would ultimately benefit everyone. Dr. Brown's patients were among the significant donors to the project.

The multidisciplinary approach involved surgeons, radiologists, pathologists, medical and radiation oncologists, and nurses. Piper Breast Center (PBC) opened in 1995 as the first comprehensive breast center in the region. In addition to Dr. Trombley and Dr. Day, Dr. Fritz Olson and Dr. Ken Primesburger also provided breast imaging services. Surgeons involved with the breast program early on included Drs. Margit Bretzke, Dan Dunn, Michael Schwartz, Ray Drew, John O'Leary, Diane Stoller, Eric Johnson, Robert Harrie, and Madeline Gaertner.

Dr. Bretzke took on the role of Medical Director for clinical services with Dr. Day as Medical Director for imaging services. Carol Bergen was appointed Clinical Manager for the Center. The medical oncologists, among the first being Dr. John Brown and Dr. Marty Oken, began to perform new patient consultations on site, thus extending the multidisciplinary approach at a single location to serve the patients. Other medical oncologists have been involved over the years, including Drs. Barb Bowers, Paul Zander, Margaret MacRae, Stuart Bloom, and Michaela Tsai.

Plastic and Reconstructive Surgery joined the program, initially with Dr. Bart Muldowney. Subsequently Drs. Mark Migliori, Dave Reubeck, Tim Schaefer, and Brian Kobenia were involved. Dr. George Landis and Dr. Pawel Stachowicz also provide this important aspect of care.

Rehabilitation services have been another important contribution to the Center, initially with access to lymphedema-trained physical therapists, with instrumental involvement by Dr. Nancy Hutchison of the Sister Kenny Rehabilitation Institute (now Courage Kenny Rehabilitation Institute). Dr. Hutchison has developed an extensive, highly regarded program of cancer rehabilitation

Dr. Hutchison has developed an extensive, highly regarded program of cancer rehabilitation services to address the many issues encountered by patients who undergo breast surgery/ reconstruction and who also receive radiation and/or chemotherapy.

services to address the many issues encountered by patients who undergo breast surgery/reconstruction and who also receive radiation and/or chemotherapy.

Genetic risk assessment is an important component of care for some breast cancer patients. Shari Baldinger, a formally trained and certified genetic counselor, became involved in the early days of the Center. She provided consultations to assess a patient's risk of heritable conditions that might predispose the patient and other family members to an increased risk of breast cancer and other malignancies. She has developed an Allina-wide program that now includes five additional genetic counselors: Shanda Phippen, Ashley Daley, Vickie Matthias Hagen, Bonnie Hatten, and Sarah Ewing.

Carol Bergen recalls that it was she, Dr. Deborah Day, and two radiology techs who were on site at the opening of the Center. The surgeons began seeing patients soon thereafter, and things became busy and grew quickly. Additional nurses were added to the staff, including Rachel Cunningham, Joyce Byrd, and Lynn Perl, with a number of others to follow. Paula Sallmen, nurse coordinator with the Virginia Piper Cancer Institute, was also involved in the early years, as was research nurse Sally Fraki. Nurse coordinators are a central and essential part of the team, guiding patients though their evaluations and treatments, providing education and support, and coordinating the multidisciplinary approach. Jeanne-Marie Bakken, a social worker, was added to the team along with Lil Pilcher, a nutritionist. Complementary therapies requested by patients were developed. Related to and as an expansion of that effort, the Penny George Institute for Health and Healing was developed, housed in a separate facility across from the hospital on 28th Street.

Continued growth in patient volume required three remodelings and expansions of the Center's facilities. The current facility on the fourth floor of the Piper Building is visually pleasing, calming, and comforting. It does an excellent job of affording patient privacy. The signature terry cloth robes and china teacups remain. Beyond that, the latest in proven breast imaging technology continues to be added. Mammography and ultrasound have been available since the beginning. Breast magnetic resonance imaging (MRI) came into use several years later and is often used once a cancer diagnosis is made. It also has a role in screening for certain high-risk patients.

The next step was digital mammography, which required new equipment and training for the radiologists. This technology allows for faster turn-around of results, which is better for patients. Molecular breast imaging capability was added in 2010 with the LumaGEM® system. This technology is an alternative for women who cannot tolerate MRI. In early 2014, tomosynthesis technology was added, which allows for greater detail.

Other aspects of breast care have also advanced. Dr. Tamera Lillemoe has specialized expertise in breast pathology and immunohistochemistry. She has been instrumental in developing and standardizing immunohistochemical studies for estrogen and progesterone receptors as well as Her-2-neu expression critical to breast cancer diagnosis, prognosis, and treatment choices. Dr. Leslie Diaz came from Northwestern University to Abbott Northwestern in 2006. He published extensively in the area of breast pathology and attained international recognition for his expertise in breast pathology. His presence enhanced the expertise of the department. He was awarded a $100,000 grant from the Susan G. Komen Foundation to study breast cancer in minority populations. Sadly, he developed cancer himself and died at age 37 in 2009. The Leslie Diaz MD Memorial Symposium for Cancer Care Improvement honors his legacy.

The multidisciplinary approach has continued and expanded. As described above, a myriad of specialists have become part of the program. In addition to the daily on-site exchange of ideas and discussions of patient care (which many view as the most significant benefit of the Center), there is a weekly conference focused on breast cancer.

Research and innovation have been a significant component of the work of the Piper Breast Center. Several locally developed studies, such as the sentinel lymph node study led by Dr. Dan Dunn, have been presented nationally and internationally. Additional work by Drs. Michaela Tsai, Tamera Lillemoe, Barbara Susnik, Erin Grimm, and Karen Swenson, Ph.D., was instrumental in assessing the value of OncotypeDx® testing in the Center's patients, the management of lobular neoplasia found on core biopsy, and the outcomes of neo-adjuvant therapy for various patient populations. These were multidisciplinary efforts that likely would not have happened were it not for the professional relationships developed as part of the PBC. The breast pathologists have worked on projects such as surgical pathology best practice guidelines to reduce re-excisions after lumpectomy, and the development of standards for intra-

Nurse coordinators are a central and essential part of the team, guiding patients though their evaluations and treatments, providing education and support, and coordinating the multidisciplinary approach.

operative inking of lumpectomy specimens to allow for removal of additional tissue from the correct margin when re-excision is needed. These practices were then implemented across all Allina hospitals. Abbott Northwestern was also the first Allina site to employ radioactive seeds to localize sites in the breast for excision. Dr. Lillemoe has also been involved with the College of American Pathologists on a program to improve breast pathology interpretation and evaluation by pathologists across the country.

The Martha Bacon Stimpson Chair in Breast Oncology to support research and program development for breast cancer was established by Martha ("Marnie") Stimpson's $1.5 million gift. It was first held by Dr. Shou-Ching Tang (2010 to 2012) and more recently by Dr. Michaela Tsai, who has expanded the research efforts significantly. Additional funding raised by "Marnie's Army," a remarkably dedicated group of donors and volunteers, matched the original donation. Ms. Stimpson provided her gift out of gratitude for the excellent care she received from Dr. John Brown, and with the hope that the breast center would attract oncologists of the same outstanding caliber.

The Center and its physicians have become involved in activities to improve breast care at Abbott Northwestern and eventually across Allina. Educational seminars for primary care, a multidisciplinary conference to discuss current cases, a journal club that meets regularly to review important medical literature, and involvement in clinical research all serve to advance knowledge and assure the most up-to-date care for patients.

In addition to Drs. Stoller, Dan Dunn, Dawn Johnson, Eric Johnson, John O'Leary, the other surgeons actively involved as of 2015 include:

- Dr. Cassandra Anderson and Dr. Natasha Rueth.

- Dr. Corrine Jordan is at the new WestHealth satellite Piper Breast Center.

- Medical Oncologists seeing new patient consults include Drs. Michaela Tsai, Paul Zander, and Stuart Bloom, along with Drs. Tim Larson, Joe Leach, Kiran Lassi, and Vinay Gupta.

- The radiologists include Drs. Lisa Schneider, Mark Austin, Sue Austin, Jessica Axmacher, Kevin Edelman, Jennifer Kersten, Trudi Parker, Damon Shearer, and Sara Veldman.

- Radiation Oncologists supporting the center are Drs. David Monyak, Patsa Sullivan, and Laura Willson.

- The breast pathology group is made up of Drs. Tamera Lillemoe, Erin Grimm, Bill McDonald, Pam Sakkinen, and Barb Susnik.

- Dr. Nancy Hutchison and nurse practitioner Noelle Andrychowicz lead Cancer Rehabilitation Services.

- Reconstructive surgeons Drs. Migliori, Kobenia, Landis, Ruebeck, Schaefer, and Stachowicz continue to play a critical role in patient recovery.

- A social worker, Sarah Johnson, and four nurse coordinators (Lisa Heideman, Amy Lenarz, Melinda Messervey, and Megan Tasler) along with a group of dedicated nurses round out the team.

- A high-risk breast cancer clinic has been active since early in the Center's existence. Patients are seen by a surgeon, genetic counselor, and nurse along with other specialists as needed. Dr. Nancy Cockson, an internist, and Dr. Bretzke were involved in developing this service.

The Piper Breast Center sees over 600 new cases of breast cancer per year. In 2015, the clinical director for the center is Dr. Dawn Johnson, and the medical director for imaging is Dr. Lisa Schneider. The Center is known throughout the region for outstanding clinical care and for the patient experience it provides. Not surprisingly, in 2009, the Center became the first breast center in Minnesota to achieve accreditation by the National Accreditation Program for Breast Centers. It is also designated as a Breast Imaging Center of Excellence by the American College of Radiology. The program, developed at Abbott Northwestern Hospital, led to the establishment of the Allina-wide Breast Committee, initially led by Dr. Dunn, to achieve his vision to improve the quality of breast cancer care across the Allina system.

The Piper Breast Center has become a destination for patients from throughout the region. This is due to the high-quality nursing staff and nurse navigators, the services of professionals in genetic counseling, social work, pharmacy, and nutrition, state-of-the-art breast imaging equipment and pathology services, along with the multidisciplinary team of physicians. The

patients are assured they will receive the highest level of care possible, delivered with a patient-centered approach.

Virginia Piper Cancer Institute

Cancer care has been taking place at Abbott Northwestern Hospital since its beginning, and before that, at Northwestern and Abbott hospitals. As cancer care became more complex and a multidisciplinary approach focused on the patient was identified as the most effective approach, many institutions began to develop cancer programs to better coordinate care. With its large, high-quality medical staff, state-of-the-art facilities, experienced and visionary hospital administrators, and an established reputation as a tertiary care facility, Abbott Northwestern Hospital was well positioned to develop a comprehensive multidisciplinary cancer program.

Virginia Piper, a well-known member of the community, died of pancreatic cancer in 1988. She had been a devoted supporter of Abbott Northwestern Hospital for many decades. Virginia ("Ginny") was born at Northwestern Hospital. She joined the hospital's all-female board in 1961 and served as its chair from 1964-69. Under her leadership, men were added to the board in 1967. Then, when Abbott and Northwestern hospitals merged in 1970, she became chair of the Abbott Northwestern Hospital Board. The physical facilities merged in 1980. She provided many more years of service after the merger, retiring from the board in 1986. Known as a gifted leader of integrity who could inspire others, the patients and their families were her primary concern.

After her death, memorials poured in, directed to Abbott Northwestern Hospital. Gordon Sprenger, then President and CEO of Lifespan, talked with her husband Harry (Bobby) Piper about developing a cancer institute as a memorial to Ginny. Mr. Piper spearheaded a fund drive for the Virginia Piper Cancer Institute in 1989 and 1990. Then as he suffered himself from cancer, Bobby handed leadership of the fundraising efforts to close friends Newell Weed and Bill George. Mr. Piper died of prostate cancer in 1990. After some considerable debate about how these funds should be used – as an endowment to be held for the future or spent to develop a program – it was decided to implement a program to honor Virginia Piper.

The Virginia Piper Cancer Institute was formed and its first medical director, selected through a national search, was Dr. Martin Oken. He came to Abbott Northwestern in 1991. Dr. Oken had trained at Roswell Park Cancer Institute in Buffalo, N.Y. He then joined the University of Minnesota Faculty and the staff at the Minneapolis VA Hospital. He was known nationally and internationally for his work in lymphomas and multiple myeloma. An endowed chair, intended to support the medical leadership costs of the Institute, was established through a generous donation from Eugene and Elizabeth Leonard. Dr. Oken was the first to hold that chair. Dr. Tae Kim assumed the position of Medical Director for Radiation Oncology in 1990, adding expertise and recognition for the program. In October 1993, the Piper Building was completed, and the Virginia Piper Cancer Institute (VPCI) opened its doors.

Paula Sallmen, who had worked with Dr. Oken at the VA, joined him at VPCI as Clinical Program Director. Dr. Oken had been active for many years in the Eastern Cooperative Oncology Group. He brought clinical research to the Institute in the Community Group Oncology Program (CGOP), which provided a mechanism for participation in national cooperative group trials. Sally Fraki provided clinical research nurse leadership. Dr. Neil Kay joined the VPCI for several years, bringing particular expertise and a national presence in the field of chronic lymphocytic leukemia and immunology. He then pursued a position with a biotech company and ultimately returned to Minnesota on the staff at the Mayo Clinic. Dr. John Allen, a gastroenterologist with a particular interest in colon cancer prevention and genetic risk evaluation, was also an associate director, returning ultimately to Minnesota Gastroenterology. He went on to be Clinical Chief of Digestive Diseases at Yale School of Medicine.

Other important professionals at VPCI in the initial years were chaplain Eva Rogness and Gregory Stavrou, who served as Arts and Humanities Coordinator. After many years of outstanding service in developing the VPCI, Dr. Oken retired from the position in 2003. Another national search ensued, and Dr. P.J. Flynn served as interim medical director during the search.

Dr. Timothy Sielaff, a hepatobiliary surgeon at the University of Minnesota, was selected and took on the role of President of VPCI in 2004. Dr. Sielaff said he was attracted to the position given Abbott Northwestern's reputation as an academically oriented hospital with a strong medical staff

Dr. [Timothy] Sielaff said he was attracted to the position [as President of the VPCI] given Abbott Northwestern's reputation as an academically oriented hospital with a strong medical staff committed to research and service to the community.

committed to research and service to the community. He built a hepatobiliary surgery program, starting from scratch, into what has become a high-quality multidisciplinary program. His focus throughout his tenure at the VPCI has been to develop multidisciplinary tumor-specific programs. This has been a very successful effort, as seen in the eleven programs developed since 2004. These are described in more detail in separate sections below.

Each program is focused on the delivery of evidence-based care with adherence to National Comprehensive Cancer Network (NCCN) guidelines. An important element of these programs is the inclusion of cancer care coordinators. These professionals, nurses or APP's, provide ongoing assistance to patients as they navigate through the multiple physicians and disciplines needed to provide their care. These coordinators are providing not only a concierge service, but rather are knowledgeable in their clinical area and provide the patients with education and guidance from a clinical perspective.

Perhaps the most remarkable aspect of the creation of these programs by the VPCI is that it was accomplished by working with a large number of independent physician practices. Their involvement and commitments of time and talent are a testament to the quality of the medical staff at Abbott Northwestern. The medical staff recognizes the quality of the multidisciplinary programs that have been created. Their resulting contribution to delivering the best care available for the patients is the ultimate benefit.

As the VPCI programs and the Piper Breast Center grew, it was clear that the patient-centered, coordinated approach to care that was at the core of their work resonated with many who experienced cancer. Harry Piper had the experience of feeling totally unprepared to care for his wife during her illness. When he learned of the approach the creators of the breast center were taking to create a patient-centered program with a coordinated approach to care, he was moved to set aside funds in the family foundation to support the work so that others would be better supported in their cancer journey. His sons, Addison (Tad), Harry, and David continue to actively support the efforts of the VPCI, along with Tad's daughter Gretchen.

A major fundraising effort took place in the Vision Campaign for the VPCI to which the Piper family contributed. Led by passionate co-chairs Chris Morrison, Terry Saario, and Kathy Farley, this remarkable effort raised $37.4

million from 2005 to 2009. Marnie Stimpson's 1.5 million dollar gift was a part of this effort (see Piper Breast Center section).

Building on the groundwork laid by Dr. Marty Oken, Dr. Tim Sielaff focused on the creation of formal programs for each tumor type, based on a multidisciplinary approach, evidence-based care and care coordination. As of 2015, there are eleven such programs, each of which is discussed in more detail throughout this chapter. Just as Abbott Northwestern is thought of as the "flagship" of Allina, so too did the VPCI become the flagship cancer program for Allina Health. The VPCI brand was sought after by a number of hospitals, but only those who can meet specifically defined criteria are given that designation by a central committee.

Administrative leadership at VPCI included of number of excellent individuals starting with Paula Sallmen, and continuing with Roy Johnson, Jennifer Stanek, and most recently Sue Nordberg. At the system level cancer service line, Clay Ahrens provided noteworthy talent, expertise, and passion in the role of Vice President at Allina Hospitals and Clinics from 2011 to 2014. He was instrumental, under the leadership of Dr. Sielaff, in developing a long-term relationship with Minnesota Oncology to provide leadership for the service line, and ultimately a co-management agreement that assures a level of stability for the program. As Dr. Sielaff began transitioning in 2014 to a position at Allina, Dr. Joe Leach took on the medical directorship.

Research is another area of activity and example of good work being done at VPCI. Beginning with Dr. Oken and Sally Fraki, who brought CGOP trials and a number of other clinical studies, research has continued under Dr. Sielaff's leadership. The Stimpson Chair was first held by Dr. Shou-Ching Tang from 2010 to 2012, with a major focus of that position being clinical research. Dr. Tang worked to develop a number of breast cancer trials during his tenure. Dr. Michaela Tsai then assumed the chair in 2012. She expanded the research activity in breast cancer and beyond into other areas, including hematologic malignancy trials being done in collaboration with the Dana Farber Cancer Institute at Harvard. Dr. Leach has been involved in bringing a number of studies to VPCI for several malignancies, some of which involve the latest immunotherapy approaches. Karen Swenson, RN, Ph.D., joined the VPCI as director of the research effort. She added considerable expertise as evidenced

The medical staff recognizes the quality of the multidisciplinary programs that have been created. Their resulting contribution to delivering the best care available for the patients is the ultimate benefit.

...the development of multidisciplinary, tumor-specific programs that bring specialists from a number of fields of medicine together to collaborate, share knowledge, and provide coordinated evidence-based care with the patient at the center of all that is done. The result is high-quality care with an approach that provides for an exceptional patient experience.

by a national award she received from the Oncology Nursing Society for her contributions to nursing research.

The quality work being done at the VPCI came to be known in the region and to be recognized by outside agencies. The VPCI achieved accreditation as an Academic Comprehensive Cancer Program by the Commission on Cancer of the American College of Surgeons (CoC). In 2013, this commission awarded the VPCI with an Outstanding Achievement Award, recognizing outstanding effort and commitment by the entire cancer team, from clinicians and volunteers to hospital administration, as well as providing high-quality patient care and exceeding the standards set by the CoC.

Insurance companies and HMOs also recognized the excellence of the programs at VPCI and the advanced level of care provided. VPCI was designated as a Blue Distinction Center for Complex and Rare Cancers in 2008. This program was developed in collaboration with a panel of leading clinicians from the National Comprehensive Cancer Network. They identified the facility as offering a comprehensive inpatient cancer care program for adults, which was being delivered by multidisciplinary teams with subspecialty training and distinguished clinical expertise in treating complex and rare subtypes of cancer.

As the cancer program at Abbott Northwestern Hospital has expanded and continues to expand to other Allina sites, the VPCI spearheaded from 2004 to 2015 the development of multidisciplinary, tumor-specific programs that bring specialists from a number of fields of medicine together to collaborate, share knowledge, and provide coordinated evidence-based care with the patient at the center of all that is done. The result is high-quality care with an approach that provides for an exceptional patient experience.

Hepatobiliary and Pancreatic Surgery

With the arrival in 2004 of Dr. Tim Sielaff from the University of Minnesota to head up the VPCI, a hepatobiliary/pancreatic (HBP) surgery program came into being at Abbott Northwestern Hospital. Dr. Sielaff, in his leadership role for the VPCI (see section on VPCI), enthusiastically promoted and developed multidisciplinary programs and tumor conferences for several malignancies. The HBP program was a prime example with involvement of medical oncology, interventional radiology, and radiation oncology in the development of patient treatment plans and clinical trials.

Initially, the program consisted of only Dr. Sielaff and Nurse Coordinator Marie Kramer. They organized care conferences, bringing in Dr. Ken Batts from pathology and Dr. John Seng in medical oncology. Very quickly interest grew from others in these specialties, and conference attendance expanded markedly. Jill May was added as the second nurse coordinator the following year, and additional HBP surgeons were brought on board, including Dr. Shawn McKenzie and Dr. Kambiz Kosari. With their departure a few years later, Dr. Yun Shin Chun joined the program after her time at the Fox Chase Cancer Center in Philadelphia. Dr. Mark Hill from Hennepin County Medical Center became involved with the program, splitting his time between that institution and Abbott Northwestern Hospital. Dr. Chun moved on to pursue other interests, and the most recent addition to the surgical group in 2015 was Dr. Srinevas Reddy.

With the expanding HBP program and its multidisciplinary approach, it became possible to pursue clinical research. VPCI/Abbott Northwestern Hospital joined the Pancreatic Research Team, an international organization that collaborates to provide clinical trials based in genomics research for these patients. Abbott Northwestern Hospital is one of 45 sites involved in these trials, in the company of institutions such as Johns Hopkins, Tufts, Virginia Mason Cancer Center, and Fred Hutchinson Cancer Research Center. Abbott Northwestern contributes significant numbers of accruals to these trials.

Since 2004, the HBP program has grown considerably. Weekly conferences have been needed for several years in order to discuss all the cases. Participation regularly includes the HBP surgeons, pathologists, and an expanded group of medical oncologists including Drs. John Seng, Tim Larson, and Joe Leach among others. In addition, interventional radiologists, along with a hepatologist or liver specialist and other physicians from Minnesota Gastroenterology have participated, as well as a representative from the University of Minnesota Liver Transplant team. Expert pathology professionals involved have been Drs. Ken Batts, Larry Burgart, Jason Daniels, and Perry Dilworth. Their specialized knowledge and experience has been a critical component of sorting out the difficult-to-diagnose lesions in the liver, bile ducts, and pancreas.

With strong nurse coordinator involvement, the multidisciplinary collaborative approach, high-quality specialists, and the availability of clinical research trials, the program offers state-of-the-art care for the region.

The program capabilities, in addition to the specialized surgery, include the availability of clinical trials, and a multidisciplinary approach to treatment planning. It also includes the expertise of interventional radiologists to provide trans-arterial chemo-embolization (injection of chemotherapy directly into the liver circulation) and complex percutaneous approaches to bile duct injuries. The radiologists involved have included Drs. Eduardo Ehrenwald, Subbarrao Inampudi, Jason Mehling, and Clark Schumaher. In recent years, they have also provided, in collaboration with radiation oncology, one of the largest radio-embolization programs in the region. This approach involves injection of microscopic radioactive spheres directly into the arteries of the liver to deliver localized radiation to tumors at that site, with minimal radiation exposure to the rest of the body.

With strong nurse coordinator involvement, the multidisciplinary collaborative approach, high-quality specialists, and the availability of clinical research trials, the program offers state-of-the-art care for the region.

Gynecologic Oncology

Dr. John Savage, after spending time at the University of Minnesota and St. Paul Ramsey Medical Center, established a private practice in St. Paul in the 1980s. He performed surgery at United Hospital and Abbott Northwestern Hospital as well as at HealthEast hospitals. In the early years at Abbott Northwestern, OB-GYN physicians performed surgery for gynecologic malignancies, with referrals to medical oncologists for patients who needed chemotherapy. One of the obstetrician gynecologists with a particular interest in gynecologic cancer was Dr. Ed Beadle. Many of these cases were referred to the University of Minnesota and the Mayo Clinic. In fact, Dr. Linda Carson, head of the gynecologic oncology division at the University of Minnesota, was on staff at Abbott Northwestern from 1987 until 2005. She served as the medical director of Gynecologic Oncology for several years. Dr. John Savage joined Minnesota Oncology in early 1996.

The program expanded considerably over the next decade. The first step involved the addition of Dr. Cheryl Bailey, who joined the staff after completing her fellowship at the University of Kentucky. Dr. Bailey was the first formally trained gynecologic oncologist to practice full time at Abbott Northwestern. Physicians were being formally trained in this subspecialty. The patients were also being seen by the medical and patient advocacy community. This was deemed essential to the care of women with gynecologic malignancies. Next, additional gynecologic oncologists were recruited to join the staff. These physicians represent a unique specialty in oncology in that they were trained to perform complex pelvic and abdominal surgery as well as to manage the chemotherapy needed for many of these malignancies. Given their specialized skills in pelvic surgery, they were also called upon to assist with complicated pelvic surgeries for benign disease.

Dr. Matt Boente joined Minnesota Oncology and the Abbott Northwestern medical staff in 2004 after spending time at Fox Chase Cancer Center in Philadelphia. He also spent time at the University of Minnesota, serving in leadership roles for gynecologic oncology and involved in clinical research. He championed the use of post-op epidural analgesia and continued to be active in clinical research with the Gynecologic Oncology Group (GOG), leading trials in ovarian cancer.

Dr. A. Catherine Casey, after training in internal medicine at Brigham and Women's Hospital in Boston, trained in OB-GYN and GYN ONC in California. She returned home to Minnesota in 2005 to practice at Abbott Northwestern, bringing added expertise in laparoscopic surgical approaches. Prior to the mid-2000s, most surgeries for gynecologic malignancies were performed by "open" technique with long abdominal incisions. She was a strong advocate for less invasive surgical approaches that could provide for more rapid patient recovery from surgery and shorter hospital stays.

When robotic surgery came to the fore for abdominal surgery, she took training in that technique and worked enthusiastically with the operating room staff to establish robotic capability for gynecologic oncology procedures. This included the establishment of a dedicated operating team and required the acquisition of a special OR table. She also convinced her physician colleagues to become trained in and adopt the robotic techniques. This technology grew very rapidly. As of August 2015, Dr. Casey has performed more than 1100 robotic surgeries at Abbott Northwestern. Dr. Bailey has performed more than 600 surgical cases.

Dr. Bailey took over medical leadership for gynecologic oncology in 1998. A gynecologic-oncology tumor conference had existed for many years to discuss cases in a multidisciplinary fashion. Gynecologic Oncology, Pathology, Radiology, and Radiation Oncology participated in this twice-monthly conference to review and discuss cases. The program is fortunate to have specialized pathologists in gynecologic malignancies.

Initially, Dr. Mark Arnesen led the program, with the later addition of Dr. Saeid Movahedi and most recently Dr. Erin Grimm. Dr. David Monyak in Radiation Oncology established the capability for High Dose Rate Brachytherapy in the 1990s. This technique has now replaced the older technique of cesium implants, which required a multiple-day hospital stay and resulted in greater patient discomfort. A dedicated room and updated equipment were put in place in 2009.

Gynecologic Oncology has evolved into a well-developed multi-specialty approach with fellowship-trained, Board-certified gynecologic oncologists, specialized pathologists, and radiation oncologists. Surgical techniques have advanced to include less invasive laparoscopic and robotic approaches. Nursing expertise has developed on Station 31/35 with specialized nurses working with the physicians. Clinical research is active with participation in Gynecologic Oncology Group trials as well as, more recently, available studies through U.S. Oncology Research. All of these efforts are focused on providing the best patient care possible.

Neuro-Oncology

Abbott Northwestern Hospital has developed a well-known Neuro-Oncology program and is a leading center in the upper Midwest for brain tumor management. In the late 1940s, Dr. Harold Buchstein established a private practice of neurosurgery in Minneapolis. Dr. Erich Wisiol joined the practice in the early 1960s, followed by Dr. Larry Seymour in 1969. Dr. Harry Rogers came to Abbott Northwestern as part of the group early on, with a particular interest in pituitary tumors. Dr. Gaylen Rockswold, who spent half time with the training program at Hennepin County Medical Center, also joined the group. Dr. Mahmoud Nagib came to the practice in 1983 after two years at St. Paul

Ramsey Medical Center. He has contributed substantially to the reputation of the brain tumor program, along with his colleagues Drs. Ed Hames, Tom Bergman, Walter Galicich, John Mullan, and Michael McCue. Abbott Northwestern is also fortunate to have other excellent neurosurgeons on staff dating back to the 1980s with the group of Drs. Gregg Dyste, Robert Roach, Dan Ahlberg, and Hart Garner. Most recently, we have seen the addition of Dr. Kyle Nelson and Dr. Kyle Uittenbogaard.

As is the case for many cancers, a multidisciplinary approach is needed in the management of brain tumors. The radiation oncologists have been involved from their beginnings at Abbott Northwestern, along with medical oncologists dating back to the 1960s, such as Dr. John Brown. Chemotherapy options were quite limited to start with, and radiation capabilities consisted primarily of whole-brain radiation. As neurosurgical techniques for brain tumor management were evolving, Dr. John Trusheim was developing an interest in neuro-oncology.

Trained in internal medicine and neurology, Dr. Trusheim wanted to pursue training in neurologic tumor management. In the 1980s, no formal training programs in neuro-oncology existed, with the possible exception of something at Duke University. As a result, Dr. Trusheim contacted Dr. B.J. Kennedy, the medical oncologist at the University of Minnesota. After repeated attempts and with much cajoling on Dr. Trusheim's part, Dr. Kennedy finally agreed to provide Dr. Trusheim with several months of fellowship training. With that training, Dr. Trusheim developed neuro-oncology clinics at the University, Abbott Northwestern, and Fairview Southdale hospitals in the early 1990s.

Dr. Trusheim worked with Dr. Walter Hall at the University of Minnesota in the late 1990s. Dr. Hall was involved in using intra-arterial chemotherapy for brain tumors. In 2004, Dr. Trusheim came to Abbott Northwestern full time as the Director of Neuro-Oncology. The Abbott Northwestern Brain Tumor Center was thus established. Two RNs, a clinical nurse specialist, and social worker staff the center.

Dr. Trusheim brought to the Center the technique of "blood brain barrier disruption" for the intra-arterial administration of chemotherapy for recurrent brain tumors. Clinical research protocols are a significant component of the program and are staffed by two RNs, a data manager, and Ph.D. nurse who is trained in leadership. One example is a vaccine protocol (DC Vax®) where a dendritic cell vaccine is created using the patient's tumor tissue. Abbott Northwestern is one of the largest accrual sites in the world for this protocol. Under development is another trial that involves injecting a retro-viral vector into the tumor. This inserts a gene into the tumor cells that codes and creates an enzyme that converts a pro-drug into the chemotherapy agent 5-FU. The pro-drug is then administered and converted into the active 5-FU compound only in the tumor cells.

Neuroradiologist Dr. Doug Yock was a key player, along with the neurosurgeons, in establishing the Brain Tumor Center and instrumental in bringing Dr. Trusheim to Abbott Northwestern full time. The Center currently sees about one third of the brain tumor cases in the state. Dr. Yock is considered by many to be a truly outstanding expert in neuro-imaging. His input was critical in driving the development of imaging technology for the program, as well as providing exceptional expertise in interpretation.

In 2004, Dr. Nagib and Dr. Yock travelled to Erlanger University in Germany to learn about the use of intra-operative MRI (iMRI) in neurosurgery. In 2006, Abbott Northwestern Hospital installed iMRI for intra-operative use. It has been used extensively by Dr. Nagib and his colleagues in nearly 2,000 surgical cases as of this writing, which represents perhaps the largest collection of cases in the country and among the top ten in the world. This approach is used not only for brain tumors, but also vascular malformations, aneurysms, upper cervical spine and skull base tumors, and conditions of the cranio-cervical junction.

Jeff Peterson, President of Abbott Northwestern during much of the development of the program and later Executive Vice President of the Allina Hospital Division, is credited as being a very supportive leader on the administrative side for the advancement of the Abbott Northwestern Brain Tumor Center. Mr. Peterson sadly died of cancer in 2013 at only 55 years of age.

Adding to the technological capability of iMRI is the use of neuronavigation with Brainlab® technology. Dr. Nagib likens this to the GPS navigation system in your car. Stickers are placed on the patient's scalp which, when used with special probes that indicate their location on an imaging screen in the operating room, allow the surgeon to navigate to the exact tumor site. The iMRI can also be used to assess during surgery whether tumor removal has been complete. Beyond this amazing technology, there is intraoperative neurophysiology, which can be used, for example, in the case of a brain stem tumor when one needs to avoid damage to cranial nerves. Neurologist/Neurophysiologist Dr. Stanley Skinner leads this effort.

Interventional neuroradiology, led initially by Dr. Dave Tubman in the early 2000s, has provided for vascular embolization to reduce bleeding in tumors that have high degree of vasculatrity. Dr. John Perl and Dr. Ben Crandall have also done this work, with more recent additions of Dr. Josser Delgado and Dr. Yasha Kadkhodayan.

Adding to the multidisciplinary approach are the radiation oncologists. Since the establishment of the Brain Tumor Center, Drs. Carol Grabowski, David Monyak, and David Pence have provided this component of patient care utilizing the Varian Trilogy linear accelerator and its stereotactic radiosurgery capabilities.

Surgical pathology is also critical to any oncology program. Abbott Northwestern has been fortunate to have expertise in neuropathology for decades. Initially Dr. William Foley was involved. Dr. Mark Arnesen subsequently provided the necessary expertise with an interest in brain tumor pathology. More recently, Dr. William McDonald has come on board with fellowship training in neuropathology, bringing the latest techniques in neurologic tumor identification and classification.

The Abbott Northwestern Hospital Brain Tumor Center and Neuro-Oncology program are a wonderful example of providing multidisciplinary care that has continuously evolved to provide outstanding medical expertise, the latest technology, and clinical research so patients receive the best care possible.

The Abbott Northwestern Hospital Brain Tumor Center and Neuro-Oncology program are a wonderful example of providing multidisciplinary care that has continuously evolved to provide outstanding medical expertise, the latest technology, and clinical research so patients receive the best care possible.

Thoracic Surgical Oncology

For many decades, surgeons trained in cardiothoracic surgery performed surgery for lung tumors and other tumors in the chest. In the 1970s, Dr. Joseph Kiser, along with Dr. Orn Arnar and Dr. Ted Peterson were among the staff who had been trained in this specialty. Cardiac surgery expanded substantially

Endobronchial ultrasound (EBUS) capability has also been developed at Abbott Northwestern, allowing for less invasive approaches to biopsy certain lung lesions, as well as to examine regional lymph nodes in the chest for possible tumor spread.

when Dr. Demetre Nicoloff and Dr. William Lindsay came to Abbott Northwestern Hospital from the University of Minnesota in 1979. Dr. Robert Emery also joined the staff from the University. They developed a heart transplant program and the increasing use of coronary bypass grafting. Cardiothoracic surgeons who took more of an interest in the thoracic area included Drs. Frazier Eales, Jim Burdine, Vibhu Kshettry, Tom Flavin, and Tim Kroshus. Dr. Kroshus was an active part of the multidisciplinary lung program for several years and was an important part of its development.

When Dr. Kroshus left to practice at Regions Hospital in St. Paul in 2010, Dr. Louis Jacques became more actively involved. Dr. Jacques, whose practice had been based in the Fairview System and was limited to thoracic surgery for many years, joined Minnesota Oncology in 2008. He had a strong interest in lung cancer. Dr. Matt Graczyk joined the practice in 2010 and has been based primarily at Abbott Northwestern. Although the fellowship training programs continue to combine training in cardiac and thoracic surgery (as does the specialty certification board), Dr. Graczyk, like Dr. Jacques, wanted to focus his practice on thoracic surgery. Dr. Graczyk was the first formally trained surgeon working full time at Abbott Northwestern to focus exclusively on general thoracic surgery. With his training at Rush University Medical Center in Chicago, he was able to bring minimally invasive approaches to thoracic surgery, allowing many patients to avoid open chest surgeries called thoracotomies. These techniques include video-assisted thorascopic surgery for removal of lung tumors as well as pleural and mediastinal lesions. More recently, robotic surgical techniques have been applied to chest surgery. Endobronchial ultrasound (EBUS) capability has also been developed at Abbott Northwestern, allowing for less invasive approaches to biopsy certain lung lesions, as well as to examine regional lymph nodes in the chest for possible tumor spread.

The multidisciplinary lung program has been in place since the 2000s, led by Dr. Michael Bowen, pulmonologist with the Minnesota Lung Center. Specialists involved in the Lung Center include pathology, radiology, medical oncology, and radiation oncology, along with the thoracic surgeons and pulmonologists. Most notably involved from pathology was, initially, Dr. John Jones, and more recently, Dr. Laurie Ryan. Physicians trained in radiology included Dr. Subi Inampudi and Dr. Rob Parker. Specialists trained in medical oncology included

Dr. Joe Leach and Dr. Tim Larson, and from radiation oncology, Drs. Dave Monyak, Patsa Sullivan, and Laura Willson. Once again, the nurse coordinator is a critical element to the delivery of multidisciplinary care and in providing an optimal patient experience. Jody Eifert, the first nurse-coordinator at the VPCI has fulfilled this role from the start. With increasing patient volumes, the frequency of the care conference was increased to a weekly schedule, with a goal of arriving at a multidisciplinary management plan for each patient. The program was further formalized by a consensus conference in 2012 that brought together an Allina-wide multidisciplinary program with programs similar to that at Abbott Northwestern Hospital. The Allina program submits data to the Society of Thoracic Surgery Database, which looks at goal measures such as length of stay, morbidity, and mortality. This allows the program to do national benchmarking with semi-annual reports reviewed by the Allina-wide program.

Like the other areas of cancer care, Thoracic Oncology has evolved to provide up-to-date, high-quality, multidisciplinary care focused on the patient.

Once again, the nurse coordinator is a critical element to the delivery of multidisciplinary care and in providing an optimal patient experience.

Urologic Oncology/Prostate Cancer Program

In the 1980s and 1990s, Dr. William Kaylor and Dr. Harry Hoppman were actively performing surgery for urologic cancers, along with Drs. John Hulbert, Abraham Kern, and John Heller of Metropolitan Urology. They focused their practices in urology at Abbott Northwestern Hospital after prior work at Mount Sinai Hospital and Metropolitan Medical Center. Dr. Paul Fadden joined the group. After Dr. Kern's sudden and unexpected death in 2013, the group eventually split up and reorganized. Dr. Irving Thorne of Aspen Medical Group has practiced at Abbott Northwestern for many years. In recent years, several members of Urologic Associates have been active at Abbott Northwestern and the Virginia Piper Cancer Institute. Dr. Paul Fadden has joined that group. Others particularly active in urologic cancer from that group include Drs. Pratap Reddy (medical director of the Prostate Cancer Center at VPCI), Chase Sovell, Bill Utz, and Mark Fallen.

For many decades, urologists primarily managed prostate cancer patients, working with radiation oncologists when appropriate for the patient's care. For more advanced disease, hormonal therapies (orchiectomy, the removal of the testicles) were used, and in recent years, luteinizing hormone-releasing hormone (LHRH) agonists such as leuprolide. Medical oncology was only involved when patients developed metastatic disease that was refractory to hormonal therapy.

As new and more effective systemic therapies were developed for prostate cancer, medical oncologists were involved earlier in the course of the disease. These included second- and third-line hormonal treatments (androgen receptor inhibitors), as well as more effective chemotherapy drugs (e.g., mitoxantrone and then cabazitaxel). Data in 2015 also indicated a potential benefit for the addition of chemotherapy to hormonal therapy early in the treatment of metastatic disease. The FDA approved an immunotherapy approach known as Provenge® (sipuleucel-T) in 2010 for minimally symptomatic hormone-refractory metastatic disease. This approach involves collecting immune cells from the patient's blood by leukapheresis. These cells are treated in the laboratory to activate these cells to attack prostate cancer cells. The treated cells are then reinfused back into the patient. This therapy has been controversial in that it only increases median survival by four months and costs more than $90,000.

Surgical techniques have evolved from open procedures to the much more frequent use of robotic surgery for performing the removal of the prostate (prostatectomy). Radiation technology has advanced over the decades from cobalt therapy to linear accelerators, to the even more focused approach of intensity modulated radiation therapy (IMRT). Latest on the scene is proton beam therapy. This radiation technique is even more focused and thus theoretically better for treating a small area such as the prostate while trying to avoid nearby structures such as the rectum, bladder, and nerves. This approach is also far more expensive, requiring a facility and equipment that together cost something in the range of $100 million. This technology is not available at Abbott Northwestern Hospital as yet. The nearest facility is at the Mayo Clinic.

With these new developments there was then an interest in developing a multidisciplinary program, particularly for prostate cancer. Not only was there the development of more options for effective treatment of advanced disease, but also the ongoing need for patients with early stage disease to select a treatment approach. Radical prostatectomy, external beam radiation, and radioactive seed implants are all options with similar outcomes. In addition, evidence accumulated that watchful waiting may be an appropriate course for patients with lower-grade tumors. Multiple disciplines came together to review recent cases at a monthly treatment planning conference.

A nurse coordinator was brought on board to educate and guide patients through their workup and treatment. Heather Christie currently serves in that role. The urologists primarily involved include Dr. Pratap Reddy as medical director, and Dr. Chase Sovell and Dr. David Streitz. For medical oncology Dr. Stuart Bloom has taken the lead, along with Dr. Dean Gesme and Dr. Burton Schwartz. Radiation oncologists Dr. Patsa Sullivan and Dr. Laura Willson are focused on this area. For imaging, the Consulting Radiology group, particularly Dr. Robin Parker, provides the expertise. Pathologists specializing in these tumors are Drs. Milt Datta, Lisa Lyons, and Anil Tadavarthy.

With the formation of a multidisciplinary team and the treatment options available, the program developed an approach for early stage prostate cancer patients to be seen by Urology, Radiation Oncology, and Medical Oncology in order to be well informed in making treatment choices. Obviously a coordinated program and nurse coordinator were critical. Patients now have the benefit of multiple opinions and the perspectives of multiple specialists, so they can choose care most appropriate for their overall medical condition and life situation.

Head and Neck Cancer

Like other areas of cancer surgery, procedures for head and neck cancer have evolved to be less extensive and less disfiguring. The overall approach once again is one of multidisciplinary care. In the 1970s, surgical resections for cancers of the head and neck often involved removal of a great deal of tissue, resulting in not only disfiguration but also severe functional impairments of speech, the airway, or swallowing. Abbott Northwestern Hospital has been fortunate to have a number of excellent ENT physicians on staff dating back to before the merger of Abbott and Northwestern Hospitals. (The reader is referred to Chapter 12 on Ear, Nose, and Throat for that history.)

Laryngeal cancer is an example of a malignancy in the head and neck region where surgery of more limited extent or use of other therapies has come into play to allow for organ preservation. Dating back to the 1930s, radiation therapy was used as an alternative to removal of the larynx (laryngectomy) for early cancers. More limited resections for early tumors became an accepted approach over the years. For locally, more advanced tumors, studies demonstrated that some combination of chemotherapy and radiation could replace surgery. A large Department of Veterans Affairs trial published in 1991 established the use of cisplatinum and 5-FU chemotherapy followed by radiation as a standard alternative to total laryngectomy. Subsequent trials have demonstrated the most effective approach to be the concurrent administration of cisplatinum chemotherapy and radiotherapy.

The concurrent radiation and chemotherapy approach has also been applied to other head and neck cancers, particularly those of the tongue base and other sites in the oropharynx. Functional outcomes are now better than with extensive surgery. Since 2000, the majority of these oropharyngeal cancers have been recognized to be related to infection with Human Papilloma Virus (HPV). These HPV cancers tend to occur in younger individuals, while head and neck cancers are more often related to alcohol and tobacco use. These latter tumors are more responsive to chemo-radiation than HPV-negative tumors. Physicians in the head and neck cancer program at Abbott Northwestern were involved in research into the role of HPV in these tumors.

As newer agents were developed for systemic therapy, they were adopted by the medical oncologists for appropriate patients. One example is cetuximab, which is a monoclonal antibody directed against the epidermal growth factor receptor (EGFR). It is used either in conjunction with radiation or alone in the case of recurrent cancer. Other targeted therapies directed at specific molecular targets in the malignant cell also have come into play.

In addition to chemo-radiation approaches, newer surgical techniques have been developed. Dr. Merrill Biel, head and neck surgeon, with fellowship training in head and neck cancer, has brought transoral robotic surgical techniques into use at Abbott Northwestern as another less-invasive approach. Dr. Biel has also pioneered research into photodynamic therapy for very early stage head and neck tumors.

As in other areas of oncology, multidisciplinary tumor conferences have been implemented for head and neck cancer. These are led by Dr. Biel and shared with other Allina sites by teleconference. Through discussion of cases at the conference and with the services of a nurse coordinator, patients benefit from a multidisciplinary approach to care. The current Cancer Care Coordinator is Suzanne Monahan, and the surgeons involved, in addition to Dr. Biel are Drs. Greg Bath, Nissim Khabie, Matthew Griebie, Carl Brown, William Garvis, Geoffrey Getnick, Mike Tedford, Darren McDonald, Michael Murphy, Ilya Perepelitsyn, Julie Reddan, and Daniel Schneider.

The radiation oncologist with particular expertise in this patient population is Dr. David Monyak. Medical Oncology has been represented by Drs. Burt Schwartz, Tom Flynn, Dean Gesme, Tim Larson, and John Seng. Imaging is an important component, as it is for most cancers. Dr. Subbarao Inampudi, Dr. Michael Plunkett, and colleagues at Consulting Radiology provide this expertise. The Pathology experts have included Dr. John Jones and Dr. Jorge Ferriero, and with their retirements, Dr. Milton Datta joined the program. Another critically important component of care for these patients is cancer rehabilitation and speech pathology. The Courage Kenny Rehabilitation Institute provides this care. Dr. Nancy Hutchison developed and continues to lead this program.

Once again one sees the evolution toward less invasive but equally effective surgery, the development of a multidisciplinary approach, professional collaboration, and the use of care coordination to provide optimal patient care.

Esophageal and Gastric Cancer

Dr. Dan Dunn and Dr. Eric Johnson were instrumental in developing a program for these malignancies. In early years of Abbott Northwestern Hospital, these tumors were approached primarily by general and thoracic surgeons. In the 1990s and beyond, more cases of adenocarcinomas began to be seen, particularly in the distal esophagus and gastro-esophageal junction. These tumors often developed due to Barrett's esophagus, related to acid reflux. Research trials began to make it clear that a multidisciplinary approach to these tumors improved outcomes and cure rates. A multidisciplinary program was developed with the combined efforts of surgery, Radiation Oncology, Medical Oncology,

As in other areas of oncology, multidisciplinary tumor conferences have been implemented for head and neck cancer... Through discussion of cases at the conference and with the services of a nurse coordinator, patients benefit from a multidisciplinary approach to care.

Pathology, Radiology, and Gastroenterology. A nurse coordinator tied it all together.

Julie Morphew, RN, OCN, was the initial care coordinator for this program and served in that role for several years. More recently, Jessica Quinlan-Woodward has filled that role. Additional surgeons have come on board with Dr. Cassandra Anderson and Dr. Peter Dahlberg. Drs. Monyak, Sullivan, and Willson have provided the radiation oncology expertise. Medical Oncology has been represented by Drs. John Seng, Burt Schwartz, Tom Flynn, P.J. Flynn, Joe Leach, Tim Larson, and Dean Gesme, among others. Dr. Robert Ganz from Gastroenterology, who has special interest and expertise in the diagnosis and management of Barrett's esophagus, became involved at the inception. Dr. Federico Rossi provided the capability of endoscopic ultrasound with needle biopsies of lesions and regional lymph nodes to aid in the diagnosis and staging of lesions. He was later joined by Dr. Nick Boetticher and Dr. Courtney Barancin, along with several other gastroenterologists. The program has been fortunate to have specialized pathologists initially in Dr. Ken Batts, followed by Drs. Larry Burgart, Perry Dilworth, Jason Daniels, and Schuyler Sanderson. Consulting Radiologists group has provided imaging expertise and social worker Sarah Johnson rounds out the team.

Attention to the precancerous condition of Barrett's esophagus can actually prevent cancer. Gastroenterologists in the program can perform diagnostic endoscopies and perform biopsies, which require interpretation by the specialized pathologists in the group. Interventions such as radiofrequency ablation can then be used to eradicate the premalignant condition non-invasively. Dr. Ganz was first in the world to perform balloon-based radiofrequency ablation.

Regular conferences support the multidisciplinary approach to these patients, facilitating communication among specialists, adherence to National Comprehensive Cancer Center guidelines, and delivery of high-quality care. Patients often receive neo-adjuvant, concurrent chemotherapy and radiation, followed by surgery. Surgery alone is done in only the earliest-staged patients. The cancer care coordinator is essential in educating the patients, guiding them to visits with specialists, and navigating through their treatment plan.

Colorectal Program

With the development of the specialty of colorectal surgery, many cases now come under its purview. While colon cancers may be operated on by either general or colorectal surgeons, rectal cancers typically are managed surgically by colorectal surgeons or specialty-trained oncology surgeons.

The colorectal surgery group, led for decades by Dr. Stanley Goldberg, has practiced at Abbott Northwestern Hospital for many years. The group has also functioned as the colorectal surgery group for the University of Minnesota. Dr. Rob Madoff was also active at Abbott Northwestern for many years before taking a position at the University. Dr. Charles Finne had a particular interest in rectal cancer and endorectal radiation. Dr. Ann Lowry has been active at Abbott Northwestern. In 2015, the members of the group participating in the program also included Drs. Amy Thorsen, Michael Spencer, and Brad Sklow. For general surgery, Dr. John O'Leary was on staff for several decades. In 2015, those most active in this area are Drs. Cassandra Anderson, Daniel Dunn, and Eric Johnson.

Screening for colorectal cancer is an effective approach in both preventing cancers by removing premalignant polyps and detecting cancers at an early, curable stage. Gastroenterologists, primarily from Minnesota Gastroenterology (MNGI), but also independent practitioners in the past such as Dr. Frank Lushine, have provided this service with screening colonoscopies and various fecal occult blood testing measures. MNGI has ten physicians involved with the program, including Drs. Cecil Chally, Caryn Fine, Robert Ganz, Scott Ketover, Robert Mackie, Robert McCabe, Coleman Smith, Dave Weinberg, and Federico Rossi. They also are involved in diagnostic exams and biopsying suspicious lesions. Virtual colonoscopy, using specialized CT imaging, has also been available as a screening technique in the radiology department.

For diagnosis, pathologic examination is of course critical. As the program has evolved, special pathologists have come on staff to provide that expertise. In addition to standard histologic examination, additional studies are done as indicated to evaluate tumors for what is called micro-satellite instability. This has significance in regards to prognosis, responsiveness to certain therapies, and the potentially inherited nature of the patient's cancer. Testing has also been developed for markers such as KRAS, which are important in identifying

Abbott Northwestern Hospital has implemented a specialized treatment technique for tumors that have spread to the liver, combining the expertise of interventional radiology and radiation oncology.

whether the tumor will respond to certain therapies in the setting of advanced disease. As in the other GI tumor categories, the group of specialized pathologists has expanded and now includes Drs. Kenneth Batts, Larry Burgart, Jason Daniels, Perry Dilworth, and Schuyler Sanderson.

Rectal cancers in particular are, with the exception of very early stage disease, managed by a multidisciplinary approach. This often involves neoadjuvant chemotherapy and radiation followed by surgery and then potentially post-operative adjuvant chemotherapy. The development of a multidisciplinary team and conferences has been critical to delivery of this care.

Regular tumor conferences became active in the mid-2000s and became more frequent as the interest of the physicians and the caseload increased. Imaging is critical here, as in other cancers, and the radiologists who developed a focus in this area include Drs. Eduardo Ehrenwald, Subbarao Inampudi, and Robin Parker. Medical oncology participants have included Drs. P.J. and Tom Flynn, Burt Schwartz, Dean Gesme, Tim Larson, Joe Leach, and John Seng. Radiation oncologists have included Drs. Tae Kim, Carol Grabowski, David Monyak, Patsa Sullivan, and Laura Willson. As with the other programs, a nurse coordinator was brought on board to tie it all together for the patient. Dusty Powers has served in that role.

Abbott Northwestern Hospital has implemented a specialized treatment technique for tumors that have spread to the liver, combining the expertise of interventional radiology and radiation oncology. Microscopic radioactive spheres are injected directly into the hepatic artery. The approach is called radioembolization. It can be used to deliver radiation directly to the part of the liver that is involved with little radiation affecting other tissues. The use of this procedure grew so dramatically that a separate multidisciplinary conference was developed to discuss these cases.

Reflecting the evolution of cancer care in general, this program evolved with the involvement of multiple specialized and subspecialized physicians from multiple fields of medicine. With tumor-specific multidisciplinary conferences, the addition of a nurse coordinator was necessary. Here continued to be a focus on delivering evidence-based, high-quality patient care.

Hematology Lymphoma Program

The newest of the Virginia Piper Cancer Institute programs, established in 2014, represents in many ways the formalization of care and services that previously existed in a less coordinated fashion. Leukemias and lymphomas had been managed at Abbott Northwestern Hospital for decades. In the 1970s, treatment for acute leukemia in adults saw a major advance with the use of chemotherapy, including anthracyclines and cytosine arabinoside. Other leukemias, lymphomas, and multiple myeloma were managed by hematologists on staff such as Dr. Seamus McKenna and oncologists such as Dr. John Brown.

The specialists in this area grew with the addition of Drs. Burt Schwartz, P.J. Flynn, Tom Flynn, and several others who followed. Hematologists also provided care for so-called "benign" hematologic conditions that weren't considered malignancies. This included abnormal blood cell counts and coagulation disorders. About a dozen new acute leukemia cases per year have been treated at Abbott Northwestern for decades, along with other bone marrow disorders. They include aplastic anemia, myelodysplastic syndromes, and chronic myeloproliferative disorders that at times require inpatient care.

Hematopathologists are essential to establish an accurate diagnosis, as well as assess the response to treatment. A number of subspecialty-trained hematopathologists joined the staff beginning in the 1980s, including Dr. John Strickler. Dr. Tracy Steeper was at Abbott Northwestern for many years before moving to Unity/Mercy Hospital. Dr. Mark Arnesen provided this expertise in the 1980s and 1990s. In 2015, the hematopathologists include Drs. Sue Wheaton, Kevin Stiegelbauer, John Strickler, Stan McCormick, and John Reinartz. The hematology/oncology staff currently is made up of Drs. Michaela Tsai, Tom Flynn, Tim Larson, John Seng, Joe Leach, Dean Gesme, Paul Zander, Vinay Gupta, and Samith Kochuparambil.

A multidisciplinary conference meets twice per month, with teleconference capabilities to other Allina sites. Participants include hematologists/oncologists, at least one hematopathologist, and a radiologist. The radiologist is usually Dr. Brent Bullis or a colleague from Consulting Radiology. A Pharm D specialist, Maria Zarambo, and Dr. John Mendiola of the molecular diagnostics lab are involved. Technologists from flow cytometry, cytogenetics laboratories, genetic counselors, and social workers are also included.

Kathy Martin, who is an RN and Oncology Nurse, was brought on as the nurse coordinator. With extensive experience in inpatient and outpatient oncology nursing, palliative care, and having worked for many years as coordinator of the autologous stem cell transplant program, she has provided valuable patient education and support. She also guides patients through complicated treatment courses, which in the case of acute leukemia may involve several weeks in the hospital. In addition, she assists with coordinating referrals to bone marrow transplant programs at other institutions when appropriate.

While care for these patients doesn't necessarily involve a multidisciplinary team at diagnosis, there are multiple specialists who become part of the care as treatment proceeds, including Infectious Disease, Surgery, respiratory care, and critical care.

Palliative Care

Palliative care, according to the National Cancer Institute, is care given to improve the quality of life of patients who have a serious or life-threatening disease. Its goal is to prevent or treat the symptoms of disease, side effects caused by treatment, as well as psychological, social, and spiritual problems related to the disease or its treatment. Physicians have been involved in the relief of pain and suffering since antiquity, but the establishment of palliative care as a formal subspecialty is a relatively recent event.

The board certification exam was first offered in 2008. A formal specialty fellowship is required in order to be certified in palliative care. The certification program was developed by the boards of internal medicine, anesthesiology, emergency medicine, family medicine, obstetrics and gynecology, pediatrics, physical medicine and rehabilitation, psychiatry and neurology, radiology, and surgery. It is a multidisciplinary approach with the involvement of many professionals, such as pharmacists, doctors, nurses, chaplains, social workers, and psychologists to address the impact of illness on all aspects of the patient's life.

Abbott Northwestern Hospital piloted a palliative care program in 2001. Established by Dr. Dean Fox (internal medicine) and Katie Herman (chaplain) the pilot assessed the benefits on patient care. Seeing favorable results, they established a formal Palliative Care consult service in 2003 with the addition of Kerstin Lappen, Certified Nurse Specialist, who received palliative care education at Harvard Medical School. In 2005, Dr. Fox moved to Duluth, where he continues to work in palliative medicine. That year Dr. Hallie Richards, who had been on faculty of the Abbott Northwestern Internal Medicine Residency Program, began devoting time to the palliative care team. In 2006, Dr. Margaret O'Connor added expertise and experience as a family medicine physician with formal training in palliative care.

The palliative care service was in high demand. With the addition of Dr. Michelle Ragen in 2011, it became possible to add an outpatient clinic to the program. In 2012, Dr. Glen Varns joined the staff as the fourth physician board certified in hospice and palliative care. Certified Nurse Specialist Mary Adams joined the team in 2011 and Certified Nurse Practitioner Leslie Muchow joined in 2014. The interdisciplinary team was completed with the addition of social worker Abbey Wiltzius. She transferred to Mercy Hospital's palliative care team in 2013, and the position is currently held by Rachel Bialostosky.

Dr. O'Connor retired in 2014. Kerstin Lappen took a position at Minnesota Oncology that year to provide palliative care expertise across the metro area as part of that large practice. In 2015, two new physicians were added to the program. Dr. David Lock came from Michigan where he had a background in emergency medicine and completed a palliative care fellowship at the University of Wisconsin Madison. Dr. Alisa Bardo-Martinson, also board certified in palliative care, came from North Memorial. The service remains strong in 2015, with a multidisciplinary team of four physicians, two advanced practice nurses, a social worker, a chaplain, and Pharm D Maria Zarambo. Coverage for consultations is provided seven days a week. The service works with the Palliative Care Fellowship at the University of Minnesota and the Minneapolis VA Hospital. The team participates on the hospital Ethics and Pain Committees and provides teaching to the Internal Medicine residents who rotate on the service.

In addition to providing expertise in the management of such symptoms as nausea and pain, the Palliative Care team is called upon to assist patients and their families as they sort through difficult decisions about treatment for advanced disease. Helping them to understand the options and make choices in the context of patients' goals for the remainder of their lives often involves

It is a multidisciplinary approach with the involvement of many professionals, such as pharmacists, doctors, nurses, chaplains, social workers, and psychologists to address the impact of illness on all aspects of the patient's life.

The Palliative Care team is called upon to assist patients and their families as they sort through difficult decisions about treatment for advanced disease. Helping them to understand the options and make choices in the context of patients' goals for the remainder of their lives often involves prolonged and difficult discussions.

prolonged and difficult discussions. These professionals provide a perspective from outside the oncology team that can be extremely valuable to all involved.

Autologous Stem Cell Transplant

Even in the early days of chemotherapy, we recognized that larger doses of these agents were capable of eliminating larger numbers of cancer cells. This was particularly true for malignancies where a high proportion of the tumor cell population was actively growing and dividing. This included most hematologic malignancies. However, this effect was also seen in solid tumors such as small cell carcinoma of the lung and breast. Higher doses of chemotherapy, however, cause more severe side effects on the normal cells in the body that are rapidly turning over, such as the mucosal lining of the mouth and gastrointestinal tract, as well as the cells of the bone marrow that are constantly producing new blood cells. For many chemotherapy regimens, the dose-limiting toxicity is the suppression of the bone marrow. Very high doses of chemotherapy can result in prolonged or even permanent suppression of the bone marrow.

An approach developed in the 1970s called for stem cells to be collected from a patient's bone marrow and cryopreserved, i.e., preserved at subzero temperatures. The patient then received high doses of chemotherapy. Following this treatment, their marrow stem cells were thawed and re-infused. This allowed for the recovery of their bone marrow, though patients still experienced weeks of very low blood counts with the associated risks of infection and bleeding; this usually required multiple red cell and platelet transfusions. With appropriate supportive care, however, the great majority survived and had recovery of their blood counts.

In 1987, Dr. P.J. Flynn developed the vision for an autologous stem cell transplant program at Abbott Northwestern Hospital. His training and experience in bone marrow transplant, and the availability of excellent pathology, laboratory, and radiology services, as well as an outstanding staff of specialists in radiation oncology, infectious disease, and pulmonology, made him believe this treatment modality was feasible at Abbott Northwestern. Dr. Tom Flynn joined the staff and had a similar interest in the program. Dr. Flynn approached

Venetia Kudrle, a member of the hospital administration, about starting such a program.

A task force was formed and issues identified and prioritized, including blood bank support, air-handling systems to prevent exposure to infectious agents, and reimbursement. Task force members visited Barnes Hospital in St. Louis, a major teaching hospital for Washington University, to observe their program firsthand. Nancy Borstad and Bill Kingston prepared a formal proposal to establish the program, dated September 10, 1987. The recommendations included the establishment of a four-bed bone marrow transplant unit on Station 30, with two of the beds having Intensive Care Unit capabilities. Some medical staff were initially concerned that this was perhaps too specialized an approach to be done at a community hospital. However, Dr. Flynn felt strongly that Abbott Northwestern had all that was needed for such a quality program.

The Bone Marrow Transplant Committee, including representatives of Hematology/Oncology, Nursing, Infectious Disease, Blood Bank, Radiation Oncology, Social Services, and Hospital Administration met during 1987-1989. Memorial Blood Centers (MBC) of Minnesota became involved to process and cryopreserve the bone marrow stem cells at subzero temperatures. Dr. Elizabeth Perry led this laboratory, and she and her staff were a critical part of the treatment team, regularly attending the monthly program meetings. Dr. Herb Polesky, followed by Dr. Jed Gorlin, both Medical Directors at MBC, were very supportive, with Dr. Gorlin actively participating in the program meetings.

The four-bed unit wasn't immediately built, but a couple of beds became available on Station 34 that had previously been used for heart transplant patients. In December 1989, a young woman with relapsed acute leukemia was the first patient. She had her stem cells reinfused on December 26 and recovered her bone marrow function. She survived the treatment to return home from the hospital.

Dr. Tae Kim came to Abbott Northwestern in 1990 as Director of Radiation Oncology. He brought expertise and extensive experience in total body radiation. This was being used in many of the transplant regimens at that time and given in conjunction with high-dose chemotherapy. The program would never have succeeded without nurse coordinators to help develop the treatment protocols. They shepherded the patients through the work-up, stem cell

The program would never have succeeded without nurse coordinators to help develop the treatment protocols. They shepherded the patients through the work-up, stem cell collection, hospital stay, and post-discharge follow-up.

collection, hospital stay, and post-discharge follow-up. The first of these nurses was Nette Kuck, followed by Mary Kay Johnston, Lynn Schroeder, and Kathy Martin. They played critical roles in all aspects of the program, including educational programs for the nurses on the hospital unit.

In 1996, the Foundation for the Accreditation of Cellular Therapy (FACT) was established. In the early 2000s, the program at Abbott Northwestern applied for this voluntary accreditation and was successful. It has remained accredited based on required re-certifications throughout its existence, meeting the rigorous quality standards established by FACT. The accreditation process required extensive work on the part of the nurse coordinator to collect data, monitor quality standards, and develop a very large number of standard operating procedures. Kathy Martin was the nurse coordinator involved throughout the ten years the program maintained FACT accreditation. The program also was approved as a designated transplant center for Eastern Cooperative Group clinical trials involving autologous stem cell transplant.

The program grew fairly quickly with fluctuations year to year. The indications for high-dose treatment evolved over time and was responsible for some of the fluctuation. As the morbidity and mortality of allogeneic bone marrow transplant improved, it became the preferred approach for many patients with acute leukemia. At one point data emerged supporting autologous transplant for breast cancer patients at high risk of developing metastatic disease. The data also supported the treatment for those patients with chemotherapy-sensitive limited metastatic disease. Ultimately the studies could not be confirmed, and one published trial from South Africa was found to have falsified data.

After the initial years on Station 34, an "Acute Observation Oncology" eight-bed unit was built on Station 30 with high-efficiency particulate air (HEPA) filtration rooms. These beds were used for the transplant patients, as well as other severely neutropenic (low white blood cell) patients, such as those going through treatment for acute leukemia. Things were evolving in the stem cell world. It was found that by using growth factors alone or after chemotherapy, one could collect sufficient numbers of bone marrow stem cells from the peripheral blood using apheresis (the removal of blood plasma from the body and reinjecting the cells). This is a technique where blood is withdrawn from a donor and certain components, such as platelets, are removed with the remainder of the blood returned to the donor. This technology and expertise were also available at Memorial Blood Centers, such that patients went there for stem cell collections as an outpatient. The older procedure of "harvesting" bone marrow in the operating room under general anesthesia was phased out. Not only were the collections of stem cells from the blood of donors much easier on the patient, these stem cells provided for more rapid recovery of blood counts after high dose chemotherapy.

On average, 20 patients were treated per year. For the last 10 years of the program, these were primarily individuals with relapsed lymphomas and multiple myeloma, conditions for which this treatment approach proved to be most beneficial. The program filled a niche as a community-based program of documented high quality. It was used primarily for patients being managed by oncologists in the Twin Cities. This allowed convenient access for the patients and easy return to their primary oncologist for ongoing care. In 2014, as Dr. P.J. Flynn and Dr. Tom Flynn were reducing their clinical time at Abbott Northwestern, and with no successors available, the program was closed. A total of 484 patients had been treated. The first stem cell infusion had been done on December 26, 1987, and the last on August 22, 2014.

Clinical Research

It is not possible to have a high-quality cancer program without participating in clinical research to advance knowledge in the field. This provides patients the opportunity to access the latest, most promising treatments. Research has always been part of the fabric of Abbott Northwestern Hospital. In oncology, this took many forms. Dr. David Hickok's laboratory focused on cancer-related activity. Dr. John Brown and other oncologists in practice in the Twin Cities, such as Drs. Irv Lerner, F. Bruce Lewis, and Ken Caldwell became part of the Community Oncology Hospital Program (CHOP). Created by the National Cancer Institute (NCI) in 1979, this program was part of the "War on Cancer" declared by President Nixon in 1971. This clinical research activity helped to lend credibility to community-based cancer care, in other words, care provided outside of University settings. The next program developed by the NCI was the Community Clinical Oncology Program (CCOP) in 1983. A somewhat parallel

Research has always been part of the fabric of Abbott Northwestern Hospital. In oncology, this took many forms.

Dealing with the side effects of treatment, the emotional stress a cancer diagnosis creates for the patient and family, and getting back to a "new normal" after treatment are some of the challenges an individual living with cancer faces.

group, the Community Group Outreach Program (CGOP) was affiliated with the Eastern Cooperative Oncology Group.

Dr. Martin Oken, the first medical director of the Virginia Piper Cancer Institute, was a leader in ECOG and CGOP. He brought the CGOP program locally with him to the VPCI. The Metro-MN CCOP, a consortium of community hospitals in Minnesota, has worked with national cooperative groups to bring clinical trials in oncology to the community setting. Dr. P.J. Flynn was the Principal Investigator for the CCOP from 1985 until 2012. Dr. Joe Leach then assumed that role. The CGOP and CCOP eventually merged to avoid duplication of efforts. The Metro-MN CCOP is recognized as one of the leading community-based programs in the country and has been consistently funded by the NCI since its inception. In 2015, the name of the CCOP was changed to Metro-Minnesota Community Oncology Research Consortium (MMCORC).

Minnesota Oncology's affiliation with the US Oncology Network in 1996 made additional clinical trials available for patients. This program has expanded. On a national network basis, working with 900 oncologists, trials were conducted that are responsible for the approval by the FDA of more than 50 new cancer therapies. Many Minnesota Oncology patients have been treated on those trials.

The Radiation Oncology department participated actively in studies with the Radiation Therapy Oncology Group (RTOG). As noted above, the HBP program became part of the national Pancreatic Research Team as this program developed.

Since 2012, the VPCI has added research capabilities in breast cancer. Dr. Tang was in the Stimpson Chair position initially, followed by Dr. Tsai. Dr. Tsai has brought on a number of trials in other areas as well. Dr. Joe Leach has made trials available for patients with lung, pancreas, and other cancers. The most recent additions have been in the area of immune-oncology. The VPCI commitment to research is also evidenced by the recent addition of Karen Swenson, RN, Ph.D. to the team. It is but another indicator of the dedication to providing quality care for cancer patients.

Survivorship

With early detection and advances in treatment, the population of cancer survivors increased steadily during the past several decades. The number of survivors continues to grow. There were three million cancer survivors in 1971, 9.8 million in 2001, and 11.7 million in 2007. In 2015, the number of survivors is about 14 million. Dealing with the side effects of treatment, the emotional stress a cancer diagnosis creates for the patient and family, and getting back to a "new normal" after treatment are some of the challenges an individual living with cancer faces. As the population of survivors has increased and as cancer has evolved into a chronic disease for many with the advances in therapy, more assistance and services for these individuals are needed.

The Virginia Piper Cancer Institute has responded, creating a survivorship program, led by Dr. Nancy Hutchison. This program helps patients regain function in general, deal with adverse effects of treatment, and return to a normal life. VPCI also developed a "healing coach" to provide emotional support, information on other therapies, and referrals to integrative therapies. This coach was put in place to assist patients in developing a healing plan, cope with uncertainties, and empower the patient within the health care system. The coach also assists with communication within the family.

Minnesota Oncology also developed a formal survivorship program using specially trained Advanced Practice Providers. These providers assist patients in a structured program at the start of treatment. The goal is to assure understanding of the treatment plan, its side effects, and methods of coping initially, during, and after treatment. This helps the patient identify his/her needs for support, education, and rehabilitation in order to recover as best possible. The programs complement one another.

Many cancer patients seek complementary therapies as they go through and recover from treatment. The Institute for Health and Healing was founded at Abbott Northwestern in 2003 by the George Family Foundation and the Ted and Roberta Mann Foundation (see Chapter 28). It was renamed the Penny George Institute for Health and Healing to honor Penny George, who is an integrative health philanthropist. As a breast cancer survivor, Mrs. George has become a national leader in advocating for integrative health. She credits integrative health as an important foundation in her own recovery. The

The goal is to assure understanding of the treatment plan, its side effects, and methods of coping initially, during, and after treatment.

The Institute's mission is to combine leading medical practice with ancient healing and wisdom. It uses a holistic, integrative approach with a "focus on the mind, body and spirit."

Institute's mission is to combine leading medical practice with ancient healing and wisdom. It uses a holistic, integrative approach with a "focus on the mind, body, and spirit." This is reflected by the sculpture at the entrance of Abbott Northwestern Hospital (see pages 74-75).

These programs have taken Abbott Northwestern Hospital and the Virginia Piper Cancer Institute to the leading edge of not only providing outstanding medical care, but also providing care for the whole person.

Conclusion

The history of cancer care at Abbott Northwestern Hospital is in many ways the history of cancer care anywhere in the country. What distinguishes this history uniquely, however, has been the extraordinary collaborative efforts of so many highly qualified specialists working effectively together to develop multidisciplinary specialized programs, while practicing in independent practices in a community setting. Strong leadership from individual physicians, VPCI leaders, hospital administrators, and the dedicated efforts of nurse coordinators made it possible to create programs and services that provide the best technology with a compassionate staff. The primary focus has always been on the patient!

References

Band, Pierre R. The Birth of the Subspecialty of Medical Oncology and Examples of Early Scientific Foundations. J Clin Oncol 2010; 28: 3653-58.

Kennedy, BJ. Medical Oncology: Its Origins, Evolution, Current Status, and Future. Cancer 1999; 85: 1-8.

Mukherjee, Siddhartha. *The Emperor of All Maladies*. Scribner, New York: Scribner, 2010.

Acknowledgements

Thanks to all of the following individuals who gave of their time and provided their perspectives, recollections, and knowledge of this history. It would not have been possible to write this without them. In no particular order: Burt Schwartz, P.J. Flynn, Dan Dunn, Bev Trombley, Margit Bretzke, Carol Bergen, John Trusheim, Tim Sielaff, Dave Monyak, Sally Lee, Cathy McLean, Tom Payne, Donn Mosser, Mahmoud Nagib, Kerstin Lappen, Matt Graczyk, Cheryl Bailey, Tami Lillemoe, Richard Meyer, and Gretchen Piper.

4

Cardiology
1951-2014
Dr. Robert A. Van Tassel

Today, Abbott Northwestern Hospital is world renowned for its expertise in cardiovascular medicine and surgery. This remarkable achievement was not by accident. Visionary physicians working in collaboration with equally talented hospital and community leaders, during a time of seismic technological advancement, have guided this institution to its current status. The emergence of cardiovascular medicine at Abbott Northwestern Hospital has been heavily influenced by advances in cardiovascular medicine at the University of Minnesota and the Mayo Clinic. Great strides were made at these two great institutions in the 1950s and '60s. These advances then gravitated to the premier private hospital in the community, namely Abbott Northwestern Hospital.

It is impossible to separate the progress in the field of cardiovascular medicine from that of cardiovascular surgery. Each discipline has benefited from the expertise of the other. The combination of outstanding talent in cardiac pathology, adult and pediatric cardiology, along with a strong surgical team at the Mayo Clinic contributed significantly to the field. Many regard the Mayo Clinic as having led the nation in this discipline. Also during this time, clinicians in cardiac surgery and cardiology, working alongside scientists doing basic scientific

...clinicians in cardiac surgery and cardiology, working alongside scientists doing basic scientific research at the University of Minnesota, led the world with transformative discoveries that represented the leading edge of this emerging field.

research at the University of Minnesota, led the world with transformative discoveries that represented the leading edge of this emerging field.

While these achievements were being realized at the Mayo Clinic and the University of Minnesota, Abbott Hospital and Northwestern Hospital were establishing themselves as the premier hospitals in the Twin Cities and greater Minnesota, largely due to excellence in subspecialty medicine. The mission of both Abbott and Northwestern hospitals was to practice and deliver the very highest quality of care. This philosophy ensured that both hospitals attracted top physicians in all specialties. For example, physicians who completed their training in cardiac surgery and cardiology at the University of Minnesota were naturally attracted to Abbott and Northwestern because of their outstanding reputations for quality and clinical expertise.

Additionally, Abbott and Northwestern hospitals developed a diversity of supporting subspecialties. Both hospitals are indebted to the founders of these institutions for instilling the quest for quality in their charters. This culture promoted the rapid and successful establishment of the practice of cardiology, developed initially at Northwestern Hospital and subsequently at Abbott Northwestern Hospital.

The Early Era 1950-1970

The decades of the 50s and the 60s were an exciting time at Northwestern Hospital. Many well-trained internists served as cardiologists for patients with heart disease. These internists were highly competent and provided an extraordinary level of care for their cardiology patients, particularly when considering the limitations of medical and invasive technology at that time. Several internists had additional cardiology training in clinical cardiology and provided advanced consultation to general internists. Drs. Frank Norman, Ray Scallen, and Robert Scott are among those physicians.

Dr. John Labree was the first cardiologist to practice invasive cardiology at Northwestern Hospital. (He was also on staff at St. Louis Park Medical Center.) He performed the first cardiac catheterization at Northwestern Hospital in 1951. His presence there was limited, however, as he subsequently dedicated his full attention to his practice at Methodist Hospital in St. Louis Park and moved his catheterization practice to Mount Sinai Hospital.

Cardiac catheterization was uncommon at that time, and the emphasis was on making the correct diagnosis of cyanotic congenital heart disease. Dr. Rolf Andreassen had just completed his cardiology training at Temple University in 1952 and returned to Minneapolis to join Dr. Dean Rizer, who had established a large, successful practice in internal medicine. Dr. Andreassen chose Northwestern Hospital because it was the premier private hospital in Minneapolis and was known for its interest in establishing expertise in subspecialty medicine.

Dr. Andreasen initially practiced both internal medicine and invasive cardiology with Dr. Rizer. However, after five years, he dedicated himself to a solo practice limited to clinical and invasive cardiology. Dr. Andreassen performed his first cardiac catheterization in the fall of 1952. The "cath lab" at that time was a single room in the Radiology Department at Northwestern Hospital. It was used for cardiac patients after the gastro-intestinal (GI) studies had been completed for the day. This "cath lab" was equipped with minimal physiologic monitoring equipment and had no cineangiography (the moving images of the heart taken by X-ray).

The specialty of cardiac surgery was also forming at large research and academic centers at this time. It had not yet been established in the private hospitals. Coronary care units and standardized treatment protocols for the critically ill cardiac patient did not exist. Patients with acute myocardial infarction were frequently hospitalized for three to four weeks. The mainstay of the treatment was limited to bed rest, oxygen, nitroglycerine, xylocaine, and sedation. The placement of deep, central venous lines was not yet accepted, and pacemakers were implanted only for complete heart block.

Chest surgeons or general surgeons performed these procedures. Coronary angiography was not available, and imaging of both adult and pediatric cardiac patients was in its infancy. Such imaging was available only at the University of Minnesota and at the Mayo Clinic. Fortunately, many of the advances in the management of cardiac patients and advances in cardiac surgical management occurred in Minnesota. These advances were readily transferable to the private hospitals after they had been thoroughly developed and tested.

The first coronary care unit (CCU) in the United States was established at the Bethany Hartford hospital in Kansas City in 1960. Soon thereafter, Dr. Andreassen visited the new CCU and was especially impressed with the new approach to the treatment of patients with myocardial infarction. This visit led Dr. Andreassen to apply these concepts and innovative methods to the patients at Northwestern Hospital. In late 1960, a coronary care unit was established at Northwestern.

The Establishment of Cardiology as a Specialty

The American Heart Association was created in 1920. Twenty-nine years later the American College of Cardiology was also established. However, the number of cardiology training programs and cardiac fellows in the 1950s was small by today's standards. Although there were significant advances in the training of cardiologists prior to 1960, it wasn't until after the establishment of the coronary care unit, the defibrillator, the "crash cart," and coronary angiography that the number of training programs greatly expanded. The number of clinical and invasive cardiologists increased significantly during this period. In 1950, there were 19 training programs in cardiology in the country with only 37 fellows. By 1995, the number of cardiology programs had increased to 210 programs with 2,633 fellows.

Dr. Mason Sones introduced coronary angiography at the Cleveland Clinic in 1962. The radiologist, Dr. Kurt Amplatz, further refined this procedure at the University of Minnesota. At the University of Minnesota, coronary angiography initially was performed by interventional radiologists and newly trained cardiac surgeons. The early surgical pioneers included Dr. Aiden Bilgatay and Dr. N. K. Jensen. Both had completed their surgical training at the University of Minnesota and had developed angiographic skills under Dr. Amplatz. They brought this technology and skill to Northwestern Hospital in the late 1960s, inaugurating the performance of coronary angiography in the catheterization laboratory. This new imaging technology allowed the cardiac surgeons to further develop their specialty and work closely with the cardiologists, who were also being trained in coronary angiography.

Dr. Robert Van Tassel completed his cardiology fellowship at the University of Minnesota in 1971 and moved to Abbott and Northwestern hospitals. As did Dr. Andreassen before him, Dr. Van Tassel initially practiced cardiology as part of an Internal Medicine group. After one year, however, he and Dr. Andreassen formally established the practice of cardiology with the creation of Minneapolis Cardiology Associates. The practice was a consultative and invasive model with all patients ultimately referred back to their primary care physicians.

In this setting, the practice flourished. However, in order for their referral practice to thrive, they needed a larger base of referrals than could be supplied by the physicians practicing at Abbott and Northwestern hospitals. This realization led to the establishment of an outreach program that became a significant part of the practice. The Lakeview Clinic in Waconia, Minnesota, was the inaugural outreach site.

As the practice grew, they needed additional expertise and more cardiologists. In 1974, Dr. James Daniel joined the practice after finishing his fellowship at the University of Minnesota. He had achieved an expertise in the exciting new imaging technology of echocardiography. At this time, Dr. Fred Gobel was the director of the cardiac catheterization laboratory at the Veterans Hospital (VA) in Minneapolis and was a highly respected clinician with a strong interest in research. In 1976, Dr. Gobel, along with the outstanding clinician Dr. Richard Nelson, left the VA system to join Minneapolis Cardiology Associates.

These five cardiologists formed the nucleus of a practice that eventually grew to more than 50 cardiologists serving more than 30 outreach sites. Those who trained at the University of Minnesota were deeply indebted to their mentors in the fellowship program. Drs. Kurt Amplatz, Howard Burchell, Jesse Edwards, Robert Eliot, and Yang Wang were among the doctors who participated in and developed the unparalleled training program at the University.

No Minnesota cardiologist is more revered than Dr. Howard Burchell. Dr. Burchell was appointed Chief of Cardiology for the teaching program at Northwestern Hospital in 1975. Prior to this appointment, he had been a Consulting Cardiologist at the Mayo Clinic. Between 1968 and 1975, he served as the esteemed Chief of Cardiology at the University of Minnesota. He also was the editor of the prestigious journal *Circulation* and was nationally and internationally known and respected.

It is impossible to overstate the importance of his presence to the success of the practice of cardiology at Abbott Northwestern Hospital. Dr. Burchell added instant credibility to the program and was an enormous asset to the clinical cardiologists, as well as to the residents in the teaching program. His advice and clinical perspective were sought daily. For years, virtually every complex cardiac case benefitted from his presence.

Minneapolis Heart Institute® and Minneapolis Heart Institute® Foundation

The growth of cardiology at Minneapolis Cardiology Associates and Northwestern Hospital was breathtaking. Remarkable and unforeseen technological advances were transforming patient care. Once coronary angiography became a prominent part of the practice, the cardiologists worked closely with the cardiac surgeons to establish the surgical revascularization program. However, a more sophisticated structure would be needed to compete on a regional and national basis, to provide a unified presence, and to allow effective marketing. Consequently, the cardiologists and the cardiac surgeons began to plan such a structure.

The goal was to create an organization that would allow each group to maintain independence, while providing an umbrella organization for marketing, outreach, and promoting general guidelines of care. In 1982, a group of 13 dedicated physicians including cardiologists, cardiac surgeons, radiologists, and anesthesiologists formed the Minneapolis Heart Institute®. These physicians included Drs. Rolf Andreassen, Orn Arnar, Kit Arom, James Daniel, Fred Gobel, Frank Johnson, Charles Jorgenson, William Kelly, Joe Kiser, William Lindsay, Richard Nelson, Demetre Nicoloff, Ted Peterson, Jonathon Rogers, and Robert Van Tassel.

The founding physicians maintained a strong interest in advancing clinical research and medical education. This culminated in 1983 with the creation of the Minneapolis Heart Institute® Foundation (MHIF) to support these endeavors. While the founding physicians initially funded MHIF, subsequently the hospital and the community became strong financial supporters. The community response was outstanding! Ray Bentdahl, Tom Keller, Rudy Luther, Ray Plank, and many others provided sophisticated leadership and financial support. Ray Sever, a former hospital administrator, served as the first president. He carefully and skillfully led the organization during its inception and for several years thereafter.

The Minneapolis Heart Institute® achieved remarkable success in developing the clinical practice of cardiology and cardiac surgery at Abbott Northwestern Hospital. The individual practices flourished under this umbrella. Patient care was outstanding, and the program achieved national recognition for excellence.

The Minneapolis Heart Institute® Foundation also grew rapidly and received national recognition for groundbreaking clinical research. By its 25th anniversary, the Foundation had received more than $10 million from the physicians alone and had invested more than $50 million in clinical research. Physician members of the Foundation had published more than 1000 peer-reviewed articles, completed more than 750 clinical trials, and participated in educating more than a half million community members.

The presence of the Minneapolis Heart Institute® Foundation at Abbott Northwestern Hospital has been a catalyst for the development of other specialties and for attracting referral patients in all subspecialties of medicine and surgery. MHIF has provided the necessary infrastructure to attract world-class researchers, such as Dr. Barry Maron in hypertrophic cardiomyopathy, Dr. Tim Henry and Dr. Jay Traverse in cardiac research, and Dr. Rob Schwartz in translational research. Without the infrastructure of the Foundation, these research physicians would not have been able to pursue their research at a private hospital. The presence of these research physicians also served as a catalyst for clinicians at the Foundation to participate in areas of interest in cardiac research. Drs. Kevin Graham, Kevin Harris, Robert Hauser, John Lesser, Michael Mooney, Wes Pedersen, Scott Sharkey, and others have been significantly involved in clinical research. They have published their findings in peer-reviewed, national medical journals.

Early recognition and adoption of promising new technology has been a signature of the cardiac program at Abbott Northwestern Hospital.

Innovation

Early recognition and adoption of promising new technology has been a signature of the cardiac program at Abbott Northwestern Hospital. Coronary angiography, coronary angioplasty, complex cardiac pacemakers, mobile ultrasound, mobile catheterization laboratory, intracoronary stents, left ventricular assist devices, and cardiac transplantation are part of a long list of pioneering efforts.

Notably, the first coronary angioplasty in the Twin Cities was performed at Abbott Northwestern Hospital. The first implantation of an artificial heart in Minnesota was performed at Abbott Northwestern Hospital in 1985 by a surgical team led by Dr. Lyle Joyce. In addition, several physicians have played key roles working with industry to create, study, and perfect medical devices that have improved the lives of our patients.

Inventions, patents, and the formation of new companies are a result of these efforts. Dr. Robert Hauser has long been a keen observer of pacemakers, pacemaker leads, and defibrillators and has been a national leader in publishing the results of the failure rates of these devices. This natural history of devices is of great value to the clinician implanting them, as well as those following such patients.

In early 2001, the cardiology group at the Minneapolis Heart Institute® elected to lead the way in the new and exciting field of advanced cardiac imaging. Dr. John Lesser volunteered to study this new imaging process at the Royal Brompton Hospital in London, recognized as an international leader in this area. Dr. Lesser returned to Abbott Northwestern Hospital to establish the Center for Cardiac Imaging, which is now a leading center in the nation in this sophisticated discipline.

In 2008, Dr. Kevin Graham conceived the Heart of New Ulm project. In partnership with Allina Health System, he developed a comprehensive preventive medicine program for an entire community. This innovative program was one of the first in the nation to evaluate an entire community in an effort to favorably influence lifestyles, eating habits, and physical activity levels. The preliminary results after five years have been impressive and demonstrate that community-based programs can have powerfully favorable results.

Minneapolis Heart Institute® was not only a leader in preventive medicine.

A highly successful cardiac transplantation program was initiated in 1986 with members from both cardiology and cardiovascular surgery: Drs. Charles Jorgensen, Maria Olivari, and Marc Pritzker from the cardiology side; Drs. Frazier Eales, Robert Emery, Lyle Joyce, and Demetre Nicoloff of the surgical team. This program was one of only a handful of national transplant programs to be operated at a private hospital.

Although there were many significant, innovative programs at Abbott Northwestern Hospital, two stand out. The Level One Heart Attack program led by Dr. Tim Henry was an approach to expedite the interventional treatment of patients with acute myocardial infarction. This program has led to significant changes in such treatment on a national and international level. The Cool-IT program, led by Dr. Michael Mooney, studied the use of an innovative cooling method for patients with an out-of-hospital cardiac arrest. The results were very favorable, and this method has been widely adopted worldwide.

In early 2001, the cardiology group at the Minneapolis Heart Institute® elected to lead the way in the new and exciting field of advanced cardiac imaging.

Subspecialization

As the practice of cardiology expanded and became vastly more complex, it became obvious to all Minneapolis Heart Institute® physicians that subspecialization was necessary. For the program to compete regionally with the University of Minnesota and with the Mayo Clinic, it would need to develop and recruit cardiologists with a refined expertise in the subspecialty areas of the practice. This process began in 1986, with the addition of Dr. Michael Mooney, who had received post fellowship training in coronary angioplasty by one of the pioneers in this field. Since then, the practice has attracted cardiologists in each of the subspecialty areas including electrophysiology, interventional cardiology, heart failure, preventive cardiology, and transplantation.

Electrophysiology is now one of the largest of the cardiology subspecialty disciplines and was developed at Abbott Northwestern Hospital by Drs. Adrian Almquist, Charles Gornick, William Katsiyannis, and Simon Milstein. Further subspecialization currently exists within interventional cardiology. Only specially trained, structural heart disease cardiologists are able to perform certain advanced procedures, such as the percutaneous implantation of heart valves. Today, specially trained cardiologists are able to deploy devices

The concept of sub-specialization distinguishes the practice of cardiology at Abbott Northwestern Hospital. It allows the most sophisticated treatment to the most complex cardiac cases and provides comprehensive cardiac care for all patients.

by a percutaneous approach to close atrial septal defects, close the left atrial appendage, and ablate areas of life-threatening, unstable arrhythmias. The concept of subspecialization distinguishes the practice of cardiology at Abbott Northwestern Hospital. It allows the most sophisticated treatment to the most complex cardiac cases and provides comprehensive cardiac care for all patients.

Merger of Minneapolis Heart Institute® and Abbott Northwestern Hospital

The practice and operation of cardiology changed dramatically in the late 1980s and 1990s. Cardiology became more hospital-centered, and the distinction between the clinical practice of cardiology and the functions of the hospital became blurred. A closer relationship between the physicians and the hospital was necessary to provide comprehensive, high-quality, innovative cardiovascular medicine at a reasonable cost.

Gordon Sprenger, the Abbott Northwestern Hospital administrator, recognized the value of this closer symbiotic relationship. Together with physician leaders, he conducted detailed and comprehensive discussions, culminating in the merger of Minneapolis Cardiology Associates with Abbott Northwestern Hospital in 1995. This merger allowed a near total alignment of the incentives and goals of both entities and greatly streamlined the cardiovascular program.

Under this new entity, the Cardiovascular Service Division was formed to promote a high level of quality and efficiency. The cardiology program gained national recognition for quality and innovation. Cardiologists from across the United States visited the Minneapolis Heart Institute® to learn details of the structure and returned to their institutions to create similar models. At the time of the merger in 1995, fewer than 10 percent of cardiology programs had established a strong hospital affiliation. Today that percentage is nearly 85 percent. The merger of Minneapolis Heart Institute® with Abbott Northwestern Hospital has been a great success and has served as a model for the nation. *U.S. News and World Report* ranked the program 15th best in the nation in 2013.

The Future

In 60 years, the Cardiology program at Abbott Northwestern Hospital was born, matured, and continues to thrive. It has served the community, the physicians, and their patients well. With dedicated physicians, a superb hospital, and a spirit of innovation and cooperation, the quality of care and the availability of the most advanced care is peerless. The future is even more exciting. Advances in the fields of biologic therapy, cardiac imaging, cell therapy, and nonsurgical minimally invasive intervention are here or just beyond the horizon.

A new era of health care delivery is in its infancy. Telemedicine, best practice guidelines, community-based programs for the prevention of heart disease, as well as novel delivery methods are expanding. A more flexible and efficient method of delivering high-quality cardiology care is imperative! The Minneapolis Heart Institute® at Abbott Northwestern Hospital is poised to help create and implement these systems.

Advances in the fields of biologic therapy, cardiac imaging, cell therapy, and nonsurgical minimally invasive intervention are here or just beyond the horizon.

5

Cardiovascular Surgery
1900-2014
Dr. Frazier Eales

Most would agree that the advances made in the field of heart surgery over the course of the last 50 years have been astounding. So much so that, as doctors, we sometimes fail to remember or acknowledge the vitally important elements that, from the beginning and to this day, underpin our ability to do what we do.

Even on a good day, cardiac surgery can be a bloody business. Dr. Joseph Kiser, a colleague who was one of the early cardiac surgeons at Northwestern Hospital, often said that, "If it weren't for the hours and the bleeding, ours would be the best job in the world." There is a lot of truth to that. Today, not unlike 50 years ago, the availability of blood products remains a critical element in the safe conduct of surgery generally, and heart surgery in particular.

Prior to 1900, there was no such thing as the safe replacement (transfusion) of blood. But in 1900, Dr. Karl Landsteiner, an Austrian-born physician and biologist, first identified the major human blood groupings. With this came the knowledge that transfusions needed to be blood type specific in order to avoid the deadly consequences of transfusion reactions. The first successful blood transfusion did not occur until 1907. Landsteiner received the Nobel Prize for his work in 1930.

Similarly, prior to the early 1900s, conventional medical wisdom dictated that it was not possible to surgically repair injured or severed blood vessels. Think of the Civil War, when the greatest surgical expertise was to perform rapid amputations of injured limbs, which was done without anesthesia and antibiotics, and with only a rudimentary understanding of basic sanitary techniques. No one believed that tissue as delicate as a blood vessel could be successfully reconstructed by suturing. No one until Dr. Alexis Carrel. Carrel was born in Lyon, France, in 1873 and received his medical degree from the University of Lyon. Perhaps more importantly, his mother was a fine seamstress and a professional embroiderer. Carrel was fascinated by her work, and he studied with another of Lyon's finest embroiderers. From this interest in sewing technique, he devised a safe and reproducible technique for suturing blood vessels. He received the Nobel Prize for this work in 1912.

Cardiac surgery involving the use of the heart-lung machine began in 1953. Dr. John Gibbon, in Philadelphia, had spent years developing such a device. The first successful "open heart" procedure was done in that year on an eighteen-year-old woman with an atrial septal defect (a hole in the muscle separating the upper chambers of the heart). Her recovery was complete and uneventful. The next two patients undergoing such a procedure died. Dr. Gibbon declared a self-imposed moratorium on open-heart surgery and never performed such surgery again.

But the challenge had been reframed, and many others began to refine the tools for diagnosis as well as for surgery. One of the true pioneers was Dr. C. Walton Lillehei at the University of Minnesota. In the mid 1950s, he did a landmark series of "cross-circulation" cases in which a child underwent heart surgery and a parent was used as the heart-lung machine. The procedures were very successful, but also raised ethical concerns. One noted physician remarked that it was the first elective surgical procedure where mortality could be 200 percent. But Dr. Lillehei, along with Clarence Dennis (who developed major improvements to the heart-lung machine) and others, persisted. And they succeeded in creating a legacy of innovation and a foundation for many cardiac surgical advances. Minnesota was well served by the early and exceptional cardiac surgical programs both at the University and at the Mayo Clinic.

Well into the 1960s, cardiac procedures were mainly directed at congenital defects or heart valve disorders, the latter frequently the result of rheumatic heart disease. The epidemic disease of the time, however, was coronary artery disease (the predominant cause of myocardial infarction or heart attack), and this remained essentially beyond surgical reach. That changed in 1967, when Dr. Rene Favoloro performed the first coronary artery bypass procedure. Dr. Favoloro, an Argentinian physician, was working at the Cleveland Clinic when this historic surgery was done. With the use of the heart-lung machine, he successfully bypassed blocked coronary arteries using the patient's own saphenous vein as the conduit. It was an event that utterly changed the course of cardiac surgery.

Cardiac Surgery at Northwestern Hospital

I have been unable to document the exact date of the first cardiac surgical procedure done at Northwestern Hospital, but it almost certainly would have been in the early to mid-1960s. This corresponds to the years in which cardiac surgery was spreading from academic (i.e., University) settings and becoming available at larger community hospitals. An article from the *Annals of Surgery*, published in February 1963, details a method for surgically repairing the aortic valve. The authors were Drs. Joseph Garamella, N. Kenneth Jensen, Michael Lynch, and W.R. Schmidt, all active at Northwestern Hospital at the time. Some, if not all, of their cases were done there. Until the advent of coronary artery bypass surgery, however, surgical volumes were quite small and surgical risks were very high.

I first set foot in Northwestern Hospital in 1970 when I was a sophomore in college. I had an interest in surgery and had taken a ten-week course for nursing students designed to expose (and attract) nurses to the operating room. Marion Jensen, the nursing director of surgery at Northwestern, hired me with these credentials as a surgical technician. It was a job that I held full-time during summers and part-time during the school year all the way through medical school. It exposed me to some of the earliest experiences in cardiac surgery at Northwestern Hospital.

Coronary artery bypass surgery today is quite a refined and expeditious exercise. That assumes, of course, that anything involving splitting the chest open can be characterized as refined. Today, the operation typically takes three hours or so to complete and involves a hospital phase of recovery of five to six days. But in 1970, surgeons, cardiologists, and anesthesiologists were working in uncharted territory. A typical bypass procedure involved eight to twelve hours in the operating room, a minimum of two to three days in intensive care and a hospital stay exceeding two weeks.

The most senior cardiac surgeons at Northwestern, including Drs. N. Kenneth Jensen, Frank Johnson, and Michael Lynch had finished their formal training in the 1950s, well before the advent of coronary artery bypass surgery. The youngest surgeons (Drs. Orn Arnar, Joseph Kiser, and Ted Peterson) were the first CV (Cardiovasular) Surgery staff at Northwestern to have had significant cardiac surgical experience as part of their fellowship training. Surgical results were excellent for that time, but nothing like today. As with so many physicians at Northwestern, these early cardiac surgeons were exceptionally talented and motivated. Their combined efforts over the next several years brought growth to the cardiac surgical program and improved outcomes. The procedures included coronary artery bypass, valve replacement, and pediatric cardiac surgery.

Cardiac Surgery at Abbott Northwestern Hospital

All of this happened literally three miles from the University of Minnesota, where the cardiac surgical program had remained incredibly robust with the likes of Drs. Aldo Casteneda, Richard Lillehei, William Lindsay, Demetre Nicoloff, and Richard Varco. Dr. Nicoloff performed the first heart transplant procedures at the University of Minnesota. He was also the lead physician in the development of the St. Jude mechanical valve (a valve that became the gold-standard for mechanical heart valve replacement). In 1979, Dr. Nicoloff and Dr. Lindsay left the University to establish a practice at what, by this time, was Abbott Northwestern Hospital. Their decision was a landmark development for Abbott Northwestern.

This was still a time when many, if not most, heart patients were referred directly to cardiac surgeons. Cardiology had made striking advances in diagnostic procedures, but "interventional" cardiology was still in its infancy. And by virtue of their work at the University, both Dr. Nicoloff and Dr. Lindsay had a referral base that included all of Minnesota and much of North Dakota, South Dakota, and Wisconsin. Over the next few years, the cardiac surgical program at Abbott Northwestern grew exponentially.

The 1980s brought changes and improvements to the management of cardiovascular disease at Abbott Northwestern. This decade marked the real beginning of interventional cardiology with the advent of percutaneous transluminal coronary angioplasty. (A catheter inserted through the skin in the groin is used to expand a blocked coronary artery.) For many patients, this provided an excellent alternative to coronary artery bypass surgery. Dr. Robert Van Tassel and his colleagues became nationally recognized leaders in the development of this therapy. By the end of the decade, coronary stenting provided an even better non-surgical alternative to the treatment of coronary artery disease.

Surgical practice was evolving as well. Mitral valve surgery, for example, had historically required replacement of the valve with either a tissue or mechanical prosthesis. But many patients with mitral valve disease could have their native valve repaired. While still a major surgical procedure, the risks with repair are lower than the risks associated with replacement and long-term results are excellent.

Many improvements across the cardiac surgical practice could be characterized as incremental. These are changes that do not garner headlines but, in the aggregate, can produce striking improvements. An example was our initiative in early extubation (i.e., a shortened length of time for a patient to be supported by a ventilator) and early ambulation. With improvements in surgical technique and anesthetic management, patients were coming out of surgery much less traumatized. A shorter operation, shorter lengths of time on the heart-lung machine, better anesthetic management, and less blood loss all contributed. "Standard practice" up to this time had been a minimum of 24 hours with ventilator support and a minimum of two days in the ICU. It became standard practice because for years it had been a true medical necessity. But by

the 1990s, a significant number of surgical patients required ventilator support for only a few hours after surgery or, in some cases, none at all.

Similarly, the pace at which activity levels were advanced after cardiac surgery had become outdated. Again, the long-standing guidelines were likely a reflection of a previous reality, leavened with a good dose of compassion. After all, it hurts to get up and start moving after a cardiac surgeon has gone to work on you. But compassion can hurt too. A corollary is found in the way obstetricians once managed mothers following delivery. In the 1950s, a new mother could anticipate four or five days of bed rest following childbirth. A very compassionate notion but extremely bad medicine. The reality is that even young, healthy people lose strength rapidly when confined to bed. And in the post-partum setting, inactivity promotes a near-perfect environment for venous thrombosis and pulmonary embolism.

The same reality applies to cardiac surgical patients, many of whom are much older and frequently not so healthy. The typical length of hospitalization after heart surgery in the 1970s was upward of two weeks. But by the late 1980s, the focus on minimizing ventilator time and implementing an aggressive early rehab protocol cut the average hospital stay in half.

While incremental changes may have made such advances technically possible, more substantial change was needed to transform possibility into reality. Transformation for Abbott Northwestern's cardiovascular program came about primarily from the recognition that we had grown into just that: a program. No longer a collection of independent clinicians and nurses, no longer just a menu of tests or procedures or medications, cardiovascular services had become an increasingly sophisticated, multidisciplinary, and inter-dependent offering. One example of our response was the development of the Heart Team among the surgical nurses. Instead of having cardiac surgical cases as only a part of their scope of practice, the Heart Team covered all cardiac cases and only cardiac cases. Doing so enhanced and made predictable the provision of a skillset that is critically important to our surgeons and our patients. Abbott Northwestern was the first hospital in the region to do this.

Similarly, the anesthesiologists, by now a group of 30 or more, chose to focus cardiovascular anesthesia care within a self-selected subgroup of eight individuals. Again, this decision addressed the reality of an increasingly challenging mix of patients and procedures. The same forces resulted in the creation of the first dedicated CV Surgical Intensive Care Unit. All of these steps contributed to tangibly improved care and outcomes.

Heart Transplant Program

Some changes did produce headlines. In 1985, Abbott Northwestern initiated its Heart Transplant program along with the use of the Jarvik total artificial heart. Dr. Lyle Joyce had come to Abbott Northwestern in 1983, following training in Salt Lake City where he was involved in the first human implantation of the Jarvik Heart, the first artificial heart. I joined the staff in 1984 after finishing training at the University of Minnesota. My last year at the University coincided with the rejuvenation of their cardiac transplantation program, a decision fueled in large part by the advent of the immuno-suppressive drug cyclosporin. The discovery of this drug had vastly improved and simplified the management of organ rejection following transplantation.

Along with Drs. Lindsay, Nicoloff, and Robert Emery, our group proceeded with our first transplant in October of 1985. In December of the same year, Mary Lund became the first woman ever to receive a Jarvik heart. While the Jarvik heart has now become something of an historical footnote, it served as an important step in the evolving technology of mechanical support for end-stage heart failure. Those in charge of the Jarvik program at Abbott Northwestern kept the worldwide registry for the device's use, and recorded the best outcomes of any program. The cardiac transplantation program quickly became robust, ranking in the top-ten programs in the country in its first decade both in terms of volume and outcomes.

This program was a rather remarkable achievement in two additional, important ways. First, it was one of the earliest transplant programs in the country to exist outside of a University setting. Second, the program was staffed (on the surgical side) by two competing private practice groups: Cardiac Surgical Associates and Minnesota Thoracic Associates. The "business model" of the time was strictly private practice, fee-for-service. In many institutions, even the notion of competing groups collaborating on an effort such as this would have been impossible.

...all of the surgeon's professional fees in this fee-for-service model were donated to the nascent Minneapolis Heart Institute® Foundation for a dedicated patient-assistance fund.

It was the visionary leap that produced the Minneapolis Heart Institute® Foundation (MHIF). This came about due to a founding group from the cardiology and cardiac surgery groups. It was rooted in the notion that Abbott Northwestern could become a world-class center for the treatment of cardiovascular disease.

But Abbott Northwestern was (and is) different. The two groups developed an integrated call schedule and shared responsibilities for both pre- and post-transplant patients. Additionally, all of the surgeon's professional fees in this fee-for-service model were donated to the nascent Minneapolis Heart Institute® Foundation for a dedicated patient-assistance fund. Many other disciplines contributed similarly to this effort, including staff from cardiology, anesthesiology, internal medicine, infectious disease, pulmonary medicine, psychiatry, and pathology.

Minneapolis Heart Institute® Foundation

The most important and enduring change that took place at this time in Abbott Northwestern's cardiovascular program was not about headlines, nor was it incremental. It was the visionary leap that produced the Minneapolis Heart Institute® Foundation (MHIF). This came about due to a founding group from the cardiology and cardiac surgery groups. It was rooted in the notion that Abbott Northwestern could become a world-class center for the treatment of cardiovascular disease. To become so would require more than being a high-quality, high-volume center. It would require tangibly advancing the discipline(s) by means of participation in research and education.

Incorporated by the founding group, membership included all of the cardiologists and cardiac surgeons at Abbott Northwestern as well as representatives from radiology and anesthesiology. The hospital leadership, most notably by Gordon Sprenger and his entire administrative staff, importantly and enthusiastically endorsed the concept. As noted by Dr. Van Tassel in his chapter on Cardiology, funding for MHIF, in the early years, came almost entirely from contributions from the participating physicians and from the hospital itself. These proved to be investments that benefitted many in our community, none more so than the patients receiving cardiovascular care at Abbott Northwestern.

Innovation and Integration

The 1990s can be characterized best as representing a decade of innovation and integration. The interventional programs within the Cardiology Department were growing rapidly in the areas of coronary angioplasty, stenting, and electrophysiology. Cardiac imaging had become a subspecialty in its own right. The surgical program saw an important shift away from coronary artery bypass surgery as the mainstay of cardiac surgery. In the late 1980s, stand-alone coronary artery bypass surgery represented 75 percent of our surgical volume; by the late 1990s, that percentage had dropped to 25 percent. In most cardiac surgical programs across the country, this produced a significant drop in the surgical caseload. At Abbott Northwestern, however, this shift was counter-balanced by steady growth in non-coronary or combined procedures. We were seeing a sicker and more complex group of patients and developed programs specifically focusing on areas such as complex valve surgery and the treatment of ascending aortic aneurysms and acute aortic dissection.

At the same time, the broad U.S. health care environment was changing in fundamental ways. The beginnings of these changes were seen in the mid-1980s with Medicare's creation and implementation of Diagnostic Related Groups (DRG). This mandated a more-or-less standardized payment system for like services, and the model was quickly assimilated into many health insurance plans. Hospitals could no longer charge on a "cost-plus" basis. They now had to look closely at their actual cost of providing a particular service, and they had to know how that cost compared to actual reimbursement. Hospitals that could provide cost-effective services were in a position to benefit from such changes; those that could not would be facing serious economic challenges.

Abbott Northwestern was well positioned for the change. The medical and nursing staff had always been known for exceptional care and excellent outcomes. And there is little in medicine that is less cost-effective than complications. The Cardiovascular Services program, due in part to sheer size, could benefit from economies of scale. But more was needed in order to maximize value.

Allina Health

Abbott Northwestern has a long history of adapting well to changes in the health care landscape. Beginning with the merger of Abbott and Northwestern

We were seeing a sicker and more complex group of patients and developed programs specifically focusing on areas such as complex valve surgery and the treatment of ascending aortic aneurysms and acute aortic dissection.

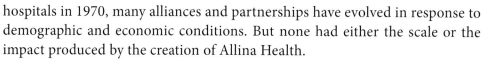

hospitals in 1970, many alliances and partnerships have evolved in response to demographic and economic conditions. But none had either the scale or the impact produced by the creation of Allina Health.

The 1994 merger between HealthSpan and Medica that became Allina Hospitals and Clinics brought under a single corporate umbrella a consortium of hospitals, physicians, and insurers. It was the first such entity in the Upper Midwest, and one of the first in the nation. At its inception, Allina had nearly a million insured lives, more than 7,000 contracted providers, and nearly two billion dollars in annual revenue. At that time, Allina was the largest nonprofit corporation and the second-largest employer (behind Northwest Airlines) in Minnesota.

In 1995, Minneapolis Cardiology Associates made the decision to move to an employed model within Abbott Northwestern and Allina. Many primary care specialties had made the change from "private practice" to "employed" in the preceding decade, but it was unusual, even controversial, for a large, single-specialty group to make such a decision. And it was very wise. It put our hospital and the cardiologists at the same table, with aligned incentives when decisions had to be made regarding programmatic needs, resources, and priorities. This setting facilitated, among other things, two of the most important changes in the last fifteen years: the transition to an electronic medical record and the building of the Heart Hospital at Abbott Northwestern. The model proved so successful that the cardiac surgical staff moved to the employed model in 2002, and the vascular surgery group was added just a few years later.

The Heart Hospital

Given the growth in the Cardiovascular Services division, planning for a Heart Hospital had begun in earnest in the late 1990s. More and better space was needed across our entire clinical spectrum: in-patient beds, ICU beds, clinic space, and procedural rooms (operating rooms, catheterization and electrophysiology rooms, space for Echocardiography, CT, and cardiac MRI). Groundbreaking for the new hospital was in October of 2002, with completion in the spring of 2005. The philanthropic donors of the Minneapolis Heart Institute® Foundation paid nearly half of the project's $120 million cost.

About the time construction began on the new Heart Hospital, the cardiovascular program faced a serious challenge in the area of the management of advanced heart failure. While our outcomes for cardiac transplantation remained excellent, volumes were declining. Nationally, there had been a renewed focus on mechanical cardiac assist devices (commonly known as LVADs—left ventricular assist device) as a management tool in "bridging" a heart failure patient to transplantation.

While LVADs had been used at Abbott Northwestern beginning in the early 1990s, we did not have a robust program. There has always been a long waiting list for available donor hearts; LVADs offered an additional tool for keeping patients alive as they waited for a donor organ. Additionally, UNOS, the national organ-matching organization, made a change that resulted in patients with LVADs being given the highest priority for available donor hearts. The end result was that transplant volumes at Abbott Northwestern diminished to the point that the program's viability was threatened.

In 2007, with input from physicians and the Minneapolis Heart Institute® Foundation, the Allina Board of Directors approved a significant investment to upgrade and broaden our advanced heart failure program. Additional cardiologists and surgeons were recruited with excellent results. Transplant volumes rebounded and the LVAD program is strong, now including the option of "destination" therapy: a life-prolonging therapy without the expectation of transplantation. An additional offshoot is a service known as ECMO (extracorporeal membrane oxygenation), which can provide shorter-term cardio-respiratory support for critically ill patients.

The Twenty-first Century

Since 2000, it seems the pace of change has only quickened. With the Heart Hospital open for less than five years, 2012 saw plans being made for a new "hybrid" operating room. This is a surgical suite that incorporates traditional surgical support capabilities with the newest imaging systems needed for interventional cardiology procedures. This suite came online in 2013.

One of the driving forces behind its creation was the development of the extraordinary procedure known as TAVR, or trans-catheter aortic valve

Part of our professional mantra should be the hope that we can make ourselves obsolete, that through the processes of research, education, and prevention, the ravages of heart disease as we have known it will become obsolete.

replacement. Patients with aortic stenosis, who also carry a high surgical risk due to other factors, can have their valve replaced without conventional open heart surgery. The technology was first used in Europe nearly a decade before, but its availability in the U.S. was more recent due to the nature of our Food and Drug Administration (FDA). The procedure requires the capabilities of a hybrid operating room, as well as the combined participation of the cardiologist and cardiac surgeon. The Minneapolis Heart Institute® at Abbott Northwestern was among the earliest centers in the country to offer this treatment. In 2014, total trans-catheter procedures at Abbott Northwestern numbered 295, a growth of nearly 200 percent over 2013.

There are many additional, exciting therapies underway and under development in cardiovascular medicine and surgery. Stem cell research, less invasive approaches to conventional surgery, and improved tools for primary and secondary prevention are among them. Part of our professional mantra should be the hope that we can make ourselves obsolete, that through the processes of research, education, and prevention, the ravages of heart disease as we have known it will become obsolete.

Until that day arrives, it is my firm belief that there are no professionals anywhere that are collectively better than those who have been providing care at Abbott Northwestern. The collective skill, compassion, and dedication of our many talented health care professionals has blessed us all at this hospital. And we have been blessed for a long time.

6

Clinical Pathology
1980-2015
Dr. Mark Arnesen

When Abbott and Northwestern hospitals merged in 1970, the consolidation led to the departure of three clinical pathologists from the Northwestern staff. In 1979 and 1980, laboratory director, Dr. Craig Freeman, recruited Drs. James Strom, John Jones, and Mark Arnesen to fill the void. Dr. Strom headed up the Microbiology Lab and oversaw laboratory referral testing. Dr. Jones headed the transfusion service and the Immunology Lab. Dr. Arnesen led Chemistry and Hematology, and took over the overall laboratory directorship after the retirement of Dr. Freeman in 1983. Under the leadership of laboratory manager Jeanette Bolstrom, laboratory testing grew steadily over the next 10 years, including a large, outpatient physician office and reference lab service.

When Dr. Terry Rosborough took over the Internal Medicine Residency Program at Abbott Northwestern, he brought an intense interest and expertise in coagulation and thrombosis. He began to consult with the coagulation laboratory and helped bring advanced coagulation and thrombosis testing to the laboratory.

Dr. Richard Bendel joined the staff of the Perinatology program and helped recruit Cindy Millard from the University of Minnesota. She set up a cytogenetics laboratory (for obtaining genetic information through the study of cells) to support the growing perinatal program. Dr. Bendel capably served as Medical Director of the Cytogenetics Laboratory until Dr. Rodney Higgins was recruited to head the service. Under Dr. Higgins' direction, the Cytogenetics Laboratory has grown into one of the largest in the region. The lab offers a wide array of services, including prenatal cytogenetics, tumor genetics, Fluorescent In Situ Hybridization, and genetic microarrays. (Fluorescent In Situ Hybridization places fluorescent markers on parts of chromosomes within a cell.) These are presently under the direction of Dr. Sue Kang.

As director of the Virginia Piper Cancer Institute (VPCI), Dr. Martin Oken recruited Dr. John Allen to start a molecular diagnostic laboratory. When the demands of Dr. Allen's busy gastroenterology practice became too great, Dr. Allen stepped down as VPCI Molecular Lab Director and Dr. Arnesen became the director. Dr. John Mendiola, a Ph.D. in molecular biology, was recruited as Lab Director. Dr. Arnesen remained as Medical Director until Dr. John Reinartz was recruited as medical director. Under Dr. Mendiola and Dr. Reinartz's capable leadership, the VPCI Molecular Laboratory (now Allina Molecular Lab) has grown, and testing greatly expanded.

In 1987, Dr. Cynthia Lais joined the Abbott Northwestern Hospital pathology staff with a subspeciality in Clinical Chemistry. She expanded our chemical pathology testing capabilities. In 1993, Dr. Charles Horwitz joined the Abbott Northwestern pathology staff after the closing of Metropolitan Mt. Sinai Hospital, which brought the department an expertise in immunology.

The Allina Central Lab

The biggest change in Clinical Pathology at Abbott Northwestern Hospital began in 1994 with the formation of Allina. At the inception, the Minnesota Attorney General laid out conditions for the merger with specific cost-cutting goals for the new organization. John Grotting, Chief Operating Officer for Allina, determined that a laboratory consolidation would be an excellent starting point for achieving cost savings. He gave the challenge to Venetia Kudrle, Vice President in charge of laboratory services; Jeannette Bolstrom, Lab Manager; and Dr. Arnesen. This team worked with their counterparts at United and Unity/Mercy Hospitals, including Dr. Don Kapps and Dr. William Natale, to create the plan for the new Allina Central Laboratory. This challenge was a tall order. The consolidation was to achieve three million dollars in annual savings, and the blueprint for the consolidation had to be completed in two months, by July 1, 1994.

The plans were completed by the deadline. The Abbott Northwestern contingent pushed for the central lab to be housed in the Abbott Northwestern campus, while the other team members pushed for a more central location along the 35W corridor. Because cost saving was the major goal, the Abbott Northwestern contingent won the day. In 1995, the Allina Central Lab was housed in the Abbott Northwestern Hospital laboratory. The other metro hospitals had their labs downsized to become rapid response labs, performing only testing requiring less than a 4-6 hour turnaround time. For the first 15 years, Allina Medical Laboratory was headed by Drs. Ron Villela, Laurel Krause, and Chris Chong.

With the merger of the Allina hospital labs, the three pathology groups also merged, forming a group of 19 pathologists called the Hospital Pathology Associates (HPA). The pathology group merger brought additional clinical pathology expertise to Abbott Northwestern Hospital. Dr. Stan McCormick, a hematopathologist, had an interest and expertise in both flow cytometry (the analysis of particles that have been passed through a filter) and molecular pathology.

When the Allina Central Lab was first formed in 1995, the scope of the lab was the four metro hospitals: Abbott Northwestern, Unity/Mercy, and United. In the ensuing 20 years, the scope of the lab grew to cover the Allina Medical Clinics, the Allina Regional Hospitals, and a growing reference lab business. As clinical services grew at Abbott Northwestern Hospital, there were a number of incursions on the laboratory space, first from the radiology department, and later from the central supply and operating room support services. As a consequence, the laboratory was outgrowing its space and bursting at the seams.

The laboratory first spread to the fifth floor of the Virginia Piper Cancer Institute and the second floor of the Harriet Walker building. Dr. Brenda Katz joined the Hospital Pathology Associates staff as a dedicated clinical pathologist in 2009. She rapidly became the go-to pathologist for lab issues and

As clinical services grew at Abbott Northwestern Hospital, there were a number of incursions on the laboratory space, first from the radiology department, and later from the central supply and operating room support services. As a consequence, the laboratory was outgrowing its space and bursting at the seams.

questions. Under the leadership of Rick Panning, Administrative Lab Director, the Allina Central Lab finally was able to move to the second floor of the old Sears Warehouse, just across 28th Street. It is now called the Tenth Avenue Facility and is connected to Abbott Northwestern Hospital by both skyways and pneumatic tube (for specimen transport). The 70,000-square-foot facility allows for the implementation of specimen handling automation and an open layout for greater efficiency. The acquisition of this property was an important accomplishment of Daryl Schroeder and the Abbott Northwestern management team.

When the Heart Hospital expansion was being planned, it became painfully obvious that parking was going to be an ongoing concern. The acquisition of this block assured Abbott Northwestern of an adequate footprint for expansion. The Mother Baby Center expansion later required further expansion on the northern end of the campus.

Dr. Lauren Anthony became Allina Lab Medical Director in 2010. Dr. William McDonald assumed the title of Abbott Northwestern Lab Medical Director in 2012. Under Dr. Anthony's leadership, the lab has engaged in a blood conservation initiative, significantly reducing the frequency and amount of blood transfusion. Recent data indicates that blood transfusion, though much safer from an infectious disease transmission perspective, is associated with inherent risks that make "transfusion avoidance" increasingly important. Dr. Anthony also began bi-monthly Transfusion Grand Rounds to build support for the ongoing blood conservation initiatives.

Dr. Susan Wheaton spearheaded development of a massive transfusion protocol to assure appropriate treatment of actively bleeding patients.

Technological Change

As clinical pathology grew more complex and pathologists became more subspecialized, HPA instituted an on-call clinical pathologist, available 24/7 through an answering service. In 2014, the microbiology lab replaced conventional microbial identification techniques with Mass Spectroscopy techniques that allow a more rapid and accurate identification of infectious organisms. This development was the result of a spectacular technological breakthrough that stemmed the inexorable trend of microbiology toward Molecular PCR (polymerase chain reaction-based assays).

Even microscopy is being brought grudgingly into the twenty-first century, though not nearly as rapidly as radiology. Cervical pap smears are now digitally scanned (with cytotechnologist oversight) and screened. This increases the abnormality pickup rates. Peripheral blood smears are similarly being digitally scanned and reviewed by medical technologists, though pathologists still prefer glass slides and microscopes. Even in pathology we are using digital slide screening for off-site consultations, and exploring use of this technology for cytology adequacies and off-site frozen sections.

7

Colon and Rectal Surgery
1916-2014
Dr. Stanley Goldberg

The specialty of colon and rectal surgery at Abbott Northwestern Hospital dates back to 1916-17, when Dr. Walter A. Fansler came to Minneapolis and joined the staff of Abbott and Northwestern hospitals. Dr. Fansler developed the first training program in proctology in the United States in 1917. This program was centered at the University of Minnesota Hospital, Minneapolis General Hospital, and both Abbott and Northwestern hospitals, where he operated on his private patients.

The first specialty to be recognized with a specialty Board was the field of Eye, Ear, Nose, and Throat. That Board gave their first certifying examination in 1914. In 1934, the American Board of Proctology was incorporated. Dr. Walter A. Fansler was one of the first Board members. Three years later, in 1937, the American Board of Surgery was founded. Because of WWII, the first certifying examination in proctology was not given until 1949. Two of Dr. Fansler's preceptees (residents), Dr. Howard M. Frykman and Dr. William C. Bernstein were certified. Dr. Frykman practiced at Abbott and Northwestern hospitals with Dr. Fansler until 1952 when Dr. Frykman decided to practice on his own, continuing at those hospitals. Dr.

In the 1970s, many new technological and surgical procedures were introduced. Fiberoptic endoscopy dramatically changed the management of colonic disease.

William C. Bernstein practiced in St. Paul, at the University Hospital, and the Veterans Administration Hospital.

The specialty was undergoing a change from anorectal surgery to colon and rectal surgery. In 1963, Dr. Stanley M. Goldberg, having completed seven years of surgical residency at the University of Minnesota in both general and colon and rectal surgery, joined Dr. Frykman in practice at Abbott and Northwestern Hospitals. He was the fifteenth person in the United States to be certified by both Boards. Unfortunately, Dr. Frykman succumbed to a renal cell carcinoma in 1969. Dr. Goldberg brought Drs. Emmanuel Balcos, Jerry Schottler, and Carl Christensen into the practice in 1970. Shortly thereafter, Drs. Frederic D. Nemer, Ann C. Lowry, and Michael P. Spencer joined the practice.

In 1972, Dr. John Najarian, the Chief of Surgery at the University of Minnesota, appointed Dr. Goldberg to head up the Division of Colon and Rectal Surgery at the University of Minnesota. The Fellows in colon and rectal surgery were all completely trained and board eligible in general surgery. The training program was enlarged to three Fellows who rotated among Abbott Northwestern Hospital, the University of Minnesota Hospital, and the Veterans Administration Hospital. Over time, the training program has evolved to five Fellows who rotate among Abbott Northwestern Hospital, Fairview Hospital, University of Minnesota Hospital, the Veterans Administration Hospital, and United Hospital in St. Paul.

Innovation

Screening for colonic cancer originated at the University of Minnesota with the cancer detection center in 1948; however, the extent of the endoscopic exam of the lower bowel was 25cm (10 inches). In the 1970s, many new technological and surgical procedures were introduced. Fiberoptic endoscopy dramatically changed the management of colonic disease. With the fiberoptic scope, the entire colon could be visualized. This technique, which uses a flexible tube to examine the colon or rectum, discovered and treated many early cancers. Benign and malignant lesions could be dealt with directly, thus preventing a major colon operation in many situations.

For many years, patients with chronic ulcerative colitis who required surgery had to have a total colectomy and permanent ileostomy established. In 1978, the first reconstruction of the rectum for ulcerative colitis in Minnesota was carried out at Abbott Northwestern Hospital. The "pouch" operation has become a standard operative procedure for these patients, and now some patients have this operation done with laparoscopy.

In the late 1970s, the intra-luminal stapler was introduced for anastomosis of the intestine. The first use of this instrument in Minnesota occurred at Abbott Northwestern in early 1978. This permitted surgeons to resect cancers of the low rectum and reconnect the bowel, dramatically reducing the need for permanent colostomies.

Dr. Charles O. Finne introduced intra-cavitary radiation for the early carcinomas of the rectum at Abbott Northwestern Hospital. This permitted patients to have rectal cancers treated as outpatients. It was used primarily in poor-risk patients. Dr. Finne accumulated one of the largest series of patients treated with this technique in the United States. He has published multiple articles on this technique demonstrating excellent results and thus saving many patients from major colonic surgery.

Anorectal surgery has also improved dramatically since the early days of Dr. Walter Fansler. Dr. Frykman developed and introduced the closed hemorrhoidectomy in 1949, which continues to be the standard operative procedure in the United States. This technique resulted in less discomfort, a shorter hospital stay, and fewer post-operative complications.

The outpatient treatment of hemorrhoids with rubberband ligation was introduced in the 1970s. This approach reduced significantly the need for definitive hemorrhoid surgery for many patients.

Over the years, anal fissure surgery has undergone a radical change from a five-day hospitalization to an outpatient procedure that allows the patient to return to work the following day.

Fistula-in-Ano

For centuries, surgeons have struggled with the malady fistula-in-ano. Frequently it required the transection of a portion of the anal sphincter muscle, resulting in anal incontinence. In 2007, Dr. Stanley Goldberg did the first LIFT

In the late 1970s, the intra-luminal stapler was introduced for anastomosis of the intestine. The first use of this instrument in Minnesota occurred at Abbott Northwestern in early 1978.

Advances in biology and genomics will change the field dramatically in the future.

(Lateral Intrasphincteric Fistula Transsection) operation for fistula-in-ano in the United States at Abbott Northwestern Hospital. This operation does not divide the external sphincter muscle, and it is now becoming the standard surgical approach for complex transphincteric fistulas worldwide.

Rectovaginal fistulas are a daunting problem for both the patient and the surgeon. Dr. Ann C. Lowry, who became the first woman president of the American Society of Colon and Rectal Surgeons, has a special interest in this condition. She has accumulated one of the largest surgical experiences with patients with this condition in the world. Dr. Lowry has taught surgeons around the globe the techniques necessary for successful outcome with this complex fistula problem.

In 1989, Dr. Robert Madoff returned from the University of Massachusetts and entered the practice at Abbott Northwestern Hospital. He developed a large practice in inflammatory bowel disease. After several years, he was tapped by Professor David A. Rothenberger to become the first Stanley M. Goldberg, M.D., Professor of Colon and Rectal Surgery at the University of Minnesota.

Pelvic Floor Center

In 2009, Dr. Anders Mellgren, M.D., Ph.D., along with Drs. Ann Lowry, Amy Thorsen, and Charles O. Finne moved the Pelvic Floor Center from the campus of Fairview Hospital to the campus of Abbott Northwestern Hospital. A variety of problems relating to incontinence, constipation, and prolapse are evaluated at the Pelvic Floor Center. It is considered the number-one Pelvic Floor Center in the United States. Sacral Nerve Stimulation is a technique that involves a pacemaker inserted to control the anal sphincters. This approach was studied in the Pelvic Floor Center leading to FDA approval in 2011. This device is used to treat both fecal and urinary incontinence all over the world.

Enterostomal Therapy

When patients require an ileostomy or colostomy, special nurses are needed to administer to these patients. A school of enterostomal therapy was set up at Abbott Northwestern Hospital under the direction of Bonnie Sue Rolstad, RN, and Joy Boarini, RN, in 1979. The care of our patients with stomas improved dramatically with the initiation of this school. (Today, enterostomal nurses are referred to as wound ostomy and continence nurses.) One of the key skills taught was pre-operative abdominal assessment and marking of the stoma site. This is still the standard of practice today.

The enterostomal training program at Abbott Northwestern evolved into webWOC Nursing Education Program. This is one of the premier web-based programs, involving students from all over the world and accredited in partnership with Metropolitan State University in St. Paul.

Training Programs in Colon and Rectal Surgery

The training program in colon and rectal surgery at the University of Minnesota has been in existence for almost 100 years. Dr. Walter A. Fansler started the first preceptorship there in 1917. Since 1960, the program at the University of Minnesota and Abbott Northwestern Hospital has trained over 175 certified colon and rectal surgeons. Many of the graduates have gone on to head up similar units. Ninety percent of the colon and rectal surgeons on the faculty at Harvard University Medical School were trained in this program. Graduates also occupy faculty positions in colon and rectal surgery at Stanford University, Mayo Clinic, Cleveland Clinic, Lahey Clinic, and Cambridge University in the United States, as well as at the University of Melbourne, Calgary, and McGill among others.

Administrative help is a major part of this story. We were fortunate to have the support of Gordon Sprenger and Bob Spinner from Administration. Their leadership led to excellent patient care and the support of multiple training programs, which have been recognized regionally and nationally.

The specialty of colon and rectal surgery has flourished and grown in these years to a point that would have been unimaginable to Dr. Fansler. Advances in biology and genomics will change the field dramatically in the future. It has been a real pleasure to serve on the staff at Abbott Northwestern Hospital for these many years. I am sure the young colon and rectal surgeons on the staff today will continue to advance the field in the future.

Since 1960, the program at the University of Minnesota and Abbott Northwestern Hospital has trained over 175 certified colon and rectal surgeons.

8

Courage Kenny Rehabilitation Institute

(formerly Sister Kenny Rehabilitation Institute)

1940-2014

Dr. Jennine Speier

The goal of physical rehabilitation is to help people achieve their full potential after devastating medical events. World War II and the polio epidemics in the 1940s and 1950s were catalysts for development of the field of physical rehabilitation. Since the 1940s, residency programs and a specialty board have certified physicians for Physical Medicine and Rehabilitation (PMR). Physicians (both PMR & primary care), nurses, and nurse practitioners work in collaboration with physical, occupational, speech, and vision therapists, social workers, and psychologists. This work continues to flourish at Courage Kenny Rehabilitation Institute.

Sister Kenny and Polio

Sister Elizabeth Kenny first encountered polio in 1911. ("Sister" was a term used in World War I England for an Army head nurse.) Isolated in the Australian bush, she was unaware of the conventional treatment of immobilizing affected muscles with casts and bracing. This

[Sister Kenny] proposed that pain had to be relieved before muscles could be retrained after paralysis and that muscle tightness or contractures interfered with movement.

approach led to deconditioning of the entire body, painful spasms and contractures, and loss of function, as well as the consequences of prolonged immobilization. She found that putting moist, hot packs on the affected areas helped loosen the tightened muscles and relieved pain. She then went on to move, stretch, and strengthen muscles, helping many to regain use of otherwise paralyzed muscles. She proposed that pain had to be relieved before muscles could be retrained after paralysis and that muscle tightness or contractures interfered with movement. She believed that polio patients would become "alienated" from awareness of function and that the earlier that remobilization occurred, the better.

In 1940, after 31 successful years of treating polio in Australia, Sister Kenny came to America to spread her treatment methods for polio-paralyzed muscles. However, she encountered resistance from physicians who did not understand her description of the treatments. The medical community was skeptical because her nursing training was limited to World War I, assisting doctors in the Australian Bush. She was tall, brash, and outspoken, which did not help her reception.

Fortunately, when she came to Minneapolis, she encountered Dr. Miland Knapp and Dr. John Pohl, who were intrigued by her treatment and helped "translate" it into medical terminology and pathophysiology. She was able to convince influential families and the City of Minneapolis that a building was needed to effectively train nurses and continue her work. A school at 1800 Chicago Avenue South was remodeled to serve as a rehabilitation center. On December 17, 1942, Elizabeth Kenny Institute was dedicated. By 1944, the Sister Kenny method was endorsed by the American Medical Association and the American Orthopedic Surgery Association as the only sound treatment for acute poliomyelitis.

Additional treatment centers in the Twin Cities were opened at Sheltering Arms, Fort Snelling, the University of Minnesota, and Minneapolis General Hospital, now Hennepin County Medical Center (HCMC). Sister Kenny received honorary degrees from Rutgers University and the University of Rochester, and lunched with President Franklin D. Roosevelt, discussing his treatment for polio at Warm Springs, GA. In 1951, she headed the Gallup Poll's list of most admired women. She was the only woman in the first 10 years of the list to displace Eleanor Roosevelt for the #1 spot. Sister Kenny made her home in Minneapolis with her adopted daughter, Mary Stewart, but had to return to Australia with failing health from Parkinson's disease in the early 1950s. She died in 1952, three years before the development of the Salk and Sabin vaccines that virtually eliminated polio in much of the world. Her treatment centers continued to deal with aftermath of the polio epidemics of the early 1950s.

Affiliation with Abbott Northwestern Hospital

In 1955, the Elizabeth Kenny Institute was planning to become a regional independent rehabilitation center. The Marvin Kline Wing was built to care not only for polio patients but also for those suffering from spinal cord and brain injuries, and stroke. The Curative Workshop, which cared for patients with disabilities other than polio, merged with Elizabeth Kenny Institute in 1956. From 1956-60, Dr. Paul Ellwood, father of the Health Maintenance Organization (HMO), was director. In the 1960s, there were fundraising problems, but Donald Dayton, Carl Pohlad, Burton Gambel, and Frank Krusen intervened to save the Institute, and the American Rehabilitation Foundation was created.

In 1976, the Elizabeth Kenny Institute merged with Abbott Northwestern Hospital and moved to its present building at 28th Street and Chicago Avenue South, becoming known as Sister Kenny Institute (SKI). The new Medical Director of Sister Kenny Institute was Dr. Richard Owen, who served until 1994. Before the new building opened, Sister Kenny had already started its Art Show for Artists with Disabilities (1963) and its innovative Golf Program for Golfers with Disabilities.

[Sister Kenny] was able to convince influential families and the City of Minneapolis that a building was needed to effectively train nurses and continue her work. A school at 1800 Chicago Avenue South was remodeled to serve as a rehabilitation center.

Inpatient Hospital-Based Rehabilitation and Accreditations

In 1981, Sister Kenny Institute received its first accreditation by the Commission of the Accreditation of Rehabilitation Facilities (CARF). In 1984, it received the Outstanding Facility Award from the National Association of Rehabilitation Facilities. Sister Kenny expanded its inpatient rehabilitation services to United Hospital in St Paul in the late 1980s, and together the units have a total of 55 beds. In 1994, Dr. Jennine Speier became Medical Director and served until

By 1944, the Sister Kenny method was endorsed by the American Medical Association and the American Orthopedic Surgery Association as the only sound treatment for acute poliomyelitis.

2007. Dr. Karl Sanders was Director until 2013, and Dr. Linda Krach is the current Medical Director.

In September 2014, Abbott Northwestern Hospital tripled the nursing stations for disabled patients. Inpatient rehab now includes 31 private rooms and 4 large double rooms. By 2014, Sister Kenny (now Courage Kenny Rehabilitation Institute) held CARF accreditations in inpatient medical rehabilitation, comprehensive stroke, spinal cord system of care, brain injury, and outpatient medical rehabilitation of spinal cord-injured patients.

Training, Research, and Technology

From 1976 through the early 1990s, Sister Kenny Institute offered training programs for health professionals from across the United States, as well as publications about its work. Their Kenny Scale of Disability was in widespread use, and SKI was a national education center for rehab professionals, especially social workers and vocational counselors. For several years, University of Minnesota Physical Medicine and Rehabilitation residents rotated through inpatient care at SKI, which is being reestablished in the near future.

In the 1980s, the Institute started working with innovative technologies and built partnerships with local business and vocational rehabilitation training programs. In 1987, it received the Governor's Award for Application of Innovation and Technology. In 1995, the Center for Advanced Rehabilitative Technologies was created, and it has partnered with researchers and businesses throughout the country.

With multiple studies showing that early mobilization contributes to improved outcomes, SKI added supported ambulation technology, including the Locomat Robotic equipment, virtual reality, and highly sensitive biofeedback equipment. A biofeedback unit developed at SKI, in collaboration with David Warner, won a national award for new medical technology.

This interest in technology led to the award of a multi-year, multimillion-dollar National Institute on Disability and Rehabilitation Tele rehabilitation grant. Sister Kenny Institute partnered with the National Rehabilitation Institute in Washington, D.C. and the Biomedical Engineering Department of Catholic University of America. At the request of the Federal government, additional funding allowed SKI therapists to conduct telemedicine rehabilitation in several Minnesota locations, as well as in American Samoa and the island countries of Palau and Yap.

In 2008, the SKI Research Center was opened at Abbott Northwestern Hospital, headed by biomedical engineer Dr. Lars Oddson (2009-2014). Ph.D.-level therapists and biomedical engineering students (from the University of Minnesota as well as universities in Sweden) participated in research projects. As of fall 2014, there were 26 active researchers whose work includes:

- Two Department of Defense-funded studies related to concussion rehabilitation.
- Two large demonstration projects: Health Care Home, funded by Centers for Medicare and Medicaid Services, and a payment improvement project, funded by Minnesota Department of Human Services.
- Dr. Mary Radomski is leading the development of a research center structure to improve our ability to deliver on the Courage Kenny Rehabilitation Institute's mission and vision.

Current areas of research also include:

- Cancer Rehab Intervention Effectiveness
- Inpatient Stroke Rehab Discharge Instruction Adherence
- Balance & Gait Rehabilitation Using Partial Body Weight in a Tilted Environment
- FOCUS FORWARD – Evaluation of a brief psychoeducational intervention for cognitive dysfunction associated with chemotherapy for breast cancer: feasibility, user-acceptance, and preliminary impact
- Factors Affecting Road Cyclists – Study closed and manuscript accepted
- Impact of LSVT BIG on Patients at Stage 1 of Parkinson's Disease – A Pilot Study
- Sensory Amplitude Electrical Stimulation Effect on Stroke Recovery

By 2014, Sister Kenny (now Courage Kenny Rehabilitation Institute) held CARF accreditations in inpatient medical rehabilitation, comprehensive stroke, spinal cord system of care, brain injury, and outpatient medical rehabilitation of spinal cord-injured patients.

OUR GOAL
Courage Kenny Rehabilitation Institute maximizes quality of life for people of all ages and all abilities. We help people achieve health and wellness by offering excellent services, innovative programs, ground-breaking research and barrier-shattering advocacy.

- Anchoring Cognitive Self-report to Performance of Real Life Tasks for Women with Chemobrain
- Impact of Prehabilitation in Total Knee Arthroplasty: Outcomes and Health Care Utilization
- Cognitive Health Prehabilitation for Women Undergoing Chemotherapy for Breast Cancer
- Sham rTMS Combined with Conventional Therapy in Acute Stroke
- Graded Exercise Testing and Aerobic Exercise Treatment for Persons with Residual Concussion Symptoms: A Feasibility Study in an Adult Sample (Maggie Weightman, PI)
- Actual or Perceived Disability: The Relationship between Oswestry Disability Index Scores and Measures of Fear-avoidance and Catastrophizing in Patients with Chronic Pain Syndromes (Murray McAllister, PI)

Outpatient Services

Sister Kenny began expanding its outpatient services with a Kenny Kids program to provide pediatric rehabilitation in the northern Twin Cities suburbs in 1989. More sites for general PT clinics were added in 1999. Dr. Richard Owen, Medical Director at that time, developed a large post-polio clinic, and Dr. Jennine Speier started a clinic for musicians with injuries.

The SKI Spine Program was established in 2006. Specially trained physicians and therapists incorporated MedX equipment into a comprehensive spine rehabilitation program that currently provides services in several metro locations. The Nasseff Spine Center (started at United Hospital) and the Courage Kenny Spine program merged in 2014. As a result, Physical Medicine and Rehabilitation comprehensive spine care providers now work with Primary Care Spine physicians on best practice guidelines.

A comprehensive Outpatient Rehabilitation Program at United and Abbott Northwestern provides continuity of care and care coordination for patients needing multiple outpatient rehab services. These include speech therapy, vision therapy, driving evaluations and training, occupational and hand therapy, and physical and lymphedema therapy. There are currently 24 outpatient Courage Kenny Sports and PT Centers in Minnesota.

Dr. Nancy Hutchison, Medical Director, Cancer Rehabilitation and Survivorship, led the development of one of the first and largest Cancer Rehabilitation programs in the country. Physicians, therapists, nurse practitioners, and care coordinators provide hospital consultation and outpatient evaluation and treatment. CKRI has more Survivorship Training and Rehabilitation certified therapists than any other rehabilitation center.

Courage Kenny Rehabilitation Institute acquired the pain clinic known as Phoenix Center in 2014. This allows the Institute to have a comprehensive pain program for patients who want to find independent strategies for managing their chronic pain. The new clinic – Courage Kenny Rehabilitation Associates Pain Clinic – continues to operate in Golden Valley, Minnesota.

OUR VISION
We are guided by our vision that one day all people will live, work, learn and play in a community based on abilities, not disabilities.

Courage Center – The Future Partner of Sister Kenny Institute

Courage Center was founded in 1928, and in 1947 became the Minnesota Society for Crippled Children and Adults. The organization was dedicated to meeting the changing needs of children and adults with disabilities, with an emphasis on advocacy and recreation as well as rehabilitation.

During the 1950s and '60s, under the visionary leadership of Wilko Schoenbohm, Courage Center established rehabilitation and training centers, opened Camp Courage, and continued public advocacy work. The Courage Center Foundation was established in 1963.

Mr. and Mrs. Walter Deubener of St. Paul donated land for a facility in Golden Valley that included a freestanding transitional rehabilitation unit (TRP). In 1973, Julie Nixon Eisenhower dedicated the Golden Valley facility. The TRP in Golden Valley is licensed as a skilled nursing facility and serves as a "bridge" between the acute care and the acute hospital-based rehabilitation needed before a patient returns to a home or community-living setting. In 2013, the TRP earned a five-star rating from the Centers for Medicare and Medicaid Services. The site also offers multiple therapies, a fitness center, and an expanded aquatic center, opened in 1994.

Courage Center has been an innovative developer of independent living

services and community living skills. They have led in the development of sports for people with disabilities including skiing, golf, sledge hockey, track and field, wheelchair basketball, and rugby. The Jr. Rolling Timberwolves won several consecutive National Wheelchair Basketball Association titles. A wheelchair-accessible softball field was built with a $200,000 Pepsi Refresh Grant, won by The Minnesota Twins when they beat out 14 other major league baseball clubs. Operation Liberty offers free sports and recreation activities to injured and disabled veterans.

In 2010, the Christopher & Dana Reeve Foundation's NeuroRecovery Network named Courage Center's Activity-Based Locomotor Exercise programs (ABLE) one of five best community-based fitness centers in the country.

In 2012, Courage Center was one of 26 nationwide recipients of the Health Care Innovation Award. The three-year $1.8 million award allows Courage Center to develop its patient-centered medical home model. Teamwork by primary care and rehabilitation physicians, as well as therapists, and programming to teach independent living skills, have reduced hospitalization costs for persons with permanent disability.

Courage Center has partnered with Habitat for Humanity to develop accessible homes. This program is one of only two advanced, primary care clinic/Health Care Homes in the nation. Activities of the clinic include:

- Telemedicine between the clinic and patient homes
- Evidence-based care pathways for five conditions most often leading to avoidable hospitalizations (diabetes, wounds, seizures, pneumonia, and urinary tract infections)
- Co-location of medical specialties most often used by our patients – psychiatry and physiatry (physical medicine and rehabilitation)
- Comprehensive care planning and care coordination provided by RNs
- Social work and community-based services to identify community resources and coordinate long-term services and supports
- Skill-building classes to improve patient self-management of multiple chronic conditions
- Round-the-clock telephone access and same-day visits

- Referrals to a full continuum of rehabilitation and community-based services
- A philosophy of care based on patient engagement and promotion of quality of life and independent living in the community

In 2015, Courage Kenny Advanced Primary Clinic was honored as one of two winners of the Medica Provider Innovation Award. Selected from 34 applicants, our model of team-based primary care and intensive care coordination stood out for its spectacular results. Reducing hospitalizations by 65 percent for a complex population is a remarkable achievement.

Courage Center was instrumental in setting up rehab centers throughout Minnesota, so its reputation and services grew statewide. At the time of the merger with Sister Kenny Institute, there were Courage therapy centers in Stillwater (Courage St. Croix), as well as in Forest Lake and Burnsville.

Sister Kenny and Courage Center, even prior to their merger, worked jointly on programs benefiting those with disabilities. In 2001, Courage and Sister Kenny Institute created AXIS Health care. This new model for people with disabilities used nurse practitioners as care coordinators to prevent common problems and avoid hospitalization.

In 2015, Courage Kenny Advanced Primary Clinic was honored as one of two winners of the Medica Provider Innovation Award... our model of team-based primary care and intensive care coordination stood out for its spectacular results.

Courage Kenny Rehabilitation Center

In June 2013, Courage Center merged with Sister Kenny Rehabilitation Institute and became part of Allina Health. The name of the center of excellence was changed to Courage Kenny Rehabilitation Institute (CKRI). Their two foundation boards merged to become the Courage Kenny Foundation, and Camp Courage was sold.

CKRI now offers a nationally unique continuum of care for persons with disabilities: acute hospital therapies and consultations, acute hospital-based rehabilitations, transitional rehab care, multiple outpatient therapies, and physician-driven training sites throughout the state. Community services include opportunities for disabled sports and other activities, in addition to teaching community living skills and vocational services.

The Institute currently has 1,500 employees, 2,000 volunteers, and serves

55,000 people annually. CKRI is the fifth largest rehabilitation service in the USA, with 45 locations serving an area of 240 square miles. It also focuses on advocacy for the disabled as well as research and integration into the community, developing best practices, and educating health care professionals.

The future of rehabilitation is bright. Intense early rehabilitation shows that recovery from neurologic injuries is possible for much longer after onset than previously thought. Improvement is seen even when rehab is used several months to years later, reflecting our new understanding of brain and nervous system plasticity. However, even with innovative treatments such as stem cells, neural growth factors, and external stimulation, rehabilitation is needed to optimize outcome. To support this practice, CKRI's intense ABLE fitness program will double its space and enrollment. Ongoing research at Courage Kenny Rehabilitation Institute will explore new techniques, including magnetic stimulation.

9

Dermatology
1932-2014
Dr. Rajneesh Madhok

The specialty of Dermatology and Syphilology began in 1932, when skin examination became critical in diagnosing syphilis prior to the discovery of serologic testing (the testing of blood or serum). By the 1940s, penicillin was recognized as an effective treatment for syphilis. Syphilis and sexually transmitted diseases gradually passed primarily to the domain of infectious disease consultants, resulting in a change of the board specialty name to The American Board of Dermatology (ABD) in 1955. The American Board of Dermatology was one of the original four organizations sponsoring the American Board of Medical Specialties. Over the years, the specialty of Dermatology has expanded to include skin surgery, immunologic diseases, pediatric dermatology, dermatopathology, and most recently, cosmetic and aesthetic procedures.

Inpatient admissions for dermatology have become less frequent in the world of hospital medicine with the evolution of care by hospitalists. The Mayo Clinic pioneered the concept of inpatient dermatology in the early 1900s, particularly for psoriasis. Dr. William Goeckerman recognized the benefit of tar and ultraviolet light therapy in the treatment that still bears his name. Even at Mayo, the former 21-day stay for inpatient Goeckerman therapy has been replaced by outpatient care, due to reimbursement issues.

Many tertiary care institutions still admit dermatology patients, but typically, care for serious and potentially lethal skin diseases is coordinated with Infectious Disease, Internal Medicine, and Rheumatology. These admissions often require intense wound care and wet dressing therapy. More severe cases such as Staph-scalded skin syndrome or toxic epidermal necrosis require care in a burn unit. Many hospitalized dermatologic cases are those who are immunosuppressed or organ transplant patients who may develop significant infections often diagnosed by skin biopsy.

Innovations in Treatment

The discovery of systemic steroids revolutionized dermatologic and rheumatologic care in the 1950s for a wide variety of inflammatory disorders. Topical steroids have become a mainstay for many skin diseases. Tools such as cryosurgery and electrosurgery have been in continued use since the early 1900s.

Recognizing the benefits of sunlight for many conditions such as psoriasis and eczema led to the development of ultraviolet light therapy in the 1920s. The original "broadband ultraviolet B" (280-320 nanometers) was found to be safe and effective for psoriasis. In the early 1980s, the narrow band of ultraviolet B at 311-312 nanometers was found to be more effective with faster and better results in psoriasis patients.

In addition, patients with vitiligo (smooth white patches of skin) and atopic dermatitis (an inflammation in the skin) have been found to benefit from Narrow Band-UltravioletB. This may be administered in a dermatologic office or with home units available for those unable to travel to a clinic. Vitiligo and psoriasis treatment has further improved with the excimer laser using the 308 nanometer wavelength of the UltravioletB spectrum. This is used for small surface areas and is typically administered two times per week over the course of several months. Lasers continue to expand in their use for vascular and pigmented lesions as well as cosmetic resurfacing and hair removal.

One of the more intriguing developments in treating skin disease came with the unexpected discovery that beta-blockers can improve vascular malformations. Infantile hemangiomas (benign tumors of blood vessel cells) occur in

5-10 percent of infants and may cause bleeding, ulceration, and functional impairment, in addition to the psychological impact of disfigurement. Although infantile hemangiomas may curve inward spontaneously, in 2008, use of the beta-blocker propranolol was found effective and well tolerated, with greater safety and less morbidity than surgical procedures or systemic steroid therapy.

The mechanism may be related to beta-adregenic receptors found on the endothelial cells of infantile hemangiomas. These receptors activate dilation of the blood vessels. Beta-blockers cause vasoconstriction and thus lessen blood flow to hemangiomas. Other mechanisms may be related to the inhibition of angiogenesis (the growth of new blood vessels) and induction of apoptosis (programmed cell death). Side effects have been minimal and well tolerated with 1-3 mg/kg/day dosing, but inpatient hospitalization is advised for those younger than two months of age. For smaller lesions topical timolol gel has been beneficial.

Newer oral treatments have evolved for non-melanoma skin cancer and metastatic basal cell carcinomas (BCC). Chronic ultraviolet radiation exposure has led to basal cell carcinomas becoming the most common cancer in the world. Eighty percent of non-melanoma skin cancer are basal cell carcinomas, while the other 20 percent are squamous cell carcinomas. Approximately 5 percent of basal cell carcinomas are considered high risk with potential for local, regional, or distant metastases. The Hedgchog inhibitor vismodegib, a cancer drug, was approved by the FDA in 2012 and has a response rate of 90 percent in advanced or metastatic BCC. A selective smoothened (SMO) inhibitor, sonidegib, has also been approved for BCC patients who are not candidates for surgery or radiation therapy. Unfortunately, 20 percent of vismodegib patients may develop a resistance to the drug over time. Recent studies suggest itraconazole or arsenic trioxide may be helpful in overcoming resistance.

Psoriasis and Sporiatic Arthritis

One of the most dramatic breakthroughs in dermatologic therapy has been the use of "biologic" drugs for psoriasis and psoriatic arthritis, both considered to be immune-mediated diseases. T-cells play a role in the pathogenesis of psoriasis via T-cell-mediated cytokines causing keratinocyte proliferation and angiogenesis resulting in chronic inflammation. These drugs, given by IV infusion or self-injection, originated in the therapy of inflammatory bowel disease and rheumatologic diseases but have expanded their scope to skin disease. They block immune proteins such as tumor necrosis factor-alpha (TNF-alfa) or interleukins (IL), which play a role in the inflammatory cascade.

They are generally safe, but raise concerns about opportunistic infection, such as reactivation of tuberculosis, and risk of malignancy, such as lymphoma. They require ongoing monitoring. Other risks include cytopenia (a reduction in the number of blood cells), demyelinating disease (damaging the myelin covering the nerves) lupus-like syndrome, and congestive heart failure. It is now recognized that the inflammation of psoriasis may contribute to increased cardiovascular risk in these patients. Other skin diseases that may respond to biologic drugs include hidradenitis suppurativa, pyoderma gangrenosum, pemphigus, and lupus.

The tumor necrosis factor-alpha inhibitors etanercept, adalimumab, and infliximab down-regulate multiple pro-inflammatory pathways in psoriasis plaques. Paradoxically, there have been cases of exacerbations of psoriasis or new onset of pustular psoriasis in these patients.

Interleukin (IL) inhibitors, beginning with ustekinumab, a human immunoglobulin G1 kappa monoclonal antibody, and now secukinumab, are the latest to enter the growing field of biologic therapies. The blocking of IL-12 and IL-23 by ustekinumab and the blocking of IL-17 by secukinumab reduces hyperproliferative keratinocytes (a growth factor that increases the proliferation of cells) Newer IL-23 inhibitors are on the horizon, with all having encouraging results.

Apremilast is a new oral anti-inflammatory drug for psoriasis and psoriatic arthritis. It works as an inhibitor of phosphodiesterase-4. Side effects are minimal, and it does not require lab monitoring since it does not cause immunosuppression. As with other systemic therapies, it may be used in combination with ultraviolet light and topical therapy.

Melanoma

Melanoma continues to cause 75 percent of all skin cancer deaths. It represents approximately 5 percent of skin cancer cases, and if detected and treated early, the 5-year survival rate is 98 percent. Metastases beyond the skin lowers 5-year survival rate to 62 percent for those with lymph node involvement, and to only 16 percent once spread occurs to organs. The past few years have led to newer immunotherapeutic and molecularly targeted therapies resulting in prolonged life. Melanoma prognosis continues to be based primarily on the level of thickness of the cancer cells in the skin. Thin melanomas (< 0.76 mm depth) and melanoma in situ are treated with excision with a 5 mm margin. Thicker melanomas require a 1 cm excisional margin and often a sentinel node biopsy is advised.

If lymph node or organ involvement is found, interferon and interleukin 2 are the primary options. High dose interferon is usually given for a few years, but flu-like side effects limit its tolerability. Dabrafenib and trametinib are two new therapies that have shown reduction in size of melanoma in 76 percent of treated patients, with benefits lasting an average of 10.5 months. Dabrafenib targets the BRAF gene mutation (occurring in 37-50 percent of melanomas) while trametinib blocks the MEK pathway. Ipilimumab is a monoclonal antibody targeting CTLA-4 that allows cytotoxic T lymphocytes to recognize and destroy melanoma cells. Studies have shown increased melanoma survival an average of 10.1 months, but some patients have had 3- to 10-year survival rates.

Dermatoscopy (also known as epiluminescence microscopy or dermoscopy) is a noninvasive advancement in the examination of skin lesions to help distinguish benign or malignant lesions. This has been especially helpful in the diagnosis of pigmented lesions, such as dysplastic nevi, and in early detection of malignant melanoma. Dermatoscopes are typically hand-held instruments that use polarized light and 10X magnification. Johan Kolhaus originally described this in 1663, with the addition of immersion oil by Ernst Abbe in 1879. Johann Saphier then added the built-in light source.

Polarized light reduces the skin surface reflection, which aids in the sensitivity and specificity of melanoma detection, thus reducing the need for unnecessary excisions. Many tumors (e.g., basal cell carcinomas, angiomas, seborrheic keratosis, and other conditions such as scabies and hair shaft disorders) have a distinct dermatoscopic appearance. The dermatoscope has

Melanoma continues to cause 75 percent of all skin cancer deaths... The past few years have led to newer immunotherapeutic and molecularly targeted therapies resulting in prolonged life.

grown in popularity over the past 20 years and has now become an integral part of the dermatologic exam in America.

Other recent drug advancements include topical brimonidine gel for the treatment of rosacea-associated facial erythema and ivermectin cream to treat Demodex mites that may trigger inflammatory rosacea.

Advancements in Technology

Finally, advancements in technology continue to have an impact on all of medicine. Nanotechnology, teledermatology, and digital imaging will play a role in the future of dermatologic care. Public awareness of skin disease, most notably skin cancer, continues to advance with the help of social media and smart phone apps. The challenge for patients and physicians will be to stay abreast of medical technology in order to reap its benefits but avoid its pitfalls.

10

Diagnostic Neuroradiology
1962-2014
Dr. Douglas Yock

The history of diagnostic neuroradiology at Abbott Northwestern Hospital has mirrored the development of the field nationally, reflecting the evolution of technology and the subspecialization of physicians.

The Early Years

Until the 1970s, most imaging of the brain and spinal cord was encompassed within general Diagnostic Radiology. In the 1960s, a few radiologists began to focus on the central nervous system. The subspecialty of neuroradiology was launched in 1962 when twelve of these individuals met at a restaurant in New York City to form the American Society of Neuroradiology.

From 1960 to 1975, the main diagnostic techniques in neuroradiology were standard X-rays of the skull and spine, X-ray tomograms of localized areas (e.g., the inner ear), cerebral angiography, pneumoencephalography, and myelography. These procedures are detailed below.

Early neuroradiologists devoted great attention to small details on skull X-rays: subtle erosion of the sella turcica (indicating an adjacent tumor or increased intracranial pressure),

Nanotechnology, teledermatology, and digital imaging will play a role in the future of dermatologic care.

remodeling of the inner table of the skull (due to an underlying mass or cyst), abnormal calcifications (of a tumor or an arteriovenous malformation), and shift of the normally midline calcification of the pineal gland. Specialized X-rays called tomograms, which provided focused layers or slices through bony anatomy, were used to better demonstrate details in some areas, e.g., widening of the internal auditory canal in patients with vestibula schwannomas – a benign, usually slow-growing tumor that develops from the balance and hearing nerves supplying the inner ear.

Cerebral angiography is the procedure of opacifying blood vessels in the brain by injection of iodinated contrast material. It developed rapidly in the 1960s and early 1970s. The technique evolved from using direct, "neck stick" punctures of the common carotid artery and the brachial artery, to the selective catheterization of the carotid and vertebral arteries via the femoral artery in the groin. Learning ever more detailed anatomy of tiny arteries and veins in the brain became important so as to recognize displacements of the blood vessels, indicating pathology.

Pneumoencephalography is a procedure performed by injection of air into the subarachnoid space following a lumbar puncture or "spinal tap." The patient was positioned in a chair that was tilted, tumbled, and/or rotated during and after the injection of air. This caused the air to ascend into the intracranial compartment and fill the ventricular system and/or the subarachnoid cisterns and convexity sulci in the brain. X-rays and tomograms were then obtained, demonstrating these landmarks and highlighting any distortion of normal anatomy. The process of pneumoencephalography was informative but very uncomfortable for the patient, with a high incidence of severe headache, nausea, and vomiting.

Myelography was the main technique for evaluating disorders of the spinal canal during this period. Iodinated, oily contrast material was injected into the subarachnoid space, usually the low back area but occasionally in the neck area. With the patient lying on a tilting table, the head was raised or lowered to position the contrast material in the lower or upper portion of the spinal canal, as indicated. X-rays of the opacified portion of the spinal canal were taken in various degrees of rotation. After the diagnostic films were obtained, the oil was removed by aspiration. The procedure was usually well tolerated, but some patients experienced sharp radicular pain when nerve roots came into contact with the spinal needle, particularly during the removal of the contrast material. A small number of patients later developed arachnoiditis, the inflammation of the tissues surrounding the spinal nerves. This was presumed to be an inflammatory reaction to residual contrast material in the subarachnoid space or to bleeding as a result of the lumbar puncture.

The Modern Era: Computed Tomography (CT)

Diagnostic neuroradiology advanced rapidly after the introduction of computed tomography (CT) in the mid 1970s. CT scanning (originally called CAT scanning as an abbreviation of "computerized axial tomography") provides images of slices or layers of the brain by computerized processing of X-ray absorption as a narrow beam is passed around the head.

The first CT scanner was limited to studies of the head positioned within a soft, rubbery cap containing water. The unit was manufactured by EMI, a British industrial research company better known as the record label of the Beatles rock band. (Beatles' record sales helped fund the research, which led to the CT scanner.) Although the scanner was considered to be a remarkable technological achievement when it was introduced, it was primitive by current standards. Each slice was 1 cm thick and took about four minutes to acquire. The resulting image consisted of a coarse 64 x 64 matrix with poor spatial resolution.

However, the contrast resolution of the images was unprecedented. For the first time, neuroradiologists were able to distinguish between various types of tissue within the head. In particular, cerebral spinal fluid (CSF) spaces were clearly defined and any hemorrhage into the intracranial compartment was apparent. As a result, the indications for pnuemoencephalography rapidly decreased. This eliminated the need for cerebral angiography to detect mass effect (e.g., from a subdural hemorrhage accumulating between the brain and the skull).

The head-only CT scanner from EMI was soon followed by whole body scanners. The EMI scanner installed in the basement of Abbott Hospital in the late 1970s was succeeded by a whole-body CT scanner made by the General Electric Company, installed in 1980.

The first CT scanner... was manufactured by EMI, a British industrial research company better known as the record label of the Beatles rock band. (Beatles' record sales helped fund the research, which led to the CT scanner.)

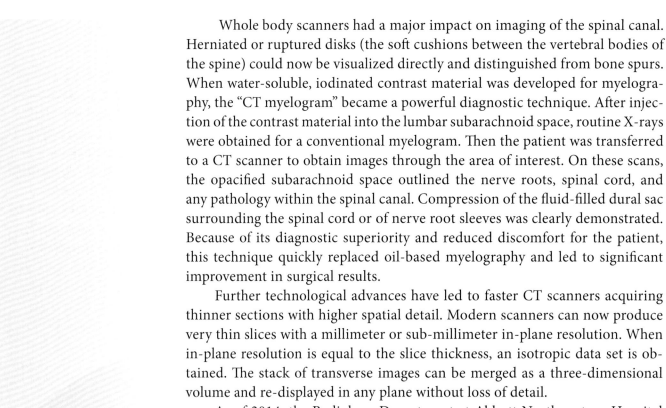

Whole body scanners had a major impact on imaging of the spinal canal. Herniated or ruptured disks (the soft cushions between the vertebral bodies of the spine) could now be visualized directly and distinguished from bone spurs. When water-soluble, iodinated contrast material was developed for myelography, the "CT myelogram" became a powerful diagnostic technique. After injection of the contrast material into the lumbar subarachnoid space, routine X-rays were obtained for a conventional myelogram. Then the patient was transferred to a CT scanner to obtain images through the area of interest. On these scans, the opacified subarachnoid space outlined the nerve roots, spinal cord, and any pathology within the spinal canal. Compression of the fluid-filled dural sac surrounding the spinal cord or of nerve root sleeves was clearly demonstrated. Because of its diagnostic superiority and reduced discomfort for the patient, this technique quickly replaced oil-based myelography and led to significant improvement in surgical results.

Further technological advances have led to faster CT scanners acquiring thinner sections with higher spatial detail. Modern scanners can now produce very thin slices with a millimeter or sub-millimeter in-plane resolution. When in-plane resolution is equal to the slice thickness, an isotropic data set is obtained. The stack of transverse images can be merged as a three-dimensional volume and re-displayed in any plane without loss of detail.

As of 2014, the Radiology Department at Abbott Northwestern Hospital operates two 64-slice spiral CT scanners and one 16-slice scanner, as well as an additional 16-slice scanner in the outpatient facility of the hospital. Each of these scanners was manufactured by the General Electric Company. A fifth CT scanner, manufactured by Siemens Medical Solutions, is located in the Heart Hospital.

The Modern Era: Magnetic Resonance Imaging (MRI)

With CT nearing maturity as a revolutionary modality in neuroradiology, an even more powerful diagnostic tool was introduced: magnetic resonance imaging, or MRI. The first MRI scanner at Abbott Northwestern Hospital, a 1.0 Tesla unit manufactured by Siemens Medical Solutions, was installed in 1985. (One tesla is equal to 10,000 gauss. For reference, the strength of the earth's magnetic field is about 0.5 gauss.)

Like CT, MRI is computerized and tomographic, providing images of slices or layers of tissue based on the computerized processing of data. Unlike CT, MRI does not use X-rays to examine tissue. It is instead based on radio waves absorbed and then emitted as an "echo" by atomic nuclei, whose magnetic orientation is temporarily disturbed while they reside in a strong magnetic field. The fact that MRI does not employ ionizing radiation is a major advantage for the technique in terms of patient safety.

The main diagnostic advantage of MRI is higher contrast sensitivity. Tissues of the brain and body differ more in their magnetic relaxation behavior, which is the basis for contrast on MRI, than they do in their X-ray absorption, the basis for contrast on CT. As a result, MRI can better discriminate between tissues, demonstrating abnormalities not visualized on a CT scan, such as the demyelinating plaques or scars of multiple sclerosis.

Magnetic resonance imaging has also made a major contribution to the diagnosis of spinal disorders. On MRI scans, nerve roots and the spinal cord are clearly outlined by the intrinsic contrast of the surrounding spinal fluid within the subarachnoid space. This eliminates the need to inject intrathecal contrast material. Similarly, compression of the subarachnoid space is apparent anywhere within the spinal canal. Finally, MRI is the first imaging modality to display pathology within the spinal cord.

The technology of MRI has advanced rapidly. Modern MRI scanners are stronger (3.0 Tesla), more open (70 cm diameter gantry aperture), and faster than earlier models. MRI now offers high in-plane spatial resolution and thin slices, generating isotropic three-dimensional data sets that can be reformatted in any plane with preservation of detail. A typical MRI scan now results in thousands of individual images that are usually reviewed by scrolling through them at a computer.

Since being built in 1985, the MRI Center at Abbott Northwestern Hospital has been expanded and remodeled twice. It now houses two modern 3.0 Tesla whole body scanners and a new 1.5 Tesla whole body unit, all manufactured by Siemens Medical Solutions. Other Siemens 1.5 Tesla scanners are located in the

On MRI scans, nerve roots and the spinal cord are clearly outlined by the intrinsic contrast of the surrounding spinal fluid within the subarachnoid space.

Intraoperative MRI imaging has been used to guide brain surgery in nearly 1,000 cases to date, enabling neurosurgeons to accomplish the greatest possible resection of tumors with the least possible damage to surrounding tissue.

outpatient imaging center adjacent to the lobby of the Sister Kenny Building and in the Heart Hospital.

In addition, a moveable Siemens 1.5 Tesla scanner was installed in Operating Room #6 in 2007. This scanner is mounted on rails in the ceiling of the room. The unit normally resides in a closet. When a neurosurgeon wants to check the progress of a cranial operation, the scanner glides into the room and over the head of the patient, with no need to move the patient or disturb the surgical field. A scan is performed, and the images are immediately available for review by the surgeon and the consulting neuroradiologist. Intraoperative MRI imaging has been used to guide brain surgery in nearly 1,000 cases to date, enabling neurosurgeons to accomplish the greatest possible resection of tumors with the least possible damage to surrounding tissue.

The Modern Era: Diagnostic Angiography

The evolution of catheter angiography within neuroradiology is reviewed in other chapters of this book. However, it is worth noting here that CT angiography and MR angiography are noninvasive techniques that have replaced catheter angiography in many diagnostic applications.

CT angiography involves the rapid intravenous injection of iodinated contrast material, followed by fast scanning that follows the arrival and circulation of the contrast through the vessels of interest (e.g., the carotid arteries and the Circle of Willis at the base of the brain). The resulting data sets can be subtracted and reconstructed to yield clear three-dimensional displays of arterial anatomy and pathology.

MR angiography can be performed with or without the intravenous injection of gadolinium-based contrast material (a para-magnetic metal ion). As in CT, data sets are obtained and processed via algorithms to yield a three-dimensional depiction of vascular anatomy. The image can be rotated and tipped for evaluation (e.g., to accomplish non-invasive screening for intracranial aneurysm).

Neuroradiology Personnel

Prior to the 1980s, neuroradiology at Abbott Northwestern Hospital was performed as part of the general radiology practice of Consulting Radiologists, Ltd. by Drs. James Finstad, Kenneth Heithoff, Eul Kang, Timothy Koelz, Kenneth Preimesberger, Ronald Seningen, and Cornelius Weins.

The first formally trained subspecialty neuroradiologist at Abbott Northwestern Hospital (1978–1980) was Dr. James Tourje. He joined Consulting Radiologists Ltd. after completing a fellowship at the University of Minnesota. Dr. David Larson and Dr. Douglas Yock provided part-time neuroradiology consultation at Abbott Northwestern Hospital from 1981-1983, through collaboration between Consulting Radiologists, Ltd. and Metropolitan Radiological Consultants. In 1983, Dr. David Tubman came to Consulting Radiologists, Ltd. from the University of Minnesota, re-establishing full-time subspecialty neuroradiology coverage at the hospital.

In the early 1980s, Dr. Heithoff left Consulting Radiologists Ltd. and formed a new group called Center for Diagnostic Imaging (CDI). This practice focused on developing outpatient centers but maintained a presence at Abbott Northwestern Hospital for several years, specializing in orthopedic and spinal applications of CT.

For a brief period in the mid-1980s, two other groups had representatives participating in neuroradiology at Abbott Northwestern Hospital. Dr. Lawrence Gold was employed by the neurologists of the Noran Clinic to interpret their imaging studies at the hospital as well as in their office. The Noran Clinic subsequently contracted with Consulting Radiologists, Ltd. for these services. For a short time in 1985-1986, Dr. Dominic Korbuly interpreted studies for patients of Park Nicollet Medical Center at Abbott Northwestern Hospital.

In 1985, Gordon Sprenger, the President of Abbott Northwestern Hospital, recruited Dr. Douglas Yock to introduce and develop the technology of MRI at the hospital. Dr. Yock served as Director of the MRI Center from 1985 to 2013. During this period, the MRI capabilities at Abbott Northwestern Hospital increased steadily, building on a productive partnership with Siemens Medical Solutions.

In the mid-1980s, Dr. Tubman and Dr. Yock shared the general neuroradiology responsibilities at Abbott Northwestern Hospital. In addition,

Diagnostic Neuroradiology has been one key ingredient in the development of an outstanding neuroscience program at Abbott Northwestern Hospital.

Dr. Tubman focused on developing diagnostic and interventional procedures, particularly angiography, and Dr. Yock focused on developing the MRI. Drs. Tubman and Yock presented a popular weekly neuroradiology conference for more than ten years, reviewing interesting cases with an audience of neurologists, neurosurgeons, residents, and other physicians. In 1986, Dr. Yock was selected by members of the Neuroscience Physician Advisory Board to chair the group, which he did until his retirement in 2013. Dr. Tubman also retired in 2013.

The increasing volume of neuroradiologic studies and procedures led to the steady expansion of the neuroradiology group of Consulting Radiologists, Ltd. The Diagnostic Neuroradiology section added Drs. Stephen Fry (1987 to present), John Steely (1989 to present), David Larson (1991-2004), William Ford (1997-2005), Neeraj Chepuri (2002-2013), Mark Oswood (2002 to present), Norman Arslanlar (2004 to present), Katherine Hug (2004-2005), Charles Donovan (2006 to present), Tanya Rath (2007-2009), Radha Inampudi (2009-2013), Jeffery Gordon (2010 to present), and Peter Lee (2013 to present).

The Interventional Neuroradiology section grew with the addition of Drs. Mark Myers, (1992-2001), John Perl II (2002-2010), Arvind Nehra (2003-2007), Benjamin Crandall (2008 to present), Josser Delgado (2011 to present), and Yasha Kadkhodayan (2012 to present). As of 2014, Dr. Mark Oswood heads the MRI Center; Dr. Jeff Gordon leads the diagnostic neuroradiology section, and Dr. Ben Crandall is the head of the interventional neuroradiology group. (See the chapter on Interventional Neuroradiology.)

Highly capable and dedicated technologists have had a major role in the operation and advances of the CT and MRI services at Abbott Northwestern Hospital. The Clinical Supervisors in CT have been Mary McDonnell (1980-1981), Terri Mitchell (1981-1986), Shary Vance (1986-1991), and Linda Hendrichs (1991 to present). In MRI, the Clinical Supervisors have been Kevin Johnson (1985-1990), John Messerschmidt (1990-2000), and Holly Mazis (2000 to present). Under their leadership, the CT and MRI technologists have managed to combine high quality and high volume, with both great efficiency and great esprit de corps.

The Neuroscience Program at Abbott Northwestern

Diagnostic Neuroradiology has been one key ingredient in the development of an outstanding neuroscience program at Abbott Northwestern Hospital. Other components have included skilled colleagues in Neurology, Neurosurgery, Neuropathology, Anesthesia. A dedicated Neurological Intensive Care Unit on Station 20, an award-winning neuroscience and spine inpatient facility on the seventh and eighth floors of the Heart Hospital, and a multi-specialty outpatient clinic on the third floor of the Piper building have supported the neuroscience program. Strong programs in stroke, epilepsy, neuro-oncology, interventional neuroradiology, spine surgery, and intraoperative monitoring of nerve conduction also contribute to the "big picture." The Neuroscience Physician Advisory Board has worked with the Hospital's administration to guide the evolution of these capabilities, meeting regularly for the past 28 years.

The multi-specialty collaboration has led to excellent patient care and exceptional programs that have been recognized regionally and nationally. Abbott Northwestern Hospital now performs more neurosurgical and spinal operations and receives more referrals of patients with neurological disorders than any other metropolitan hospital. For the past 10 years, *U.S. News and World Report* has ranked Abbott Northwestern Hospital among the best hospitals in the country for neurology and neurosurgery.

For the past 10 years, U.S. News and World Report has ranked Abbott Northwestern Hospital among the best hospitals in the country for neurology and neurosurgery.

11

Diagnostic Radiology
1960-2015
Dr. Ken Preimesberger

The Early Years – 1960-1970

Diagnostic radiology at Northwestern Hospital was initially located on the sixth floor of the early hospital. The hospital was expanded in 1963, and Radiology was moved to the ground floor. Dr. Stanley Von Drashek, Chief of Radiology at that time, was instrumental in obtaining a major equipment purchase that became operational in 1964. This was a biplane angiocardiographic X-ray unit for performing diagnostic studies on the brain, heart, and circulatory system. At a cost of approximately $120,000, this was a major expense that required the Board of Trustees to approve the funds. However, it was an important acquisition. This equipment enabled the radiologist to perform angiographic studies on the patient and to view various organ systems in two planes. This equipment has now been replaced by real time digital imaging, which subjects the patient to much less radiation. The use of X-ray film has now largely been replaced by digital imaging. The fourth and fifth generation CT and MRI scanners cost $1.5 - $2.7 million.

The Middle Years – 1970-1980

The Abbott Northwestern merger occurred in 1970. Prior to that time, two separate groups served the radiology sections of these two hospitals. After the merger, a single radiology group, Consulting Radiologists LTD, was formed. This continues to the present day. In the 1960s, radiology residencies trained physicians in both diagnostic imaging and therapeutic radiology. Board certification required expertise in both modalities. In the 1970s, Board certification changed, and separate exams were given for radiation therapy and diagnostic radiology.

Radiation therapy was an integral part of Northwestern Hospital Radiology until 1964 when Dr. Don Mosser was named Chief of Radiation Therapy. The two sections, radiation therapy and diagnostic radiology, split into separate departments.

Diagnostic imaging remained largely X-ray based until the early 1970s. Body imaging at this time was limited to routine plain film X-rays and X-ray fluoroscopy. This included upper gastrointestinal studies, barium enemas, X-rays of the spinal column (Myelograms), and basic nuclear medicine exams of the brain, lungs, and bone. Developing technology in the mid-1970s included ultrasound, computerized axial tomography (CT Scans), and magnetic resonance imaging (MRI). The basis for these changes was the ability of computer technology to process data.

Ultrasound is a technology that allows for the imaging of organs deep within the body. This technology uses sound waves to penetrate the body, and the resulting reflections produce an image. The ability to visualize these deep organs and structures represented a marked advancement in patient evaluations.

The first ultrasound units at Northwestern Hospital occupied an entire room. In the early 1980s, "real time" ultrasound became a reality. Smaller, portable units that could be moved from room to room and from patient to patient replaced the large machines. Currently some ultrasound units are so small that they can be carried by hand.

By applying principals of Doppler sonography to these ultrasound machines, physicians were able to visualize and measure blood flow in the body organs. This was especially useful to evaluate blood flow to the brain (i.e., carotid arteries). However, while ultrasound represented a major advancement in body imaging, it had limitations.

The Later Years

Diagnostic whole body imaging became a reality in the early 1970s with the advent of computerized axial tomography (CAT Scans). Godfrey Hounsfield of England is regarded as the inventor of CT scanning. The invention and development of CT scanning is considered to be the greatest innovation in the field of radiology since the discovery of X-rays.

CT scanners use an X-ray beam to produce a volume of data that can be computer manipulated to produce cross-sectional images of the human body. The first CT scanners for clinical practice were available in 1973. These early CT units were limited to head imaging because of long scan times that resulted in motion artifacts. One of the earliest patient head scans was performed at the Mayo Clinic in 1973. The first body CT scan was performed at the Mallinkrodt Institute at Washington University in St. Louis in 1974. These early body scanners were relatively slow and generally took up to 1-2 minutes for one image. This required the patient to hold his/her breath for this period of time, which was difficult for patients who were quite ill.

Dr. Jerry Hopperstad was Chief of Radiology at Abbott Hospital in 1975 and instrumental in obtaining one of the first body CT scanners in Minnesota. This was a Delta-Ohio Nuclear CT scanner. It became operational at Abbott in August 1975 and performed until the Abbott Northwestern Hospital consolidation in 1980. Dr. Ken Heithoff was instrumental in establishing one of the first hospital-based CT imaging centers at Abbott Hospital.

Northwestern Hospital had purchased its own third-generation GE CT scanner. Once the consolidation was accomplished, the older Abbott Hospital model was discarded. Presently, there are four CT scanners in the Abbott Northwestern Radiology Department. These are fourth- and fifth-generation GE scanners that scan the entire abdomen and pelvis in 12 seconds. Volumetric sections of the body are computer-processed, creating image sections of the body as thin as 0.35 mm.

The basic hardware of a MRI scanner is essentially powerful magnets coils and a computer to process the collected data... the physical principle... involves magnetizing the nucleus of atoms within tissue and applying radio waves to change the steady state to orientate these atoms.

MRI

Magnetic Resonance Imaging (MRI) was the next major advancement in body imaging. The principles of magnetic resonance (MR) had been known since the 1950s. Again, new technology allowed these principles to be used to obtain body images. The first MRI body images were obtained in England in 1977. The first MRI prototypes were tested on clinical patients in 1980. This technique was cleared for patient studies by the Food and Drug Administration (FDA) in 1984 and became a reality in 1985.

With the leadership of Gordon Sprenger, Abbott Northwestern Hospital built a MRI center. The first unit was a Tesla unit. The basic hardware of a MRI scanner is essentially powerful magnet coils and a computer to process the collected data. However, the physical principle behind the technology is complex. It involves magnetizing the nucleus of atoms within tissue and applying radio waves to change the steady state to orientate these atoms. Coils measure the energy released when these atoms return to their normal orientation once the radio waves are turned off. Thin section images of any part of the body, in any plane and orientation, can be obtained without the use of X-rays.

Presently Abbott Northwestern Hospital has 3 MRI units that are housed in the MRI building. The magnets are so heavy that they can only be installed at ground level. Two of the units are 3 tesla magnets, and the third is a 1.5 tesla unit. The cost of these individual scanners ranges between $2 and $2.7 million. Dr. Doug Yock was placed in charge of the MRI center until his retirement in 2013.

Nuclear Medicine

Nuclear Medicine has been a staple of body imaging since the development of the scintillation gamma camera in 1957. This imaging technique involves the administration of radiopharmaceuticals, which have an affinity for certain tissues and are labeled with radioactive tracers (i.e., isotopes). Commonly used isotopes include technetium -99m, iodine 123, thallium -201, and fludeoxy glucose (18F-FDG). Although the resulting images are not comparable to those of CT or MRI, this technique has the advantage of demonstrating the metabolic function of organs and tissues.

Routine scanning such as bone, lungs, heart, and brain improved greatly with the introduction of SPECT (Single Photon Emission Computed Tomography) and PET (Positron Emission Tomography). SPECT scanning is a technique that produces images of thin sections of the entire organ. This allows the physicians to look deep into tissue and greatly increases the sensitivity for detecting small abnormalities located deep in the organ. PET is used primarily to evaluate and stage malignancies. This unit projects anatomical images as well as metabolic activity of the malignant tissue. Abbott Northwestern Hospital has very active PET and SPECT programs.

Breast Imaging

The various techniques labeled Mammography have allowed more precise evaluation of breast tissue in an attempt to find malignancies within the breast. Early imaging in the 1960s and 1970s with routine X-ray film was somewhat limited for detecting small abnormalities. Xeroradiography was developed in the 1970s and allowed for less radiation exposure to the breast, as well as better detail in the resulting image. This enables the detection of smaller breast lesions at an earlier stage of the malignancy process.

The xeroradiography technique uses selenium-coated aluminum plates to record the radiographic image instead of X-ray film. The images are then transferred to a special plastic-coated paper for interpretation. This technique was used at Abbott Northwestern Hospital into the early 1980s. Improvements in X-ray film mammography in the 1980s became possible with new machines, improved X-ray film, as well as better screens to display the images. As a result xeromammography is now only of historical interest.

From the late 1980s until 1995, breast imaging was performed in the first floor radiology area. The entire section consisted of one mammography unit and one stereotactic needle biopsy unit. The X-ray stereotactic breast needle biopsy technique became a widely used procedure in the early 1990s. Abbott Northwestern Hospital purchased one of the early units.

When it became apparent that breast imaging and the diagnosis of breast cancer was becoming an important and high volume medical tool, a larger area was needed. Under the leadership of Dr. Beverly Trombley and Dr. Deborah

Xeroradiography was developed in the 1970s and allowed for less radiation exposure to the breast, as well as better detail in the resulting image. This enables the detection of smaller breast lesions at an earlier stage of the malignancy process.

Day, breast imaging moved to its present location in the Piper building in January 1995. These two physicians along with the breast surgeon, Dr. Daniel Dunn, are credited with the formation of the Piper Breast Center, as we know it today. The Piper Breast Center was the first in Minnesota to be recognized by the American College of Radiology as a "breast center of excellence."

The Twenty-first Century Radiologist

Prior to 1990, a general radiologist could perform any of the studies and procedures offered in the Radiology Department. This would include routine X-ray, mammography, nuclear medicine, ultrasound, neuroradiologic exams, angiography, and/or general fluoroscopy. Often 4-6 radiologists could cover the entire radiology department at Abbott Northwestern. These general radiologists included Drs. Ken Preimesberger, James Finstad, Tim Koelz, Anthony Cook, Eul Kang, Cornelius Weins, and Fritz Olson, just to name a few. (In 2015, 21 full-time radiologists serve the Radiology Department.)

The rapid expansion of imaging technology made the subspecialization in radiology necessary to ensure skill and expertise. These subdivisions included neuroradiology, interventional radiology, interventional neuroradiology, musculoskeletal imaging, and heart imaging. Many of these subspecializations now require Board certification and regular proficiency exams.

Interventional Radiology

Cardiovascular/interventional radiology (now termed Interventional Radiology or "IR") at Abbott Northwestern Hospital had its roots in "Special Procedures," a term used until the late 1970s. For decades, Special Procedure described a miscellaneous assortment of exams that could be performed by all radiologists. This might have included a translumbar aortogram, a knee arthrogram, or a lumbar myelogram.

In the late 1970s, a number of remarkable technological advances converged to produce a dramatic increase in the number and types of procedures that could be done using sophisticated imaging guidance. The advances in imaging detail that led to these changes were based on the introduction of the computer into diagnostic imaging. The new digital technologies led directly to the development of CT scanning, which in turn permitted exquisite anatomic images of any part of the body. They also led to development of digital subtraction angiography, which permitted faster angiographic exams with significantly lower radiation doses and contrast images.

At the same time, other technological advances were occurring that led to marked growth in interventional procedures. The development of extremely safe, flexible, biopsy needles (Chiba "skinny" needles) allowed safe, image-guided biopsies of, or access to, virtually any organ. New guide wires, catheters, balloons, stents, and medications could now be safely placed or delivered anywhere in the body. All of these developments resulted in a remarkable increase in both the number and types of diagnostic and, for the first time, therapeutic procedures that could then be done within the radiology department.

By 1980, Interventional Radiology (IR) had been identified as a distinct subspecialty; the term and the fellowship-training programs for interventional radiologists had started up around the country. The evolution of IR at Abbott Northwestern closely mirrored these larger changes. Even a partial list of the types of interventions now performed routinely at Abbott Northwestern is illustrative. The list would include CT-guided biopsies, abscess drainages, angioplasty and stenting for atherosclerotic stenosis or occlusions. Also included are sub-selective vascular embolization in the management of gastrointestinal bleeding, chemo-embolization or radiofrequency ablations for liver malignancies, and placement of Inferior Vena Cava (IVC) filters, i.e., filters in the large vein in the abdominal area, for the treatment of recurrent pulmonary emboli. In conjunction with vascular surgeons, IR aids with implanting stents in the abdominal aorta to treat abdominal aortic aneurysms and prevent rupture.

Two other aspects of the history of Interventional Radiology at Abbott Northwestern deserve mention. The first is the contributions of three interventional radiologists who helped build the foundations of this subspecialty at Abbott Northwestern. Dr. Murthy Tadavarthy was the first fellowship-trained cardiovascular interventional radiologist to practice at Abbott Northwestern. He arrived in 1980 and spent the next 25 years helping build a solid IR presence. Along with Dr. Willie Castaneda from the University of Minnesota, he

The new digital technologies led directly to the development of CT scanning, which in turn permitted exquisite anatomic images of any part of the body.

*Medical
conditions
that previously
required
open surgical
procedures can
now be diagnosed
and treated by
an interventional
radiologist.*

co-authored one of the seminal textbooks of the field, *Interventional Radiology* (1990). Dr. Tadavarthy was joined in 1983 by Dr. Phil Murray. Together, they anchored the department from the 1980s into the 2000s.

Dr. Murray and Dr. Tadavarthy pioneered the creation of an IR admitting service at Abbott Northwestern. They also established an outpatient IR clinic to facilitate pre-procedure consultations and post-procedure follow-ups, quite novel practices in the 1980s. Dr. Murray was also the only non-cardiologist to be the president of the Minneapolis Heart Institute® (1990-92).

The third fellowship-trained IR who played an extremely important role in the growth and success of IR at Abbott Northwestern was Dr. Subbarao Inampudi. He arrived at Abbott Northwestern in 1991, after practicing at Metropolitan Mount Sinai. A cardiovascular surgeon, Dr. Ted Peterson, had seen Dr. Inappudi work at Mount Sinai and encouraged him to come to Abbott Northwestern. Dr. Inampudi was the president of Consulting Radiologists for many years. He also was elected as the Chief of Medical Staff at Abbott Northwestern. He is the only radiologist to receive such recognition. Dr. Inampudi served on the Allina Board of Directors and was Chair of the Quality Control Committee for six years.

A second aspect of IR history at Abbott Northwestern worth noting is the close working relationship with the Cardiology section. This seems almost anachronistic today, but it was alive and well back then. This collaboration contributed to the great success of the Minneapolis Heart Institute® in its formative years.

Interventional Radiology has become a subspecialty of Radiology. These image-guiding procedures utilize CT scan, ultrasound, digital fluoroscopy, or MRI to obtain tissue and/or to treat disease states. Medical conditions that previously required open surgical procedures can now be diagnosed and treated by an interventional radiologist. These procedures are generally considered to be minimally invasive, resulting in less physical trauma to the patient. This reduces the likelihood of infection and shortens the recovery time. These procedures are generally performed on an outpatient basis.

The first image-guided interventions were performed at Abbott Hospital in the late 1970s prior to the physical merger with Northwestern Hospital. These early interventions were needle biopsies to determine tissue histology.

Nearly every organ in the body, with the exception of the brain, were/are biopsied using minimally invasive image guidance. Treatment of diseases by interventional radiology include catheter drainage of abscesses, angioplasty, stent placement in diseased vascular structures, dilatation and stent placement of biliary duct stenosis or obstruction, drainage of obstructed kidneys, and the placement of filters into the inferior vena cava to prevent pulmonary emboli.

All areas of medicine and radiology underwent enormous, transformative change during these years. Nowhere have the changes been more dramatic or affected patient care more than those brought about by the emergence of Interventional Radiology. Less invasive than traditional surgical procedures, the IR approaches have had lower morbidity and resulted in shorter hospital stays. This has profoundly changed medical practice at Abbott Northwestern. It has indeed been a long, exciting, and gratifying journey since the early days of "Special Procedures."

Interventional Neuroradiology

Interventional neuroradiology is a separate subspecialty. It plays a critical role in the diagnosis and treatment of stroke. Strokes caused by clots can be treated by intra-arterial thrombolysis, thus getting rid of the clot obstructing the artery. In some cases, angioplasty and stent placement are utilized to treat strokes. Strokes caused by intracranial bleeding from a ruptured aneurysm may be treated by embolization and/or metal coil placement into the aneurysm. The Interventional Neuroradiology program at Abbott Northwestern Hospital was established and led by Dr. David Tubman. His program is considered a leader in this subspecialty. (See Chapter 17 on Interventional Neuroradiology and Diagnostic Neuroradiology.)

The Future

Radiology will continue to evolve as technology develops. Abbott Northwestern Hospital has been a leader in applying new technology to diagnostic imaging. The old X-ray films have been replaced by digital imaging, which uses less radiation and is much faster in producing real-time images, immediately available to

Teleradiology allows for the transmission of digital images from one location to another within the hospital, and these images can even be transferred from hospital to hospital, as well as to locations in other cities or states.

the examining physician. These images can be transmitted electronically to another location outside of the radiology department through teleradiology. Teleradiology allows for the transmission of digital images from one location to another within the hospital, and these images can even be transferred from hospital to hospital, as well as to locations in other cities or states. Images are easily archived and stored, and rapidly accessed for evaluation and comparison.

This technology is not limited to those physicians trained in radiology, but will also include, for example, cardiologists. The cardiologists, using ultrasound, will be able to evaluate cardiac function in a patient in an outstate emergency room or hospital. They will be able to render an opinion and make a recommendation for further care.

In summary, the dramatic developments in the Department of Radiology at Abbott Northwestern Hospital demonstrate just how accurate hospital administrator Stan Nelson was in his report to the Northwestern Hospital Board of Trustees in 1966. He stated that, in the future, advances in medicine would come at tremendous cost and, as compared to the Salk vaccine, would benefit a relative few. Gordon Sprenger, in speaking of the merger of Abbott and Northwestern hospitals, cited the costs of these new technologies, which necessitated larger facilities that could absorb the changes practically and financially.

12

Ear, Nose, and Throat

1800-2014

Dr. Thomas A. Christiansen

Otolaryngology, the care of ear, nose, and throat (ENT), has a rich history at both Northwestern and Abbott hospitals. These institutions were founded in the earliest years of the transition from pioneer medicine to standards of excellence for both the health care practitioner and facility. The ENT history cannot be separated from that of eye care (Ophthalmology) as the early training in specialization was known as Ear, Eye, Nose, Throat (EENT). I have been unable to discover hospital rosters prior to the mid-1960s, but it is possible to review other biographical sources linking names to medical staff affiliations. Alas, senior partners, colleagues, and teachers who knew details of the earliest years of these hospitals and medical specializations have departed. Their experiences would have been wonderful to include. Nonetheless, we know that the physicians connected to the earliest years of Abbott and Northwestern hospitals were highly educated among peers. They were leaders and teachers who profoundly shaped their profession in the hospitals where they worked. That tradition of excellence is uncompromised in the modern experience of Abbott Northwestern Hospital.

Early to Mid-nineteenth Century Medicine

In *Pioneering Specialists, History of the American Academy of Ophthalmology and Otolaryngology*, Sharon Bryan notes that in the first half of the nineteenth century, less than 10 percent of physicians were graduates of a medical school, and few ever attended a lecture in a school of medicine. There was no such thing as licensure or certification. Apart from the schools of medicine in Chicago or in the East, medical training was mostly by preceptorship with someone already established. Doctors were variously known as herbalist, homeopathic, or allopathic physicians.

Dr. Edward Purcell was the first physician to practice in Minnesota, as he accompanied the Fifth Regiment Infantry sent by the federal government to establish Fort Snelling in 1819. There followed a few medical missionaries and others employed by lumber companies, but Christopher Carli was the first permanent civilian physician who established practice in Stillwater in 1841. John J. Dewey was the first physician in St. Paul in 1847. Ira Kingsley was an herbalist in St. Anthony in 1849, but said to have been more interested in his job as a constable. The colorful John Murphy, a graduate of Rush Medical College, was established in St. Anthony by mid-century. Another Rush graduate, A. E. Ames, joined him in 1851. When Dr. Ames moved across the river to the nascent Minneapolis on the west bank in 1851, the local population was 15. It swelled to 500 in one year, and by the end of the 1850s, 24 doctors practiced on either side of the river.

Minneapolis was a booming pioneer town, fueled by water power from the Mississippi River, facilitating lumber and grain milling. Minnesota became a territory in 1839, and in 1851, the territorial legislature and Governor Ramsey enacted a bill to establish a university, although this was not fully implemented until 1868. Delay was partly due to debt (partially repaid by John S. Pillsbury), the Civil War, and implementation of Lincoln's land grant concept for state universities.

In 1853, the forerunner of the Minnesota Medical Association was established, followed by the Hennepin County Medical Society in 1855, and by 1860, the beginning of the Ramsey County Medical Society. The Minnesota State Medical Society formed in 1869.

The first hospital in Minnesota was St. Joseph's founded in 1854 in St.

Paul. In 1858 Minnesota became a state. By 1860, the population had swelled to 172, 000. In 1870, of the 29 doctors in Hennepin County, only 18 were medical school graduates. In 1871, the first hospital in Minneapolis was the Cottage Hospital, transformed into St. Barnabas in 1881.

1880s to the Turn of the Century

The population of Minnesota was 300,000 by 1880. The 1880s-1900s brought changes to medicine. The Civil War focused attention on battlefield injuries and their treatment. A number of Minnesota physicians served with distinction, even electing to become prisoner rather than abandon the wounded. The 1880s brought Koch's microbial or germ theory along with Lister's demonstration of aseptic technique. Tuberculosis, often called consumption, killed one out of seven worldwide in the nineteenth and twentieth centuries. Curiously, Minnesota had a somewhat undeserved reputation as a favorable climate for treating consumption. The area's first quarantine hospital (Pest House) was established at rural Lake Calhoun in 1883, just one year after the establishment of the Northwestern Hospital for Women and Children.

Minnesota had a somewhat undeserved reputation as a favorable climate for treating consumption.

The earliest hospitals were established as charitable facilities, which was the case for the Northwestern Hospital for Women and Children. The more successful generalists favored office calls and home visits, with less affluent patients and indigents more likely to need hospitalization.

Specialization by a physician was by personal choice or interest. An example is that of Edward B. Zier, who earned a medical degree in 1877 from Louisville, Kentucky, did graduate work in Vienna and London, and came to Minneapolis as a general practitioner in 1881. He was the first to limit his practice to diseases of the throat and lung in Minneapolis, and it was regarded as rather successful.

From Preceptorship to Private Medical Colleges

Apprenticeship or preceptorship was rapidly yielding to private, medical college-based education. Even the established eastern schools affiliated with a university retained, for a while, a remnant of apprenticeship, whereby students paid course fees directly to the instructor, hardly eliminating incompetents. The nation's first medical school, the University of Pennsylvania, opened in 1765 and was among the first to require tuition and a unified faculty. Minnesota's relatively strict Medical Practice Acts of 1883 and 1887 stipulated that all persons wishing to practice medicine and surgery must apply to the Board for a license, submit to an examination, and present evidence of taking a minimum of required course work and lectures. It is said that 200 "physicians" left the state rather than face examination.

Minnesota was the first state to create an independent State Board of Medical Examiners. By 1896, only 23 states even had licensing boards. The best, the brightest, and those fortunate to have financial backing would obtain training in established schools in Chicago, New York, Boston, or Philadelphia. Many went to Europe for additional training.

In Minnesota, the shift to private medical colleges is a complex story. In St. Paul, a preparatory school of medicine was formed in 1860, and by 1878, it had been transformed into the St. Paul Medical Collage. Minneapolis-based faculty commuted by train. Dr. F. A. Dunsmoor of Minneapolis, a founder, began to believe that enhanced clinical instruction would be better achieved by forming the Minnesota College Hospital (1881) on the east bank of the river at the Winslow House. He was joined by A. W. Abbott, Frank Todd (EENT), T. S. Roberts (founder of the Bell Museum, and Roberts Bird Sanctuary), and others. In 1885, the Minnesota College Hospital reorganized and moved next to St. Barnabas under the new name of Minnesota Hospital College. Faculty of the dissolved St. Paul Medical College joined the physicians in Minneapolis. In 1883, the Minneapolis College of Physicians and Surgeons was formed and became part of Hamline University in 1895. In 1886, the Homeopathic Medical College was formed. In 1885, the St. Paul Medical College was reconstituted using some of the Minnesota Hospital College faculty.

Meanwhile, in the 1880s, the University of Minnesota would grant a Bachelor of Medicine degree (M.B.), which was essentially a warrant of the University that the graduate could practice medicine and surgery. An M.D. degree could only be granted if the graduate studied under the direction of a physician in active practice with an M.D. degree from a medical college recognized by the Board of Regents. From 1884 to 1887, only nine M.D. degrees were granted. This reflects the fact that the University of Minnesota Medical School was established in 1888, facilitated by the Minnesota Hospital College and the St. Paul Medical College surrendering their charters and offering their buildings for use by the University.

The Minnesota Homeopathic College was merged into the University medical school with Dean Wesbrook accepting this concept as long as students wanted to take courses in homeopathy. He predicted, correctly, that the homeopathy division would cease to function for lack of student interest. Ultimately, Hamline's medical school folded into the University of Minnesota as well (1908). At that point, the transformation from preceptorship to private medical college to university-based medical education was nearly complete. In 1892, Medical Hall was dedicated on the University campus, renamed Millard Hall in 1908.

Other Late-nineteenth Century Events

In 1887, physicians in St. Paul and Minneapolis formed the prestigious Minnesota Academy of Medicine. The first president was John F. Fulton, an EENT specialist of St. Paul, who had been a founder of the St. Paul Medical College and first professor of EENT at the University of Minnesota. Dr. Hal Foster started the Western Association of Ophthalmologists, Otologists, and Laryngologists in Kansas City, Missouri, in 1896. This quickly became known as the American Academy of Ophthalmology and Otolaryngology (AAOO) and by 1907 was the largest specialty society in the United States.

The 1883 opening of the Northwestern Hospital for Women and Children, with financial backing of Harriet G. Walker, was followed by a new facility in 1887, with large gifts from Mrs. William Harrison and Mrs. M. L. Stewart. Though originally staffed by women physicians, consultants using the hospital were of either gender. The hospital had departments of gynecology, obstetrics, surgery, eye, and ear. Other notable dates are the establishment of:

- St. Mary's (1890)
- Swedish Hospital (1898)
- Rochester St. Mary's (1887)

- Maternity Hospital (1886)
- St. Anthony Hospital (1886)
- Deaconess Hospital (1889)
- Asbury Methodist (1892)
- Minneapolis City Hospital (1887)
- The Thomas Hospital for Tuberculosis opened in 1907 and would be succeeded by Glen Lake Sanitarium in 1929
- Fairview Hospital was started in 1916

The Twentieth Century through World War I

By 1900, the population of Minneapolis was 202,718, and the city was milling 14 percent of the nation's grain. The turn of the century brought more refinement to medical education. The University Medical School no longer needed the Minneapolis and St. Paul facilities. Elliot Memorial Hospital arose on campus in 1912. Clinical teachers worked without salary, dependent on their private practices in the Twin Cities. Only the basic science faculty were both full-time and salaried. Abraham Flexner gave high marks to the medical school's basic science curriculum in his report about medical education in 1909. Amos Abbott's first hospital opened in 1902, replaced by a new building with William Dunwoody's backing in 1910.

Both Frank C. Todd of Minneapolis and William R. Murray of Michigan were born in 1869. Todd had medical and dental degrees from Minnesota and did graduate work in Europe. Murray was a graduate of Rush Medical College and the Illinois Eye and Ear Infirmary, also doing postgraduate work in Philadelphia, Vienna, and London. Both were faculty at the University of Minnesota and published numerous articles – both eye and ENT for Dr. Todd and chiefly ENT for Dr. Murray.

Departmentalization came to the University Medical School in 1909. Dr. Todd became the first head of EENT, and Dr. Murray was the first Assistant Chief. Murray had an active practice at Abbott Hospital. Todd and his associate John S. Macnie were active at Hillcrest Surgical Hospital – sometimes referred to as Franklin Hospital (1910 to 1931), in addition to the University. Additional faculty included:

- John Pratt (licensed 1894) and his nephew Fred Pratt (licensed 1901). Both were educated in Michigan, Chicago, and Vienna, and they coauthored a textbook of intranasal surgery. Fred Pratt was active at both Abbott and Northwestern Hospitals.

- Justus Mathews, a Minnesota graduate, was active at Eitel and Northwestern hospitals. He wrote a paper on "Technique of Tonsillectomy" and one on "Relation of Nasal Conditions to Anaphylaxis and Asthma."

- Douglas Wood (licensed 1905) was Canadian- and European-trained in EENT and active at Abbott and Northwestern.

- Arthur Edward Smith (licensed 1905) was Minnesota- and European-trained and on the staff of Northwestern. He wrote articles on tuberculosis of the eye, acute complications of mastoidectomy, and the effects of head injury on vision.

- Horace Newhart, born in New Ulm in 1872, was a graduate of Dartmouth and of the University of Michigan Medical School in 1898. He did postgraduate study in otolaryngology in Vienna at various times from 1895 through 1912. He studied in Adam Politzer's clinic and under Dr. M. Hajek. He was one of the first in Minnesota to do fenestration surgery of the lateral semicircular canal for otosclerosis, a predecessor procedure to stapedectomy. Fenestration was the forerunner of the current ear surgery for deafness, in which the surgeon creates an opening in the middle to inner ear to lessen deafness. He was on the staff at the University of Minnesota and at Northwestern Hospital. He translated German texts and wrote numerous professional articles of EENT substance. Like Dr. Todd, he championed hearing and vision screening in school-age children and promoted accurate audiometry. He was active in local and national societies.

- Ken Phelps, born in 1888, was a graduate of Minnesota's Medical School in 1913 and did postgraduate study at the Manhattan Eye and Ear, Johns Hopkins, and also in London and Edinburgh. He was an early bronchoscopist at the University of Minnesota, as well as at Abbott and

Northwestern hospitals. He published articles on "Maxillary Sinusitis of Dental Origin," "Extraction of Foreign Bodies from Bronchi," "Orbital Abscess," as well as anesthetic for tonsillectomy, sinusitis in children, bones of the esophagus, and visual defects in West Point cadets. He was truly a pioneer of bronchoesophagology.

- Howard McIlwain Morton (born 1866) was a medical graduate of the University of Pennsylvania in 1891 and did EENT training there before starting private practice in Minneapolis in 1891. He became professor of ophthalmology and otology at Hamline University and was known as an oculist and aurist at St. Barnabas. He was said to be an inventor and prolific writer. In fact, archival letters demonstrate his communication with two Boston otologists (Blake and Jack) who were removing otosclerotic stapes (scarring of the stapes bone in the ear) in the late 1890s. This was about sixty years before that was "invented" by John Shea as a replacement for the fenestration procedure. He queried ophthalmologists around the country relative to meningitis as a possible complication of enucleation (removal without cutting) of the eye.

In 1910, Morton wrote 30 colleagues in Minneapolis and St. Paul, inviting them to form a state specialty society. The enthusiastic response facilitated the Minnesota Academy of Ophthalmology and Otolaryngology (MAOO) in 1911. The previously mentioned EENT specialists were included in addition to Minneapolis doctors C. J. and C. M. Spratt (licensed around 1900 and active in EENT specialty societies), James Reynolds (licensed 1905), Willard Pineo (of the first graduating class of the U of M Medical School with postgrad training in New York, London, and Paris), E. J. Brown, E. H. Parker, William Porteous, F. C. Stout, R. A. Campbell, J. D. Simpson, J. A. Watson, and J. H. Morse.

Their hospital affiliations could not be ascertained in my study. Additional archival letters show that Morton would give coupons to guest speakers of the new Academy, so they could stay courtesy of the Minneapolis Club. He even received a thank-you letter from Dr. Harvey Cushing (often called the "father of modern neurosurgery") who stayed at the University Club in St. Paul while attending an AMA meeting in 1928.

In 1914, Dr. Frank Todd successfully petitioned Dean Lyon and the Board of Regents to set up a two-year specialty training program for two individuals in EENT that would also lead to an advanced degree. The 1914 EENT proposal became the first residency program established at the University of Minnesota.

In 1916, the first specialty board in America, the Board of Ophthalmology, was created. The second specialty board, Otolaryngology, was created in 1924. These occurrences are amazing considering that all training programs were EENT.

World War I forever changed the experience of European specialty training, with the American universities seizing responsibility of educational tasks. The University of Minnesota was one of the first seven schools to offer graduate programs in EENT with specific degrees, awards, etc. For Minnesota, this was also the first establishment of Base Hospital 26 whereby the University would assemble a team of medical specialists. Dr. Frank Todd was recognized as a brilliant academician, teacher, and administrator, and he became head of another hospital at Camp Dodge, Iowa, and was slated for additional work in France. While inspecting cantonment (temporary) hospitals, he contracted a respiratory illness in 1918 (likely Spanish Influenza), and he died at the Presbyterian Hospital in Chicago. Dr. William Murray succeeded Todd as head of the department. Dr. Todd's legacy led to an attempt to create an eye and ear hospital, but the Todd Amphitheatre is the only visible remnant of the Todd Memorial Hospital. His loss was deeply felt.

Carl William Waldron was born in Canada in 1887 and held both M.D. and D.D.S. degrees from Toronto. He took EENT training at Johns Hopkins with a special emphasis on maxillofacial (upper jaw and face) surgery. He served in the Canadian army medical corps and decided to open a practice in Minneapolis in 1919. The earliest plastic surgeons were EENT trained, like Dr. Waldron. He practiced at Abbott and Northwestern Hospitals. His son was John Waldron, a member of the pediatric surgeons' group from Abbott and Northwestern hospitals that founded Minneapolis Children's Hospital.

Erling Hansen was born in Minneapolis in 1890, and was awarded his MD degree from University of Minnesota in 1915, and did graduate specialty work at the New York Eye and Ear Infirmary. He was highly decorated in World War I by both the United States and France. Initially, he was a scholar in otology (study of the ear) but later confined his practice to ophthalmology. He joined

Dr. Horace Newhart in practice and was active at Northwestern and the University. William Edward Patterson is another Minnesota graduate with New York specialty training who began his career in 1917 out of Abbott Hospital and Hillcrest Surgical Hospital.

Post-World War I to 1950

In 1904, there were 2000 ENT physicians in North America, and by 1923 that number had increased to 10,000. A much smaller number belonged to the American Academy of Ophthalmology and Otolaryngology (AAOO), and quite a few were actually general practitioners focusing in this area. In 1930, 30 percent of medical school graduates were going into specialty practice, including 13 percent in EENT (down from 22 percent in 1910). Despite dual training in eye and ENT, some chose to practice in only one area. Bryan further notes that of AAOO members in communities of less than 500,000, 2/3 of the specialists were AAOO members and most practiced EENT. In communities greater than 500,000, eye and ENT practices were more separate. Still, of those claiming to specialize, 75 percent of them actually did work in both areas.

The nation's second specialty board (Otolaryngology in 1924) lagged behind the Ophthalmology Board of 1916. This perhaps reflected the conundrum of assimilating the component otology, laryngology, bronchoesophagology, and rhinology subspecialties. This is remarkable with dual training still under one roof at academic training centers. Emphasizing a commitment to continuing education, the AAOO introduced a postgraduate education course in 1921 that continues to this day for both specialties.

The Janney endowment to Abbott Hospital created one of the first non-specialty pediatric hospital wards in the Midwest. Ear and sinus complications were commonly seen in children and adults in the pre-antibiotic era. In 1926, while William R. Murray was doing a mastoid operation at Abbott Hospital, he cut his finger during the surgery, typically done with loupes, mallet, chisel and gouges. He developed an infection in the wound and died of overwhelming sepsis at Abbott Hospital on December 27, 1926.

Dr. Frank E. Burch of St. Paul succeeded Dr. Murray and became the third head of EENT. Burch limited his practice after the war to ophthalmology and had a national reputation in eye muscle surgery. In 1930, while still head of EENT, he divided the department into an ophthalmology division, which he headed, and an otolaryngology division headed by Horace Newhart. Some dual training continued in the affiliated teaching hospitals (Ancker, Minneapolis General, Veterans) until the 1940s.

Just prior to World War II, some important names surfaced. Jerome Hilger finished the ENT residency in 1939 and will be mentioned later. Robert E. Priest was a Minnesota graduate who completed his training in 1949 in ENT. He would start practice in the Medical Arts Building and was on the staff at the University, St. Mary's, and Northwestern Hospital. He was chief of staff at Northwestern in 1954 and became nationally recognized as a laryngologist and bronchoesophagologist. Clearly, he continued the tradition started by Dr. Ken Phelps in 1913. Dr. George M. Tangen also finished his specialty training at Minnesota in 1941 and was on the staff of both Abbott and Northwestern hospitals and a frequent lecturer at the University. He is the father of George V. Tangen, who came on the staffs of Abbott and Northwestern in the 1960s.

Conrad Holmberg, a Rush Medical School graduate, finished ENT in 1941 and had some eye training. He served in World War II in the Pacific theater and later did a fellowship at the House Institute in Los Angeles, where he learned the fenestration procedure. He joined the practice of Dr. Horace Newhart (ENT) and Erling Hansen (eye), and all three of them were active at Northwestern.

Lawrence R. Boies was born in Renville, Minnesota in 1898, and was a corpsman in World War I. A graduate of the University of Wisconsin, he received his M.D. degree from the College of Physicians and Surgeons of Columbia University in New York in 1926. He did graduate work in eye and especially ENT at Harvard's Massachusetts Eye and Ear Infirmary. He joined the University of Minnesota faculty in 1931. According to his son, Dr. Lawrence R. Boies Jr., he worked at Abbott, Northwestern, the University hospital, and met his wife at Asbury Methodist.

When Horace Newhart retired in 1942, Dr. Boies took over as head of the ENT division at the University. When Dr. Frank Burch retired in 1943 as head of EENT and its eye division, Dr. Erling Hansen succeeded him as head of the eye division, and Dr. Boies became the fourth head of the EENT department.

A natural transition point in Otolaryngology came in 1937 with the introduction of sulfanilamide into clinical practice, followed by penicillin in 1942. As a result, surgery for patients suffering from suppurative disease, causing infections of the nasal sinuses, middle ear, mastoid, and throat frequently could be avoided. There was some doubt about the viability of the specialty in the antibiotic era. In 1950, 33 percent of approved residencies in otolaryngology were vacant, and in 1957 40 percent of first-year ENT residency positions were unfilled. Clearly, the energy for otolaryngology would need to be directed from other avenues.

One such source of new energy would come from the Second World War. World War II reactivated Base Hospital 26 of the medical school faculty. A branch of that program did go to Southeast Asia (i.e., Dr. Holmberg in New Caledonia), but the main involvement would be in North Africa and Italy. Some of the ENT surgeons would gain enormous experience with care of massive head and neck wounds and reconstructive repair of the associated defects.

Of perhaps singular excellence in this was the experience of Jerome Hilger of St. Paul. He was called upon by Dr. Boies to lead Otolaryngology in the progression of head and neck tumor surgery, plastic and reconstructive surgery, and maxillofacial trauma surgery, assisted by one of his associates, Dr. Albert Hohman. The department and the ENT community owe Dr. Hilger much gratitude. His clinical professorship at the University was demonstrated at other academic institutions to the benefit of ENT departments. Drs. Boies, Priest, and Hilger authored a widely used textbook of otolaryngology that was revised over several clinical generations.

Harold Ulvestad finished ENT at the University in 1948, having done military orthopedic work in London and Berlin. He joined with Dr. Boies in their private practice in the Medical Arts Building, and Dr. Ulvestad went on to be a transition founder with the transfer of Asbury-Methodist to the Methodist Hospital of St. Louis Park. Drs. Boies and Ulvestad were joined by Dr. Conrad Holmberg after Horace Newhart retired.

1950 to the Present Day

By 1950, the Minneapolis population had peaked at 500,000. In 1955, the University decided to adopt the "Harvard Model" of geographic full-time department heads. Dr. Erling Hansen (eye) was now full-time at the University, as was Dr. L. R. Boies for ENT. At that point, the practice of Drs. Ulvestad and Holmberg merged with that of Dr. Robert Priest. This early post-World War II downtown medical group would continue to be joined by many who contributed to Abbott and Northwestern hospitals, and were fully utilized as active clinical faculty of the University and its affiliated teaching hospitals.

Dr. Graham Smith was a 1958 ENT specialty graduate who enjoyed an active practice at Abbott and Northwestern. He was joined by a contemporary, Dr. Benjamin Bofencamp, who achieved national recognition for making a movie showing the usefulness of cricopharyngeal myotomy in bulbar polio in association with the Sister Kenny Institute. Dr. John Glaeser later joined that practice and was widely respected for his clinical judgment and excellence in surgery. His career was abruptly ended with a tragic death.

The 1950s proved to be the second watershed that gave new energy to otolaryngology. The Zeiss oto-microscope allowed the surgeon to enlarge the visual field of tiny middle ear structures. German and Swiss otologists (Wullstein, Zoelner, Plester, Ruedi, et al) laid down the principles of microscopic surgery of the temporal bone, including tympanoplasty, mastoidectomy, and the hugely successful redeployment of stapedectomy for otosclerosis, eclipsing the fenestration operation. Those in training at that exciting time included Drs. Robert Richardson, George V. Tangen, John S. Huff, Richard Lund, Hyman Paisner, and Melvin Sigel. The latter two were the foundation of ENT at Mount Sinai, and were joined by Dr. Gary Garvis. All were active in practice at Northwestern.

When the prestigious pediatric surgery group of Drs. Tague Chisholm, Bernie Spencer, et al moved from Abbott and Northwestern to Minneapolis Children's Hospital (of which they were founders), Dr. George V. Tangen adapted a large percentage of his practice to that of pediatric otolaryngology. Dr. Carl Brown and Dr. Richard Levinson joined Drs. Paisner and Sigel and similarly gave a large share of their effort to pediatric otolaryngology, in addition to work at Northwestern Hospital. Dr. Tom Christiansen picked up the effort at Northwestern with the retirement of Dr. Robert Richardson and practice modification of George Tangen. By 1970, Abbott Hospital merged with Northwestern; the medical staffs combined in 1976, and the Abbott location closed in 1980. Eitel Hospital would merge with Abbott Northwestern in 1985. (It was also known as Doctors' Memorial Hospital, 1912-1985.)

In 1967, Dr. Michael Paparella became head of the ENT at the University. Medicare was formed in 1966 and provided increased income to the University medical staff. NIH teaching grants were plentiful, and under Dr. Paparella, full-time academic positions increased, changing the role of the clinical faculty in teaching.

Dr. Robert E. Priest had been head of ENT at Minneapolis General Hospital from 1946 to 1956. He was succeeded by Dr. John Glaeser, and he, in turn, by Dr. Melvin Sigel. The responsibility for Ancker/Ramsey was in the Jerome Hilger group of St. Paul. The VA Hospital was different, having Dr. Henry V. Hanson (1889-1971) as a full-time head through both World Wars. Dr. Hanson's research demonstrated the utility of vestibulotoxic streptomycin to address the sense of loss of equilibrium in the treatment of Meniere's Disease. He may have done the first laryngectomy in Hennepin County in 1934. He retired in 1957.

ENT residents continued to rotate through private practices (i.e., Priest and Hilger) and were utilized at Abbott and Northwestern among others. Dr. John Huff taught at the University. Drs. Robert Richardson, Tom Christiansen, and Matthew Griebie gave regular time to teaching at the VA Hospital. Phase B medical students had clinical rotations in some of the private ENT clinics and, for a short time, Abbott Northwestern medical residents were offered a similar elective. Despite the augmentation of full-time academic faculty, the teaching partnership with clinical faculty continued during the Paparella leadership years, as it also did with his successor, Dr. Arndt J. Duvall. When Dr. George Adams became department head, there was marked contraction of the utilization of clinical faculty.

At the same time, the length of the ENT residency had increased to five years, including a year of general surgery. The degree of specialization in otolaryngology and a change in the mix of private pay/charity patients would preclude many graduates from complete competence in all areas of the expanding specialty. This ushered in post-residency fellowships in otology, neurotology, head and neck tumor, skull base, pediatric ENT (i.e., Dr. James Sidman and Dr. Ben Soumekh), facial plastic and reconstructive surgery, and numerous high-quality research opportunities. Less invasive techniques such as endoscopic sinus surgery have been transformational (i.e., Dr. Karin Evan and Dr. Michael Tedford). Dr. Merrill Biel is an example of fellowship-trained head and neck cancer competence at Abbott Northwestern, and he was joined by Dr. Greg Barth and others.

Dr. Biel did original work in photodynamic therapy of head and neck cancer at Abbott Northwestern and also introduced robotics to the specialty. Head and neck cancer treatment brought collaborative efforts for ENT with oncology, radiation therapy, speech pathology, diagnostic and interventional radiology, occupational and physical therapy, as well as reconstructive surgeons with skills in microvascular free flap repair. Dr. Tom Christiansen worked with neurosurgery and neuroradiology with increasing interest in transnasal transphenoidal hypophysectomy for the removal of the pituitary gland.

Skull base surgical teams of ENT and neurosurgery were increasingly doing combined excision of lesions involving the skull base. Drs. Rick Nissen, Hamid Sajjadi, and Bill Garvis took neurotology and skull base surgery to new levels, with an external approach to the eighth nerve, cerebrospinal fluid leaks, Meniere's surgery, and chemodectomas in difficult areas.

ENT continues to play a role in the investigational protocols and treatment of patients suffering from obstructive sleep apnea. The American Academy of Facial Plastic and Reconstructive Surgery gives a platform to those in ENT with an interest in cosmetic surgery. At the same time, the specialty has lost ground in bronchoesophagology, with pulmonary medicine and gastroenterology more widely adaptive of flexible diagnostic and therapeutic endoscopy. It remains for ENT, and especially the pediatric ENT doctors, to remain facile in rigid endoscopic techniques, especially in dealing with foreign bodies of the upper aerodigestive tract.

In 1979, the American Academy of Ophthalmology and Otolaryngology split into two separate organizations, reflecting the reality that EENT practice was over. The ENT brand is the American Academy of Otolaryngology-Head and Neck Surgery. The state MAOO hung on a bit longer out of deference to collegial attitudes between the two specialties, although the scientific sessions had been separate for eye and ENT for many years. In 1985, the state

Head and neck cancer treatment brought collaborative efforts for ENT with oncology, radiation therapy, speech pathology, diagnostic and interventional radiology, occupational and physical therapy, as well as reconstructive surgeons with skills in microvascular free flap repair.

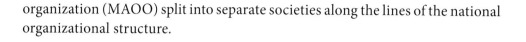

organization (MAOO) split into separate societies along the lines of the national organizational structure.

Conclusion

I have attempted to show the remarkable role of those EENT and ENT physicians in private practice who helped transform pioneer medicine into a high quality, scientific experience. They were physician leaders in the community, and many were very involved at Abbott and Northwestern hospitals. They figured prominently in the transformation of preceptorship medical education to that of the private medical college and the adoption of university-based medical education. When it became necessary to transition into full-time academic positions, in many instances these leaders were drawn from the Abbott and Northwestern environments.

Most of the physicians I have named are long departed, many have retired, and those still in active practice are becoming senior in their group associations. They are joined by younger physicians of enormous talent. To try to name all of them would risk missing some and would soon be incomplete, which would not be consistent with the purpose of this retrospective and historical analysis.

In an era of remarkable health care change, the role of independent practice of otolaryngology may be challenged. It is a small specialty that barely registers as a blip on the health care dollar expenditure. But ENT is a hugely diverse head and neck medicine and surgery specialty. It not only survived its expected demise but grew in strength and diversity. This is an asset that makes it attractive to those in medical training. It is from them that we expect continuation of excellence and leadership.

References

- Bryan, Sharon A., "Pioneering Specialists, History of the American Academy of Ophthalmology and Otolaryngology," American Academy of Ophthalmology (San Francisco) and American Academy of Otolaryngology-Head and Neck Surgery (Rochester, MN) 1982. Taken from *A Century of Excellence, a 100th Anniversary History of the American Academy of Otolaryngology – Head and Neck Surgery and its Predecessor Organizations*, Loring W Pratt, Jerome C Goldstein, Sharon A Bryan. Editor T. Susan Hill. AAO-HNS Foundation, Inc. Alexandria, VA 1996.

- Dunsmoor, F. A., "Medicine and Surgery-Part 1," and "Charitable Institutions," in *History of the City of Minneapolis*, Isaac Atwater editor, Munsell and Co, New York, 1893.

- Hamilton, Arthur S., "The Early History of Medicine in Minneapolis," *The Journal-Lancet*, vol 38 no 5, Minneapolis, March 1, 1918.

- Leaf, Sue, *A Love Affair With Birds – The Life Of Thomas Sadler Roberts*, University of Minnesota Press, Minneapolis, 2013.

- Medical Bulletin, University of Minnesota, Minneapolis, Nov-Dec 1970.

- Myers, J. Arthur, *Masters of Medicine – An Historical Sketch of the College of Medical Sciences University of Minnesota 1888-1966*, Warren H Green, St. Louis, MO 1969.

- Unpublished archival material from the Hennepin County Medical Society collected from the Twin Cities Medical Society, Minneapolis including:
  - Obituary files
  - Otolaryngology 1955-1975 by Robert E Priest and Conrad J Holmberg

- Bulletin of the Hennepin County Medical Society Special Anniversary Issue. Hennepin County Medical Society, Editor Holly Ebel, Minneapolis, MN 1980.

- *Who's Who in America – The Book of Minnesotans: A Biographical Dictionary of Leading and Living Men of the State of Minnesota*, Abner Nelson Marquis editor, A M Marquis, Chicago, 1907.

- Wilson, Leonard, Medical Revolution in Minnesota – A History of the University of Minnesota Medical School, Midewiwin Press, St. Paul, MN 1989.

13

Internal Medicine at Abbott Hospital

1911-1980

Dr. Richard Sturgeon

Dr. Amos Abbott started several hospitals in Minnesota, most notably the Hospital for Women and Children in 1902 and the Abbott Hospital in 1911. Three successful businessmen, William Dunwoody, Thomas Janney, and Oliver C. Wyman made sequential gifts to Abbott Hospital allowing for expansion. They were all associated with Westminster Presbyterian Church, so the financial responsibilities of the hospital were placed in the hands of the Board of Trustees of their church. Thus, Westminster Presbyterian Church of Minneapolis became the only individual church in the U.S. to own and operate a hospital.

Dr. Abbott helped determine the quality of the early Abbott medical staff by controlling appointments. His choices were based on academic excellence and the candidate's interest in teaching. He chose the elite of Minneapolis medicine. The Abbott Hospital staff was, in effect, an extension of the medical staff at the University of Minnesota School of Medicine. The pediatrician, surgeon, and internist who practiced at Abbott Hospital were all heads of their respective departments at the University. As time went on, he added physicians of similar stature and interest.

Dr. Reuben Johnson was the first addition to the staff of Internal Medicine. He had been a football player at the University of Minnesota and was a clinician with a distinguished academic reputation. He brought to private practice an early interest in parathyroid diseases and was able to quarterback the management of a large number of cases of parathyroid tumor when doing so was a real achievement. Dr. Johnson served the University as a clinical professor throughout his career.

In the 1920s, the names of other internists show up in medical staff meeting minutes: Dr. Archie Cardle, who was later killed in an early commercial plane flight; Dr. Jay Davis, who subsequently invited Dr. Lowell Weber and Dr. Mark Hanson to join him; Dr. A.H. McFarland, the world's most modest internist; and Dr. George D. Heads' son Doug, who practiced only at night. And then there was Dr. Henry Ulrich. The June 1927 minutes of the medical staff meeting record Dr. Ulrich's generous offer to make his electrocardiograph available for a small fee, at anytime, to anyone who could get to his office at 14th and Willow.

Dr. Abbott had planned well, and as time went on, the tradition of excellence and teaching he started became self-sustaining. Minneapolis General Hospital (MGH) was one of the last and best examples of a public teaching hospital using a part-time, unpaid clinical staff. Volunteer members of the Abbott medical staff had carried the majority of the teaching load. In 1923, the major attending surgeons at MGH were all practicing physicians on the Abbott staff. Drs. Giessler, Henry Ulrich, Huenkens, and Adair were the Chiefs of Orthopedics, Medicine, Pediatrics, and Obstetrics-Gynecology, respectively. There were not many subspecialties in those days. Forty years later at "The General," in 1963, members of the Abbott Hospital medical staff chaired all nine additional subspecialty sections.

Dr. Tom Lowry became the head of Internal Medicine Department at Minneapolis General in 1950. He presided during the period when so many active and future Abbott doctors were involved as students, interns, residents, or part of the attending staff, as well as serving as the aforementioned department chiefs. Dr. Lowry later became Medical Director for the entire enterprise during the last days of the old hospital. During the early 1960s, the bottom line was finally catching up with MGH. Dr. Lowry was part of the group instrumental in arranging for its survival as a county hospital, now called Hennepin County Medical Center. The vote by the populace of Hennepin County to assume the financial responsibilities of the hospital was overwhelmingly positive. Dr. Lowry was also instrumental in creating the Minneapolis Medical Research Foundation.

Dr. Boyd Thomes first met Dr. Lowry in 1942 when Lowry was Dr. Thomes's attending physician at the University of Minnesota Medical School. Dr. Thomes said that Dr. Lowry and his contemporary, Dr. John Boehrer, were near-perfect examples of the type of clinician Dr. C. J. Watson was trying to create. Dr. Watson was the Chief of the Internal Medicine Department at the University of Minnesota Medical School. (Dr. Watson was later the Medical Director at Northwestern Hospital.) He valued physicians who were practitioners and teachers in equal degree and ready to tackle any problem that might turn up.

After World War II, Abbott Hospital made the transition from a good community general hospital to an "academic lite" specialty hospital populated with specialty and subspecialty physicians who also had close ties to teaching and research activities. Their subspecialty training, together with continuing day-to-day interaction with training programs, set the tone of excellence in their practice. A self-imposed standard of care reflected this specialty and subspecialty best practice behavior. This expansion of subspecialty medicine at Abbott was attractive to newly trained specialists and subspecialists who found it a comforting place and an attractive practice model.

In the 1950s and 1960s, there was a movement away from a solo practice model to Internal Medicine group practices. Most Internal Medicine physician groups had medical staff privileges at two or more metro hospitals. This allowed the physicians to make accommodations for their patients who may have been admitted urgently or who needed a special procedure at that specific hospital. However, these Internal Medicine groups focused on or gravitated to one hospital site for efficiency and familiarity.

There were three such groups of Internal Medicine physicians who focused their practice at Abbott. Dr. Lowry was joined by Dr. Bill Paule and eventually Drs. Malcom Clark, John Bradley, Vince Fromke, and Dave Carlson. Dr. John

Abbott Hospital became a pioneer in providing comprehensive health care to the elderly poor through the Minneapolis Age and Opportunity Center (MAO).

Boehrer took on Dr. Bill Schultz and my senior partner, Dr. Boyd Thomes. The group eventually grew to include Drs. Ray Scallen, Jim McKenna, Bob Maslansky, Bill Torp, Bob Van Tassel, Dick Adair, and me. Dr. Reuban Johnson added lovable Dr. John Johnson and then Drs. Bill Petersen, Art Lindeland, Bruce Jacobsen, Jerry Swanson, and Dave Plimpton, forming the practice that became fondly known to many as the Lutefisk League.

Collaboration and collegiality united these three groups of providers of medical services at Abbott Hospital. They were competitors only in the business sense. On a day-to-day basis, they were mutually supportive colleagues. In growing their practices, each group would bring on new medical subspecialists, for example Dr. Bob Van Tassel in Cardiology. "Competing" groups would encourage and enhance the building of new subspecialty efforts. It did not matter to whom the new recruit "belonged." The groups developed these individual medical sub-specialists, bringing elevated expectations in the practice of medicine to the staff at large and an elevated level of care to our patients.

Until the late-1970s, many Abbott Hospital Internal Medicine specialists continued the attending-teaching volunteerism that had existed at Minneapolis General Hospital and its specialty clinics. These stellar physicians attracted like-minded and capable new partners into their competing group practices. This close connection and interaction with Minneapolis General and the University of Minnesota gave them an inside recruiting position to survey the draft choices for their Internal Medicine group practices.

In the mid-1960s, Westminster Presbyterian Church trustees decided that the church should detach itself from Abbott Hospital. Nevertheless, community responsibility remained a key mission of the Board. During this time Abbott Hospital became a pioneer in providing comprehensive health care to the elderly poor through the Minneapolis Age and Opportunity Center (MAO). Abbott Hospital President George Adamovich, in collaboration with Daphne Krause from MAO, brought innovation to the program. It received national praise for its creative use of existing facilities to provide physician services, hospital care, and social services under the same roof. In the very early stages of this program, the MAO program would use Abbott Internal Medicine private practice office space in the evenings to deliver outpatient care. Internal Medicine Department physicians made themselves available to assist the MAO clinicians. That program successfully recruited a highly sought after Internist-Geriatrician, Dr. M. Kasahara, who soon had other partners practicing Geriatrics.

From the beginning, Dr. Abbott expressed his appreciation for a pleasant setting in which to treat private patients. The establishment of the Doctors' Dining Room in 1968 would do the same for the medical staff. In the friendly atmosphere of the lunchroom, the special features of the Abbott spirit found a garden in which to flower. The easy interpersonal relationships and the increased awareness of each other's style and character led to spontaneous "curbstone consults" occurring effortlessly. This comfortable environment increased the quality of medical care and enjoyment in providing it. Newly appointed physicians were instructed to "hang out in the doctors' lunchroom," to get to know and be known by their physician colleagues. At that time, no other metropolitan hospital medical staff was lucky enough to enjoy a similar environment that allowed the development and continuance of friendship amongst one's "competitors." The Abbott Hospital Doctors' Dining Room was, justifiably, the envy of every other medical staff in the city. Once the transition was made in 1980 to Abbott Northwestern Hospital, the Doctors' Dining Room /lounge was replicated.

(These thoughts, in large measure, are plagiarized from remarks by Dr. A. Boyd Thomes, given at the final Abbott Medical Staff meeting Oct. 2, 1979.)

Dr. Abbott expressed his appreciation for a pleasant setting in which to treat private patients. The establishment of the Doctors' Dining Room in 1968 would do the same for the medical staff. In the friendly atmosphere of the lunchroom, the special features of the Abbott spirit found a garden in which to flower.

14

Internal Medicine
Northwestern Hospital • 1882-2014
Abbott Northwestern Hospital • 1980-2014
Dr. Eugene Ollila

Two Hundred Years and Counting

The late 1800s was important for developing what today we call hospitals, especially with the impetus of the Civil War. In Minneapolis, Cottage Hospital was built by the Episcopal Church in 1870 and later became St. Barnabas Hospital. Harriet Walker Maternity Hospital was built in 1880 for charitable care to unwed mothers, and this later became Walker Methodist Care Center. Dr. Martha Ripley helped build Maternity Hospital in 1886, and a year later, General Hospital was built.

In 1882, Harriet Walker convened a group of influential women, supported by Dr. Mary Hood and Dr. Mary Whetstone. They opened Northwestern Hospital for Women and Children, which had eight rooms, and soon became too small. (I believe Northwestern Hospital did not have a male on its executive committee or Board of Trustees until 1967.) After two moves, they finally settled on a Minneapolis location at 27th and Chicago, with Dr. Amos Abbott as the first consulting physician. Twenty years later, Dr. Abbott opened his own hospital for the carriage trade about a mile away, followed by Dr. George Eitel, who built Eitel Hospital on Loring Park in Minneapolis.

During the twentieth century, improvements in health care delivery and changes in health care financing caused established hospitals to look at mergers, while physicians often were on more than one medical staff. This was especially true with Abbott and Northwestern hospitals. On January 1, 1970, these hospitals merged, and in 1980 moved to the Northwestern Hospital site. Five years later, Abbott Northwestern Hospital and Sister Kenny Institute merged. In 1993, this merger process culminated with the current Allina Health System.

Solo Practice, Partnerships, and Internal Medicine Groups

Early in the twentieth century, medical practice consisted of solo practices or very small partnerships. Several groups became the primary physicians admitting their patients to Northwestern Hospital. In the late 60s and early 70s, physicians were allowed to incorporate for the first time. Popularized by the legal profession, incorporation started the medical profession on a long learning process.

As far as I can determine, the first Internal Medicine physician at Northwestern Hospital was Dr. Robert Rizer, who practiced from 1916 to 1954. He moved to the hospital in 1921, where he introduced the Sippy Diet for ulcer patients (a bland diet of milk, farina, and egg, eaten hourly). His son, Dean, joined him in 1945. Dr. Rolf Andreasson joined the practice in the 1950s, and later formed what is now the Minneapolis Heart Institute® with Dr. Bob Van Tassel. Dr. Tom Arnold joined in 1965 (and later went to the Southdale area), followed by Dr. Jack Shronts in 1972, Ron Vessey in 1975, and Mark Johnson in 1979. Drs. Ben Whitten, Kathy Ayaz, Jean Anderson, and Margaret MacRae all joined later. The office closed in 1996, and all joined other groups, except for Ron Vessey, who continued in solo practice, and Margaret MacRae, who became an oncologist with a group and solo practice.

The second Internal Medicine group was later called Internist's Ltd. and became one of the founders of the current Allina-Nicollet Mall. Dr. Jay Davis began this group either in the late 1920s or early 1930s. He had spent time in China and was impressed with the low fat, i.e., low cholesterol, diet in dealing with coronary artery disease. He later invited his nephew, Dr. Lowell Weber to join him, as well as Dr. Mark Hanson in 1947-48, Dr. Bob Scott in 1965, and

Dr. Doug Kjellson in 1967. Doug later went to Hennepin County General. In 1977, Bob Scott recruited me from Hennepin County General, where he was my consulting physician.

Abbott Northwestern Hospital graduates joined the group, including Dr. Doug Godfrey in 1982, and later Dr. Jeanne Stocks and Dr. Karen Blackstone. This group was the first to go to the Southdale (Edina) area in 1985 and was in the first Allina office in the new Centennial Lakes Building that opened in 1990. Later Drs. Andana Gutter, Padma Gadella, and Rosalie Siy joined. Rosalie later became lead physician at Allina-Edina. In addition, Bob Scott and Doug Godfrey were among the earliest Abbott Northwestern physicians at WestHealth in Plymouth.

In 1945, Dr. Fred Schoff and Dr. Harold Miller formed a third group, and later added Dr. William Nuestle, who was one of the founders of the Fargo Clinic in 1959. After Fred Schoff's death in 1961, Dr. Franklin Norman was recruited. (He became famous or infamous because of his sponsorship of the "Not Necessarily Annual Lutefisk Dinner," for which he also served as head chef.) Dr. David Vagneur joined in 1974, and after Miller and Nuestle's retirements, this group joined Internist's Ltd in 1993.

Following World War II, a fourth group formed with Tom Lowry, but he left to join a separate group at Abbott Hospital. This group eventually had Drs. Robert Blomberg, Gordon McKinley, Herb Plass, and Jerry Dougan. (Dr. Plass came from an Abbott group that included Drs. Tom Lowry, Bill Paule, and Malcolm Clark.) Dr. Jim Shanks and Dr. Tom Davis joined in 1976 and merged into Minneapolis Internal Medicine in 1990. This group included Drs. Dave Carlson, John Bradley, Bill Paule, and Vince Fromke.

Dr. Jerry Dougan left and formed a rheumatology group in 1971 that included Dr. Walt Dorman (1978) and later Drs. Gary Baker, Archie Skemp, and Chip Bergstrom. This group merged with Dr. Paul Waytz's group in Edina in 1998. Dr. Vince Fromke had been the first Chief Resident under C.J. Watson when he formed the Internal Medicine residency at Northwestern Hospital, and he joined in 1972. He continued his porphyria research at Abbott Northwestern Hospital. (His lab was next to Dr. David Hickok's lab; he was doing research on breast cancer.) Vince is still in practice in Tennessee.

The fifth mostly Northwestern Hospital group included Drs. James Myhre,

Pat Ylvisaker, and Gerald Swanson, who transferred to Bill Petersen's group in 1972. Dr. Don Fisher was in this group for a while, but overall this group disbanded with retirements.

There were several other smaller groups or solo physicians at Northwestern Hospital. Dr. J. C. Miller was solo until joined by his son, Todd, in 1972. They later added Dr. Bob Coates and Dr. Brad Heltemes from the Abbott Northwestern Internal Medicine Residency Program. Dr. David Jones was in solo practice until his retirement in 1999. Dr. Albert Greenberg was also solo for many years. He had additional cardiology training, so he was the EKG reading guru. Dr. Elliot Francke joined him in 1981, and, after being certified by Columbia University Medical School, he became the first full-time Infectious Disease specialist at Abbott Northwestern. John LaBree and Tom Cooke were at Northwestern for a time, with the latter going to Hennepin Medical Society.

There were also several other groups for whom Northwestern Hospital was a secondary home initially, but who became prominent at Abbott Northwestern, especially after the closure of Abbott. One of these groups included Drs. William Petersen, Arthur Lindeland, Bill Bergstrom (who was also an endocrinologist), Khalid Mahmud (later at North Memorial as an oncologist), Jerry Swanson, David Plimpton, and Bruce Jacobson.

A second group was later known as Minneapolis Internal Medicine Associates (MIMA) and co-located to Medical Arts with Internist's Ltd. That group included Drs. Boyd Thomes; Jim (Seamus) McKenna, later an oncologist at Abbott Northwestern Hospital; Ray Scallen, who also served at the Minneapolis Veterans Administration Hospital and returned to become the physician director of the Cardiac Care Unit; as well as Drs. Richard Sturgeon, William Torp, Richard Adair, and Charlie Petersen. (Charlie is now practicing in Steamboat Springs, Colorado.)

After these changes, Drs. Ben Whitten, Kathy Ayaz, Paul Sutter, Micheal Cummings, Noelle Nelson, Paul Phillips, Donna Rodel, and several others joined. This group became known as Abbott Northwestern General Medicine Associates (ANGMA), and moved to Edina, separate from the Allina-Edina clinic. They also have a site on the Abbott Northwestern campus. Finally, Dr. Jeanette Lowry practiced with her husband Dr. Paul Lowry, at both Abbott Northwestern Hospital and Fairview Southdale Hospital.

Several Abbott Northwestern women graduates formed a clinic at Southdale called Sharpe, Dillon, Cockson and Associates, which continues to be active. Others, including Dr. Betty Stryvoky, joined with Dr. Caroline Toll to form Allina-Uptown Clinic.

After the closure of Metropolitan-Mount Sinai Hospital in 1990, other changes occurred among medical groups. Dr. Ray Scallen joined Drs. James Stevenson, Robert Schultz, and Paul Olson and co-located to an office with MIMA and Internist's Ltd. Another group that included Drs. David Berman, Al Devine, Harold Wexler, Stu Borkman, and Dan Rischall were at Abbott Northwestern starting in 1984. Dr. Peter Kieley and Dr. Ron Kaufman joined the Abbott Northwestern staff.

Geriatrics really developed as a subspecialty in the 1980s, and the Minneapolis Age and Opportunity Clinic was active beginning in the 1970s. It included Drs. George Bonnewell, Masajuki Kasahara, Wesley Brugger, Dionisio Pastones, John Hill, and later, Ed Ratner.

Many presidents of the Medical Staff came from the groups named above, including Drs. Bill Petersen, Bob Scott, Malcolm Clark, Boyd Thomes, Bill Torp, Todd Miller, Dick Sturgeon, and Gene Ollila. Dr. Jason Reed is Chief of Medical Staff at the time of this writing. He is in one of the few private groups, which also includes Dr. Dudley McLinn and Dr. John Egan. Dr. Bill Petersen, after his stint as Vice President of Medical Affairs, started the St. Thomas Health Care MiniMBA program.

Allina Health

Over the past 20 years, most internists have become employees of Allina. Allina clinics are located in downtown Minneapolis (Nicollet Mall), Uptown (The Doctors and Uptown), Richfield (previously called WoodLake), Edina, and Plymouth (WestHealth), along with the ANGMA offices previously mentioned. In addition, other offices developed when Aspen Clinics and Quello Clinics became part of Allina, and they now operate under the Allina name. A large group of Hospitalists, as well as a group of Intensivists in the ICU areas, now provide inpatient care.

Allina presently consists of 12 Hospitals and more than 90 Clinics, and is

Allina presently consists of 12 Hospitals and more than 90 Clinics, and is the sixth largest employer in Minnesota.

the sixth largest employer in Minnesota. The hospital that began by delivering medical care to women and children more than 100 years ago is now a regional health care center, involved in teaching and tertiary/quaternary research. From humble beginnings indeed.

This concludes my history of Internal Medicine at Northwestern and Abbott Northwestern Hospital. I am certain I have left out individuals who were important. I apologize for those inadvertent omissions.

Selections from the Internal Medicine Department Meeting Minutes

I reviewed the existing monthly meeting notes of the Internal Medicine Department from January 1963 to October 1979. The following are some of the more interesting dates and topics.

July 1963 – New Radiation Therapy area.

Dec 1963 – Discussion begins about having a full-time physician leading education.

March 1964 – The first defibrillator arrives, under direction of Dr. Rolf Andreasson.

Nov 1964 – Department makes recommendations that nurses be trained to handle medical emergencies and that there be a special unit for Acute Myocardial Infarction.

Oct 1965 – Recommendation for identifying and marking patients who have incurable cancer for DNR (Do Not Resuscitate).

July 1966 – Teaching program begins under Dr. C.J. Watson, recently retired medical chief at University of Minnesota.

April 1967 – First approval for radioisotope scanning.

Feb 1968 – Department recommends a physician statement in patient's chart, verifying patient understanding before undergoing high-risk procedures, and requiring a complete work-up.

April 1968 – Twelve-channel autoanalyzer becomes available – SMA12-60.

Sept 1968 – First delineation of special privileges for certain procedures, such as angiography, EK interpretation, liver biopsy, BM biopsy, and thoracentesis.

Feb 1969 – New Intensive Care Unit (ICU) and Cardiac Care Unit (CCU) opens in tower addition.

Jan 1970 – Dr. C.J. Watson decries diminished federal funding for research.

July 1971 – Dr. Robert Howard joins as Director of Medical Education, and succeeds Dr. C.J.Watson.

August 1971 – Educational meeting concerning Health Maintenance Organizations.

Dec 1972 – Outstate communities requesting onsite consultation services.

Jan 1973 – New EKG exercise area (stress test), with $20 charge for hospital and $12 for physician.

July 1975 – Ultrasound of abdomen available.

April 1976 – Routine orders for CCU available. First full-time cardiac fellow – Dr. Hans Bauer.

April 1977 – Recommendation for family practice to become part of Internal Medicine Department.

Jan 1979 – Recommendation to have separate nursing station for Neurology/Neurosurgery patients.

March 1979 – One bed in ICU designated for renal dialysis.

Sept 1979 – New protocol for coronary angioplasty, making ANWH the 19th USA center to perform this procedure.

These records help place the changes at Abbott Northwestern Hospital into an historical perspective. As Minnesota Public Radio likes to say on its classical music station, "All music was once new." All medical procedures were also once new, and many significant changes occurred in our lifetime.

15

Gastroenterology
1800s-2014
Dr. Arnold Kaplan

Pioneers

Based on citations from Egyptian papyri, practicing physicians had significant knowledge of gastrointestinal diseases during the period of the pharaohs. Irynakhty, who was a court physician in the tenth dynasty, 2125 B.C., specialized in gastroenterology, sleeping, and proctology. Gastrointestinal endoscopy may have begun in 1805 when Philipp Bozzini made the first attempt to observe inside the living human body using a tube he named Lichtleiter (light-guiding instrument) to examine the urinary tract, the rectum, and the pharynx.

In 1868 Adolf Kussmaul, a well-known German physician, developed the gastroscope to examine the stomach pouch. He perfected the technique based on observation of a sword swallower. In 1871, at the society of physicians in Vienna, Carl Storek demonstrated an esophagoscope made of two telescopic metal tubes. Waldenburg had initially devised this in 1870. However, it wasn't until 1932, when Rudolph Schindler and Georg Wolf developed a semiflexible endoscope, that systematic observations could be made and catalogued. The next major advance was not made until 1957, when Basil Hirschowitz introduced the first prototype of a fiberoptic gastroscope. Wolff and Shinya introduced colonoscopy into clinical practice in 1969.

The American Board of Internal Medicine has certified Gastroenterologists since 1941.

Ultrasound was developed after World II, based on sonar devices used for military purposes.

Prior to 1970, specialties in Internal Medicine were practiced largely by certified internists with more or less formal subspecialty training in their area of directed interest and experience. Their efforts were divided between general care and specialty consultation. Certification has become nearly universal amongst subspecialists only since the late decades of the last century. Until 45 years ago, a gastroenterologist might be invited to consult on a case and render a diagnostic/therapeutic opinion that only occasionally required ongoing treatment.

Diagnosis was based significantly on the ongoing clinical events. In fact, disruption of the "natural" healing process was of such concern that even an upper GI barium X-ray might be delayed for days for fear of inducing a relapse of gastrointestinal bleeding. Further diagnostic efforts included common laboratory results (chemistry tests on blood, urine, and feces) and radiologic procedures, commonly employing barium as a contrast. Imaging by scanning was less commonly used, and radioisotopes were considered of dubious safety.

Nonsurgical treatment consisted of restricted diets, nasogastric aspiration, postural changes, and a small number of medications including analgesics, antacids, and corticosteroids, as well as nonselective secretory and motility inhibitors such as probantheline, and antiemetics. When employed, surgery was always open, as opposed to the laparoscopic approach used today.

Ultrasound was developed after World War II, based on sonar devices used for military purposes. Endoscopy was infrequently employed owing to the need to insert rigid hollow tubes through the mouth or rectum. These instruments made it difficult for the endoscopist and involved risks and discomfort for the patients.

Adequate and safe biopsy of the liver became possible in the post-war period through the use of aspiration needling. The small intestine was biopsied as necessary, using a guillotine device triggered by suction or a spring applied through a long tube in the mouth. Dr. James Carey at the University of Minnesota used one such tube. For reasons of ease and safety, it was widely used in the local private hospital setting. Prior to the local introduction of fiberoptic gastroscopy in 1967, Dr. R.S. Ylvisaker and Dr. James Myhre advanced the use of gastroscopy in clinical diagnosis at Northwestern Hospital. They collaborated in the study of gastritis using gastroscopic biopsy while still at the University of Minnesota School of Medicine.

Minnesota claims two other important pioneers of gastrointestinal study: Dr. Walter Alvarez of the Mayo Clinic, who did the first electrogastrography research in 1921-22, and Dr. Charles Code. In 1958, Dr. Code, along with Dr. Franz Ingelfinger, introduced esophageal manometry, a method to measure the pressure in the esophagus. Subsequently, while he was at the Mayo Clinic, Dr. Code published a systematized study of esophageal motility in health and disease.

Later, the University of Minnesota became a leader in the field through the contribution of nationally recognized clinical educators such as Dr. Jack Vennes and Dr. Stephen Silvis. They attended patients at Abbott Northwestern Hospital as well.

Advances in Endoscopy and Radiology

The picture changed dramatically between 1970 and 1990 as a result of technical advances in endoscopy, radiography, and pharmacology. Flexible endoscopy was developed initially through the use of fiberoptic imaging and subsequently video technology. These instruments provided the ability to visualize the mucosal surface of the gastrointestinal tract more accurately and without most of the risk and discomfort, which had previously been part of the process. This improved the timeliness and appropriateness of treatment of many disorders, including peptic ulcer disease, upper gastrointestinal bleeding of many causes, cancer of the stomach, celiac sprue, ulcerative colitis, and reflux esophagitis. Endoscopy supplanted most of the barium contrast radiological tests dominant at the time, which included upper GI series and the barium enema. Independent advancements in radiographic diagnosis, including digital scanning (CT scans and MRIs), enhanced ultrasound, and safer and more selective isotope scans, provided additional diagnostic options.

Endoscopic biopsy provided a new level of diagnostic accuracy, and treatment became possible through the use and development of tube placements, injectors, dilators, electrocoagulating devices, snares, and staples. The treatment of bile duct stones, strictures, and tumors was revolutionized by this technology, which combined endoscopy with radiology. This often took place in the X-ray suites, providing stimulus for growth in these departments.

Endoscopic biopsy provided a new level of diagnostic accuracy, and treatment became possible through the use and development of tube placements, injectors, dilators, electrocoagulating devices, snares, and staples.

In the past decade, a more intimate combination of the radiographic and endoscopic techniques became possible through Endoscopic Ultrasonography. A probe is applied internally through an upper gastrointestinal endoscope, thus providing a more accurate anatomical display than ultrasounds obtained by probes applied on the skin.

Colonoscopy

A major impetus to the use of colonoscopy occurred in the 1990s, when it was demonstrated conclusively that colon cancer most often developed in benign colon polyps. This was largely preventable through timely polyp removal by means of trans-colonoscopic wire snare and cautery. The endoscopy center became the site for a marked expansion of polyp-seeking screening colonoscopy. Following this expanded use of colonoscopy, which promoted the addition of expert gastrointestinal pathologists to our staff, the hospital has become a proving ground for the detailed examination of the removed polyps. This has resulted in a number of collaborative studies that have contributed to the critical differentiation of polyp types, as well as DNA studies of removed tumors, yielding greater accuracy of treatment and prognosis.

An Expanding Field

These advances required more gastroenterologists with additional training and experience. Medical educators responded quickly, adding full-time gastroenterologists to the practicing medical community. As a rough measure, there were no more than several physicians with gastrointestinal privileges at the time of the merger of Abbott and Northwestern Hospitals in 1970, and today there are 46 physicians with such privileges.

Endoscopy was initially performed in the emergency department or operating room and thus supported by the respective unit personnel. However, a specialized endoscopy unit was created in the 1980s. This has been expanded repeatedly to allow for skilled support of upper and lower gastrointestinal endoscopy, endoscopic ultrasound, and endoscopic cholangiopancreatography

Following this expanded use of colonoscopy, which promoted the addition of expert gastrointestinal pathologists to our staff, the hospital has become a proving ground for the detailed examination of the removed polyps.

(an X-ray of the gall bladder and pancreas) with on-site video, as well as liver biopsy on both in-patients and out-patients.

Colorectal Surgery

The vigorous independent growth of colorectal surgery at Abbott Northwestern Hospital included active participation of surgical fellows from University of Minnesota Medical School. Abdominal surgery methods have evolved significantly through the expanded use of laparoscopic and natural-orifice approaches, as well as robotic devices. The latter have become a notable part of the esophageal and gastric care program at the Virginia Piper Cancer Institute. Cultivation of hospital and physician-group relationships provided an atmosphere of cooperation and interaction among gastroenterologists, surgeons, radiologists, pathologists, and oncologists. Enhanced patient care, as well as the support of clinical studies that have contributed to medicine nationally and internationally, has been the result.

Pharmacology

Pharmacological advances include potent gastric antisecretory drugs and many antibiotics used in gastrointestinal infections. In 1976, cimetidine, a histamine-2 antagonist that inhibits acid secretion by the gastric parietal cell, was introduced into clinical use. This changed the treatment of peptic ulcer disease by eliminating dependence on strict diets and frequent antacid doses. Omeprazole, a far more potent acid antisecretory drug and a revolutionary advance, was made available in the United States in 1990.

In 2005, Barry Marshall and Robin Warren of Australia were awarded the Nobel Prize in Physiology and Medicine for their discovery of the causal role of the bacteria Heliobacter pylori in peptic ulcer disease. This discovery, along with the aggressive use of omeprazole or similar drugs, and antibiotics, allowed for widespread cure of peptic ulcer disease, nearly eliminating the need for surgery. Immunomodulators and biological agents have added to treatment effectiveness of multiple conditions, including ulcerative colitis, Crohn's disease, and liver disease. Hepatits C, which had become the most common cause of

*Dr. Robert Ganz...
along with Dr.
Brian Zelickson...
invented the
treatment
of Barrett's
esophagus, a
precancerous
lesion, and
other conditions
through the use
of radiofrequency
ablation.*

cirrhosis requiring liver transplantation, is now curable through a new generation of medications.

Education and Research

Medical education and research has been an integral part of Gastroenterology. In 1966, after 20 years of leadership in research and education at the University of Minnesota, Dr. Cecil J. Watson moved his laboratory to Abbott Northwestern Hospital. Dr. Watson specialized in porphyrin metabolism-related conditions and liver disease at the University of Minnesota. (Porphyrin metabolism studies the pigment of the blood.) His work contributed to the treatment of Acute Porphyria and added to Abbott Northwestern's reputation as a center for graduate and undergraduate medical education. During the ensuing fourteen years, he published a total of 77 papers.

The light-sensitizing characteristic of some porphyrins was used to detect and treat cancers (and other conditions) of organs including the esophagus, stomach, and colon. This method, called photodynamic therapy, was based on the applied discoveries of Dr. Watson, and his coworker over the decades, Dr. Samuel Schwartz.

Dr. Robert Ganz, current Chief of Gastroenterology at Abbott Northwestern Hospital, along with Dr. Brian Zelickson, a member of the Abbott Northwestern Hospital Dermatology staff, invented the treatment of Barrett's esophagus, a precancerous lesion, and other conditions through the use of radiofrequency ablation. This is a method for delivery of thermal energy in a controlled fashion, applied through an endoscope, and has emerged as the standard of care for advanced Barrett's Esophagus.

The Future of Gastroenterology

Health care delivery is evolving from a physician-based practice to an organization-based system with a team-practice orientation. Gastroenterology has been affected, as have all medical specialties. The pace and precise organizing principles are difficult to predict given the influences of costs, complexity of medical technology, and government mandates.

The electronic medical record that tracks diagnoses, treatments, costs, and frequency of patient encounters has been a stimulus in this direction. It has proved to be expensive, as have other technologies, inducing physicians to form or join corporations. Handheld devices or personal digital assistants allow for improved data access and communication among doctors, physician's assistants, nurses, and pharmacists. Once the issue of security has been resolved, patients may also use this technology.

Technology allows for physicians to focus more on their skills and thus ameliorates the predicted shortage of gastroenterologists. Such technology might include peroral capsule endoscopy with external control, whereby a capsule-sized endoscopic device can be swallowed to provide a continuing optical record during transit through the stomach, esophagus, small bowel, and colon. These might perhaps be assisted by computer readouts much as electrocardiograms are interpreted. The dexterity and trained eye of endoscopists could be invested in more technical diagnostic procedures involving spectroscopy, ultrasound, microscopy, and other advanced optical tools. These include operative therapeutic procedures involving the biliary tract, treatment of gastrointestinal bleeding and gastroesophageal reflux, as well as neoplasms of the colon and upper GI tract.

Technical aids such as balloons or straighteners might extend the reach of an operative endoscope further into the small bowel. Intraluminal operative endoscopy might easily be combined with external laparoscopic or natural orifice approach (Natural Orifice Transluminal Endoscopic Surgery, whereby access is gained via the stomach or bowel rather than through the abdominal wall) for resections now requiring open abdominal surgery.

Endoscopic evaluation and treatment of focal lesions, especially tumors, may be aided by advances in new technology such as fluorescence, light scattering reflectance, spectroscopy, laser confocal microscopy and endomicroscopy, optic coherence tomography, and integrated ultrasonic probes allowing for "optical biopsies" of lesions. Local treatment of gastrointestinal cancer with agents administered via endoscopy is an exciting prospect. Potential agents include engineered viruses that either selectively kill malignant cells or sensitize them to chemo- or radio-therapy. The application of immunotherapy is another approach, wherein an allogeneic, mixed-lymphocyte culture (cytoimplant)

Handheld devices or personal digital assistants allow for improved data access and communication among doctors, physician's assistants, nurses, and pharmacists.

is injected into the cancer to initiate a strong tumor-specific immune response. This approach already has been used with apparent benefit in pancreatic cancer.

Colon tumor screening is likely to shift significantly from colonoscopy to other imaging methods. Blood and other abnormalities in the colon may be detected by fecal markers, utilizing immunological or other analytical methods. Conceivably, the detection of DNA mutations or specific cancer-associated proteins in blood or feces could be a sensitive and specific indicator of high-risk neoplasms. Other investigations utilizing radiological techniques such as CT colonography and MRI colonography might also have an increased role in screening, particularly if sensitivity and specificity can be improved without the preceding use of laxatives. PET scanning can also detect most cancers and at least some of the larger polyps. With some modification, the PET scan, an X-ray that produces a cross-section of an organ, might also become an alternative screening modality.

The twenty-first century brought recognition of the role of the microbiome and its impact on health and disease in disorders of the gut (Crohn's, colon cancer, colitis). Treatment of resistant Clostridium difficele infections by microbiome transplant (via capsules or enemas containing material derived from normal stool) are already in use. It is likely that research on the human microbiome will continue to demonstrate other correlations, such as a relationship with the increased prevalence of autoimmune diseases, including Type 1 Diabetes.

There is no doubt that DNA identification will provide a powerful diagnostic tool regardless of specialty.

In the coming decades, it is likely that we will face a continuing tension between many of these advances and strained resources. This will be, perhaps, the major factor in any attempt to predict the future of health care.

Physicians Credentialed in Gastroentrology

There are many contributors to this history, involving specialties whose names will not be noted here, but a complete list of those credentialed in Gastroenterology follows.

Past Members

Jeffrey H Albrecht, MD

John Irvin Allen, MD

Matthew Bagamery, MD

Arnold M Brier, MD

Oliver W. Cass, MD

Paul B Dickinson, MD

Richard A. Dubow, MD

Mahnaz Farahmand, MD

Martin L. Freeman, MD

Robert A Gill, MD

Deborah A Goldman, MD

Agnes H. Han, MD

Arnold P Kaplan, MD

Phillip M Kibort, MD, MBA

James P Kromhout, MD

Robert B Lasser, MD

Frank G Lushine, MD

Thomas R Martin, MD

Randolph M McConnie, MD

Ronald J Pizinger, MD

Pete A Pooler, MD

James Pries, MD

Michael J Rensch, MD

Kelly Salfiti, MD

John E Sandgren, MD

Michael J Shaw, MD

Jerrold M Stempel, MD

Jan Tanghe, MD

Joseph M Tombers, MD

Dorothy I Whitmer, MD

James R Wood, MD

Paul N Yakshe, MD

Randy J. Yanda, MD

Current Gastroentrologists

Nouredin Alebouyeh, MBBS

Sundeep Arora, MD

Ramalingam Arumugam, MD

Michael Bader, MD

Courtney Barancin, MD

Neville Basman, MD

Nicholas Boetticher, MD

Fernando Carballo, MD

Cecil Chally, MD

Zongyu Chen, MD

Sandra Denman, MD

Nissa Erickson, MD

Elizabeth Fallon, MD

Samuel Feldshon, MD

David Ferenci, MD

Caryn Fine, MD

Robert Ganz, MD

Stephen Gilberstadt, MD

April Grudell, MD

Michelle Kennedy, MD

Scott Ketover, MD

John Lake, MD

Samuel Leon, MD

James Levine, MD

Aaron Link, MD

Jeffrey Lisko, MD

Philip Lowry, MD
Robert Mackie, MD
Robert McCabe, MD
Benjamin Mitlyng, MD
David Perdue, MD
Alison Platt, DO
Timothy Potter, MD
Erica Roberson, MD
Federico Rossi, MD
Stephen Rudolph, MD
Irfan Sandozi, MD

Mark Schmidt, MD
Cynthia Sherman, MD
Coleman Smith, MD
Richard Stafford, MD
Bradford Stone, MD
Bertha Toriz, MD
David Weinberg, MD
David Wiechmann, MD
Kirk Wilson, DO
Donald Zogg, MD

16

General Surgery
1983-2014
Dr. Jack Graber

A little more than 30 years ago (August 1983), I first walked into Abbott Northwestern Hospital. I had joined the practice of Moos, Hickok, Schultz and Graber, as it was called at that time. Drs. Arthur Zierold and Daniel Moos established the practice in the years after World War II. Dr. Zierold was a highly regarded surgeon, recipient of the Charles Bowles-Rogers Award from the Twin Cities Medical Society in 1963. He and Dr. Dan Moos were founding doctors of the Minneapolis Medical Research Foundation in 1952. He died before the Abbott and Northwestern Hospitals merged in 1970. In the mid-1960s, Dr. David Hickok joined the practice. I didn't get the opportunity to meet Dr. Zierold, and by the time I arrived in Minneapolis, Dr. Moos' vision had failed him such that he no longer performed surgery. Dave Hickok was the leader of our group then.

Dave was a remarkable man, a graduate of Blake High School in Minneapolis and Princeton University where, incidentally, he was an outstanding football player. He was even on the cover of *Time* due to his football prowess. (I've seen a copy!) Besides being tall, dark-haired and handsome, he was a remarkable surgeon. Always in control, he could accomplish surgical feats through the smallest incisions, quickly, and his patients uniformly did well. He was regarded as

...we devised a technique of removing the gallbladder via a laparoscope using laser wands.

one of the premier surgeons in the area throughout his entire career. He was a doctor 24 hours a day, and essentially, whenever he was needed at the hospital, he was there. The practice of medicine was highly competitive then, and it was largely based on direct referrals from internists and family physicians. He was very busy, and he told me to expect "one case per week per year in practice"!

Bill Stephens joined our group for the last several years of his practice after a long, excellent career in General Surgery that took him from the old Abbott to the new Abbott Northwestern Hospital.

By the time he retired, David Hickok was slowing his practice down. David had a vast number of friends, and they never hesitated to call him for advice or help. At his retirement party (he initially refused the event, but Dr. Schultz and I convinced him, with the help of his wife Hope, to allow a small one), a man stood up to toast Dave. He said, "I want to thank Dave, especially noting that he saved my wife's life." Everyone applauded, and then another man stood and said, "I want to thank Dave for he not only saved my wife's life, he saved mine, too." After a knowing laugh and more applause, a third man stood and said, "Dave not only saved my wife's and my lives, but also my daughter's and two of my horses!" By then everyone was laughing, but it was true; he was a valued doctor to all these people and so many more. I thought he knew everything. It was a tragedy when he died suddenly only a year after retiring in 1996.

At that time, Abbott Northwestern was doing very well. There was still the sense of an austere medical society within its walls. New therapies were becoming available, such as Hyper Alimentation or Total Parenteral Nutrition (TPN). Dr. Leonard Schultz was a man to try new things, and he pioneered TPN at Abbott Northwestern. From then on, it was one new idea or procedure after the other for Leonard and me. I wasn't working in Minneapolis long when we started Laser Angioplasty to treat artery blockages, or for that matter, Laser Anything to treat problems of a variety of natures. Most of these procedures didn't hold up, but Leonard applied laser to make Laparoscopic Cholecystectomy (removal of the gallbladder) work. At that time there was no other way commercially available to cut tissue using a laparoscope without causing excessive bleeding. We thought laser was the only way. And we devised a technique of removing the gallbladder via a laparoscope using laser wands. After testing this on a series of 20 dogs in the lab, we offered the procedure to a patient who was totally adverse to a large incision. It worked well.

Leonard reported this case at the Society for Laser Surgery and Medicine in Washington, D.C. in the late 80s. We thought we were the first surgeons to do this procedure (we weren't), but we were the first surgeons in the world to report it. At that presentation, another surgeon got up to comment on our paper, and he had 15 patients for whom he had done "lap choles." We dove into this new operation headfirst and developed a training program to teach other surgeons. At one time, all of our Abbott Northwestern workshops were full (60 physicians each), and we had 300 surgeons on the waiting list. It wasn't long before all surgeons in the country found someplace to train, and the need for our workshops disappeared. Laparoscopic Cholecystectomy is now the procedure of choice throughout the world.

Acceptance of the new laparoscopic procedures for General Surgery operations at Abbott Northwestern was scattered, with some surgeons saying it was "malpractice" to those who quickly adopted the procedure. The laser gave way to more efficient electrocautery. Years of improved technology made the use of laparoscopic techniques one of the greatest advances in General Surgery in decades. Abbott Northwestern was the site for development of many new or vastly improved laparoscopic techniques in the years to follow.

Dr. Leonard Schultz made his name with "lap choles," but further, he was the true originator and populist of Laparoscopic Hernia repair. It was the early 1990s, and this change in an age-old operation was not received well by the majority of surgeons. This operation is now done routinely and internationally; however, Leonard retired before it blossomed to its magnificence well after the turn of the century. By that time, Abbott Northwestern had developed the Laser Center, which morphed into the outpatient surgery sites of today. Surgery was being done much less invasively, and the Laparoscopic Cholecystectomy became an outpatient procedure. Stomach, esophageal, splenic, appendicular, adrenal, kidney, and colon surgeries were being done laparoscopically, and much of it was done first, or differently and better at Abbott Northwestern.

A similar phenomenon and another story can be told regarding Cardiac Surgery and the development of the world-class Cardiology group, which

Abbott Northwestern was the site for development of many new or vastly improved laparoscopic techniques in the years to follow.

...in 2008, we were doing typical, though excellent, open incisional abdominal aneurysm repairs.

eventually became the Minneapolis Heart Institute®. But that story is for another chapter in this book. (See chapters on Cardiology and Cardiovascular Surgery.)

There were several excellent General Surgical groups working at Abbott Northwestern in 2000. Dr. Henry Sosin and Dr. Michael Schwartz led one, which eventually included Drs. Ray Drew, Ed Chute, Dan Dunn, Eric Johnson, and Michael Hoo. Drs. John Parrot, John O'Leary, and Ernie Lampe were another group. Dr. Leonard Schultz and I parted ways in 1996, and soon Dr. Peter Alden joined me from Methodist Hospital, bringing a new vascular surgery expertise. Dan Dunn left Henry Sosin's group, and after a brief stint in Texas, joined Peter and me. Soon we hired Dr. Eric Johnson right out of residency, and Dr. Margit Bretzke came to us from a group operating at Fairview Riverside Hospital. We were a happy, high-quality group of surgeons, and it wasn't long before the other groups left or disbanded. Drs. Michael Schwartz, Ray Drew, and Ed Chute stopped doing general and vascular surgery and successfully focused solely on bariatric surgery (mostly laparoscopic gastric bypass operations). They continued to operate at Abbott Northwestern, leading to the Abbott Northwestern Hospital Bariatric Center. John O'Leary shed his other partners and operated with our group at an arm's length. That relationship exists to this day.

By 2008, an excellent young vascular surgeon, Dr. Alex Tretinyak, had joined our group, and the time was right for Alex, Peter Alden, and me to leave General Surgery to further develop Vascular Surgery at Abbott Northwestern. We joined with Dr. Tim Sullivan, who had a nationally renowned practice in Vascular via the Cleveland and Mayo Clinics. We became hospital employees within the large Minneapolis Heart Institute® as the Division of Vascular Surgery. With Tim as the program's leader, Vascular Surgery at Abbott Northwestern was forever changed for the better.

For example, in 2008, we were doing typical, though excellent, open incisional abdominal aneurysm repairs. By 2011, 70 percent of the aneurysms were repaired with Endovascular Technique, meaning by use of needle puncture of the femoral arteries and X-ray visualization. The patients would have their abdominal aortic aneurysm repaired and walk out of the hospital the next day. It was yet another effort at Abbott Northwestern that led the community and region. We now have eight members in our Vascular Surgery group including the additions of Drs Addi Rizvi, Jason Alexander, Andy Craig, Neda Skeik, and Jesse Mananga. Dr. Alex Tretinyak left the group in 2013.

Meanwhile, the General Surgeons comprising the practice known as Surgical Specialists of Minnesota made great advances as well. Dr. Dan Dunn and Dr. Margit Bretzke were instrumental in developing the Virginia Piper Cancer Institute and specifically the Breast Center. Dr. Eric Johnson and Dr. Dan Dunn also honed the laparoscopic stomach and esophageal surgeries, leading to procedures like robotic total esophagectomy for cancer. Adding Dr. Casandra Anderson to the group has enhanced areas of cancer surgery. Other excellent surgeons who joined by leaving successful practices or came right out of residency were Drs. Tor Aasheim, Dawn Johnson, Jesica Guiterez, and Peter Dahlberg. They remain a financially independent organization.

The complex field of Hepatobilliary Surgery was separated out from General Surgery, and Dr. Tim Sielaff was brought in to do the pancreatectomies and liver resections as well as to be the Director of the Cancer Center.

One cannot practice surgery for too long, maybe 30 to 35 years at most. As such, surgeons came and went through the operating rooms at Abbott Northwestern Hospital. The difference from most other facilities was that at Abbott Northwestern, you could leave your mark. So much excellence, so much opportunity and progress, and so much comradery with other surgical leaders led to programs others try to emulate. We have done something special here, and it is recognized the world over. The sense of accomplishment is quite gratifying.

The patients would have their abdominal aortic aneurysm repaired and walk out of the hospital the next day. It was yet another effort at Abbott Northwestern that led the community and region.

17

Interventional Neuroradiology
1984-2014
Dr. David Tubman

Interventional neuroradiology was in its infancy when I began practicing at Abbott North-western Hospital 30 years ago. During those decades, interventional neuroradiology became an integral part of the treatment of cerebrovascular disease worldwide. The following is a brief description of some of the early history, device development, and current techniques in place.

The first reported use of embolization of cerebral arteries to treat brain arteriovenous malformations was in 1960 by Dr. A.J. Lussenhop, an American neurosurgeon. This procedure destroyed malformations in arteries in the brain with the injection of small pebbles (emboli). In the mid-1970s, Dr. F.A. Serbinenko, a Russian neurosurgeon, reported the use of detachable balloons to treat cerebral aneurysms (abnormal dilation of an artery) and carotid cavernous fistulas (an abnormal communication between the cavernous sinus and the carotid arterial system).

Dr. Gerard Debrun, a French neuroradiologist, was credited with bringing the balloon technology out of Russia in the late 1970s. I was able to work with Dr. Debrun in 1981 following his move to the University of Western Ontario.

More than 2,000 cerebral aneurysms have been treated at Abbott Northwestern Hospital since 1995.

In 1982, I performed the first balloon repair of a carotid-cavernous fistula in Minnesota. At the time, I was working with Dr. Kurt Amplatz in his research lab at the University of Minnesota. Since all 1983-era endovascular devices had to be hand-assembled, we worked to modify and improve both devices and technique.

I joined Consulting Radiologists Limited in 1983 to work at Abbott Northwestern Hospital. The focus was improving computed tomography, purchasing MRI equipment, and building a robust neuroangiographic suite with the associated staffing. The first major neurointervention or radiology procedures were performed in 1988. This was following the development of microcatheters and microwires that allowed intracranial vascular navigation.

During the 1980s and 1990s, a number of babies were born with high-flow cerebral arteriovenous fistulas. We treated 20 of these children with a multi-staged balloon/coil/glue procedure and had the opportunity to follow them in the ensuing years. All cases had surprisingly good outcomes. We developed a strong relationship with Children's Hospital Department of Anesthesia, as well as the intensivist staff at that hospital. Additional support came from the Department of Neurosurgery via Dr. Mahmoud Nagib and his nurse practitioners.

We were asked to treat the University of Minnesota's neurosurgery patients for seven years from 1989 to 1996. All these patients had endovascular treatments at Abbott Northwestern Hospital and were transferred to the University of Minnesota for neurosurgery when necessary.

This relatively new specialty has always been driven by innovation. This innovation has been rapid and continuous over the past 20 years. Advances included digital subtraction angiography and digital roadmapping. The Guglielmi Detachable Coil (GDC), approved in 1995, has become the cornerstone of endovascular aneurysm treatment. Multiple iterations have followed. The international subarachnoid aneurysm trial (ISAT) demonstrated that patients treated with coils had improved outcomes compared with those who were treated with open surgery.

More than 2,000 cerebral aneurysms have been treated at Abbott Northwestern Hospital since 1995. A unique group of aneurysm treatment devices, called flow diverters, were developed to treat those aneurysms not amenable to coil embolization. These devices are called mesh devices. They are placed in the parent arteries, disrupt inflow into the aneurysms, and result in thrombosis of the blood in the aneurysms. Vasospasm, or the contraction of blood vessels in the brain following subarachnoid hemorrhage, can cause brain damage. Treatment to combat the spasms with medications injected through a microcatheter and/or a balloon inserted into intracranial arteries has helped improve patient outcomes.

Arteriovenous malformations treatment has progressed from the injection of plastic balls into the arteries of the brain to the current use of ONYX, a nonadhesive liquid embolic agent. The improved safety of this polymer and the ability to treat deep cerebral vascular lesions has resulted in the obliteration of many of these dangerous lesions. Embolization with subsequent neurosurgical removal or radiosurgery has become the mainstay of the treatment options.

Multiple devices have been developed for clot removal from intracranial arteries and veins following a stroke. Currently, use of large bore, highly trackable catheters placed into the intracranial arteries with or without mechanical retrieval devices has produced the best results when used soon after the onset of a stroke. The entire stroke program at Abbott Northwestern Hospital has evolved into a multidisciplinary team with rapid response teams and improved patient outcomes.

Cement-assisted vertebral body augmentation (vertebroplasty) has become an effective means for treating vertebral body, i.e., bony, compression fractures and its associated pain. This procedure is utilized along with multiple spinal injection techniques in our spine pain management program.

Devices and techniques may have started and expanded our practice, but its success has to do with the people who worked in this area. The nurse clinician, Mary Mahre, started in 1989 and has been a cornerstone of the practice for 22 years. The nurse practitioners Lana Buck, Ruth Anderson, and currently Jill Schultz and Anna Blum have carried the huge load of patient management. Jen Fease joined in 2006 to enter data for us. She went on to develop a robust database and become a top regulatory affairs person and information expert. Coordinator Sandee Verootis has been the entry point for most of the patients coming into the practice. She is a solid, patient, and extraordinarily loyal member of the team. The Radiology Department and nurses have provided exemplary service on a 24/7 basis for the 30 years of my hospital practice. These

The entire stroke program at Abbott Northwestern Hospital has evolved into a multidisciplinary team with rapid response teams and improved patient outcomes.

people are largely responsible for the success of the practice outcomes we have enjoyed.

I have been fortunate to have a number of exceptional and hard-working physicians as partners over the years. Drs. Mark Myers, John Perl, Arvind Nehra, and Ben Crandall have all made great contributions to the practice. Dr. Josser Delgado and Dr. Yasha Kayan, both of whom are fellowship-trained interventional neuroradiologists, are currently providing quality patient management and technical expertise.

Hospital administration and the Boards of Directors have obviously made positive contributions to the practice by providing the equipment and devices needed. More significantly, the hospital's development of the Intensivist and Hospitalists programs has been important in improving patient outcomes and satisfaction.

Finally, the trust and expertise of our Neuroscience colleagues has made for a collaborative, satisfying, and high-quality medical practice. The neurosurgeons, neurologists, neuroradiologists, otolaryngologists, and spine surgeons should be congratulated for the common vision that resulted in the best patient care possible.

18

Library Services
1970-2014
Jim Bulger, MLIS

History of Hospital Libraries

Hospital libraries date back into the 1800s. The Office of Librarian for the Hennepin County Medical Society was established in 1862, and by 1890 it contained 1,692 volumes. The Medical Library Association in the U.S. was founded in 1898 and included librarians from 24 hospitals. Hospital libraries came into being as clinical medicine grew, influenced by the need for education and training with the growth of internships and residencies. As the practice of medicine moved out of the home and into the hospital, the influence of physicians led to the development of medical libraries in hospitals. However, in most hospitals, the "library" may have consisted of nothing more than a shelf of books.

In the early part of the twentieth century, many hospitals also had a "patient library" (as distinguished from the "medical staff library"). The patient library provided bibliotherapy to patients, emphasizing the use of books as a therapeutic tool. The librarian was seen as a trained therapist, working alongside physical and occupational therapy. In an address to the Minnesota Hospital Association in 1938, Gordon R. Kaman emphasized the value of therapeutic reading for hospitalized patients. He said that a "skilled bibliotherapist can help materially in

The librarian was seen as a trained therapist, working alongside physical and occupational therapy. In an address to the Minnesota Hospital Association in 1938, Gordon R. Kaman emphasized the value of therapeutic reading for hospitalized patients.

reducing the patient's morbidity and in shortening his convalescence (sic) in a great number and variety of illnesses."

The 1934 meeting of the American Hospital Association stressed the importance of hospital libraries in meeting patient care. And in 1940, the American College of Surgeons' Manual of Hospital Standards included a minimum standard for hospital libraries, including resources, housing, and personnel. Medical library education in Minnesota began in 1937 when the University of Minnesota's Division of Library Instruction offered a lecture course and six-week internship in an approved hospital library. The staff of the BioMedical library at the "U" continues to offer occasional classes in medical librarianship through St. Catherine University's master in library and information science program.

The 1960s saw a shift in focus from collections and resource building to one of service: primarily reference and document delivery. There was also a greater integration of nursing and medical libraries, which had been separate entities within the hospital.

Abbott Northwestern Hospital Medical Library

Not much is known or remembered about the hospital libraries at Abbott Hospital and Northwestern Hospital prior to 1970. Both hospitals, as well as Sister Kenny Institute, maintained libraries with a book collection. They also participated in some sharing of materials with the Hennepin County Medical Society and other local hospital libraries. The medical library at Northwestern hospital was a small room located near the medical staff lounge. The school of nursing at Abbott Hospital was staffed by Mrs. Andrea Espe as librarian until 1961, when she was replaced by Mrs. Ethel Peters.

When the newly formed Abbott Northwestern School of Nursing opened its doors in 1970, new space was made available to support both the medical and nursing staffs. The library was (and is) located in the lower level of the Education Building. This allowed easy evening access to nurses through the tunnel from their dorm in the Harriet Walker Building.

In 1970, Donna Johnson was hired to be the Chief Librarian for Abbott Northwestern Hospital. Donna's career was to span the next 32 years. This was a period of remarkable expansion and growth in library services. Donna had completed her Master of Library Science degree at Case Western Reserve University in Ohio. Her studies included a focus on medical libraries. Her visionary efforts and calm but determined leadership soon put the Abbott Northwestern Library Services at the forefront both locally and nationally.

Throughout her career, Donna played an active role in the profession. She served as president of the Medical Library Association Hospital Libraries Section in 1979-80 and was a member of the prestigious Nominating Committee for the MLA in 1984. She served as Chair of the Minnesota Health Sciences Library Association from 1974-76 and Chair of the Twin Cities BioMedical Consortium in 1977.

Donna's involvement would set the tone for a high level of professional activity on the part of library staff on the local, regional, and national level. There was active participation by the staff in hosting two national and three regional conferences, serving in officer positions, and submitting papers and/or conference posters almost annually.

In 1974, Abbott Northwestern Hospital formed a partnership to provide library services to the new Children's Health Center of Minneapolis.

Children's Hospital

In 1974, Abbott Northwestern Hospital formed a partnership to provide library services to the new Children's Health Center of Minneapolis. This was the forerunner of Children's Hospitals and Clinics of Minnesota. The Edward J. Huenekins Memorial Library at Children's was supported by the staff of the Abbott Northwestern Hospital Medical Library.

Preliminary planning for the library at Children's had begun in 1971. Donna Johnson worked with Dr. Tague Chisholm, a pediatric surgeon, to secure pledges from the medical staff for donations of books and journals to begin the medical library collection. In addition to the print collection, the Children's library soon included a computer terminal with access to MEDLINE. In 1974, Dr. Chisholm gave this report to a colleague about this amazing new technology:

> You can type a logged, keyed request into Bethesda [home of the National Library of Medicine] in the state of Maryland

The partnership with Children's Hospital also provided the foundation for an extensive outreach program designed to close the information gap experienced by rural physicians and other health care providers.

asking for the best five articles on a given subject that have been published in the last two years. Within five minutes the computer in Bethesda can scan as many as several thousand references and give you a print-out before your very eyes of the five best references from the world's literature…

In time, a library assistant was hired to manage the Children's library. The Abbott Northwestern Library Services staff provided oversight, back-up reference services, literature searches, document delivery, and acquisition and cataloging. This partnership continues to the present day, as Allina Health Library Services provides the backbone of library support to Children's.

Outreach

The partnership with Children's Hospital also provided the foundation for an extensive outreach program designed to close the information gap experienced by rural physicians and other health care providers. The program was able to extend the rich library resources of Abbott Northwestern to small community hospitals and clinics across the state, making available professional library services and high-tech resources at an affordable cost.

The outreach program began in the early 1980s with a grant from the National Library of Medicine. Fourteen hospitals received seed money to create or improve their local hospital libraries. The program targeted hospitals that were part of the referral base for Abbott Northwestern in Minnesota and western Wisconsin. By 1994, 22 hospitals and their affiliated clinics were receiving services on a contractual basis. A full-time "circuit rider" librarian, Mary Ellinghuysen, was hired. She logged an average of 14,000 miles per year in visiting these locations. In visits to hospitals, she would analyze their current book and journal collection, recommend changes, meet with the local library manager (who typically devoted one to two hours per week to maintain the local library), make rounds with hospital departments, and promote awareness of the service.

In 1997, Donna Johnson was the recipient of the Michael E. DeBakey

Services Outreach Award by the Friends of the National Library of Medicine (FNLM), in recognition of the outstanding success of Library Services' Outreach program. The award included a cash prize and travel to the FNLM second annual conference in Washington, D.C.

Media Services

Like many medical libraries in the early 1970s, the Abbott Northwestern library established audio-visual services, to make available as well as produce information in a variety of formats. This eventually grew to become the Media Services Department, a branch of Library Services. By the mid-1980s, Media Services was providing photography and video services to the hospital including in the surgical suite. In addition, the Media Services Department provided graphic design for a variety of media, maintained satellite and audio-visual equipment, as well as other media production and services.

A significant undertaking for Library-Media Services was the establishment of the Videoconferencing and Telemedicine Network in 1995. This was a joint project between Allina and the Rural Health Association. It included 25 hubs and was used for education, meetings, clinical consultations, and teleradiology. The network was a groundbreaking initiative that paved the way for Allina's expanding work in delivering telehealth medicine. These services were delivered for a number of clinical conditions including strokes, cardiology, mental health, and other clinical areas. This allowed patients to receive high-quality specialist care close to home.

Media Services supported Closed Circuit TV (CCTV) production for patients at Abbott Northwestern and Children's, providing health information, educational programming, and patient-interactive programs. In 1983, the CCTV crew daily produced 2½ hours of live broadcasts.

In 1983, the CCTV crew daily produced 2½ hours of live broadcasts.

Growth and change

Under Donna Johnson's leadership, the Abbott Northwestern Library saw many years of growth in programs and services offered. In 1980, the Cecil Watson book collection was established in a Special Volumes room added to the library.

Dr. Cecil J. Watson was the first director of the Medical Education program at Northwestern Hospital and subsequently Abbott Northwestern Hospital. This room was later repurposed as the Current Periodicals room, and eventually became dedicated to AudioVisual Services. The Watson collection contained medical and literary classics collected and donated by Dr. Watson himself.

The library was also involved in health promotion efforts during the mid-1980s. The program was targeted to employees, selected community members, and corporations. It focused on weight reduction, smoking cessation, stress management, and employee wellness.

Library Services took on an international flair in 1984 and 1986, hosting two Cunningham Fellows in cooperation with the Medical Library Association. They were here as part of a six-month stay, studying medical libraries in the United States. Mr. Mahesh Palled, Chief Librarian at the JJM Medical College, Davangere, Karnataka State, India, spent the month of April 1984 at Abbott Northwestern observing and interacting with the library staff. Mr. Chandraiya, from the Fiji School of Medicine, Suva, Fiji, visited in May 1986. He was able to conclude his U.S. tour by attending the national MLA meeting held in Minneapolis that year. The gentlemen were each housed in a room rented at 2606 Chicago for $50 per week.

Library staff was also beginning to grow. The 1985 annual report lists a library/media director, secretary, two library professionals, and three library support staff, including Marcia Gabriel-Tanner, who remains a backbone of Library staff to this day. Media Services had 13 staff members: a manager, art director, photographer, TV producer, graphic artist, and a media assistant.

Library Services was also growing in the volume of work as illustrated by this table.

	Articles Supplied	Literature Searches	Books & Journals Circulated
1983	17,849	4,767	5,708
1987	40,120	7,323	6,119
1990	38,585	8,242	4,464

A note in the 1990 Library/Media Services annual report states that the decrease in articles supplied is by design in an, "ongoing attempt to educate users in appropriate and effective use of library services." The report also notes that the literature search data includes, for the first time, searches done by "end-users."

Medical Literature Analysis (NLM) and Retrieval System (MEDLARS)

The National Library of Medicine began publishing Index Medicus in 1879. It provided a monthly guide to the medical literature from thousands of journals. Hand-searching of these large-print volumes was required to find articles on a given topic or by a particular author. After several years of planning, the NLM awarded a $3 million contract to the General Electric Company to develop a mechanized system, MEDLARS (Medical Literature Analysis and Retrieval System). Completed in 1964, it ran on a Minneapolis-Honeywell 800 computer. At the time, no other publicly available, fully operational, electronic storage and retrieval system of its magnitude existed.

In addition to speeding the production of Index Medicus for the burgeoning volume of medical literature, the MEDLARS system provided rapid searching capabilities. This was useful for answering complex bibliographic questions that cannot be handled efficiently by referring to the printed indexes. Medical librarians were trained to perform the MEDLAR searches to provide answers to the requests. Average delivery time to receive the results was two weeks.

In late 1971, an online version called MEDLINE ("MEDLARS Online") was developed as a way to do online searches from remote medical libraries. It could support as many as 25 simultaneous users. Librarians travelled to Bethesda, Maryland, to complete a two-week training prior to using the system.

It was probably in the mid-1970s when the Abbott Northwestern library began to make use of this resource, logging in to MEDLINE via a computer terminal and modem. This represented a significant leap forward in access to information, though perhaps few foresaw the technology shift that was to come over the next 25 years.

Library staff was also beginning to investigate electronic access to journals and books and to consider the impact of the new "information highway" – the Internet. Little did we know!

Early Computers

The first Library computer network was purchased at Abbott Northwestern Hospital in 1987. An AT&T B32/400 computer, which was used for the billing system, provided a database for library services contracts, a data file of library users, word processing, as well as access to a new online inter-library loan system called DOCLINE. By the early 1990s, a new computer system allowed physicians to dial-in to a dedicated workstation in the library.

Also newly purchased in 1990 was the first online catalog system (Sydney), replacing the beloved but inefficient index card system for tracking circulation. The library staff was also now able to access the online catalog at the University of Minnesota and other medical libraries, rather than rely on a printed catalog.

In 1992, the PlusNet II system was installed, allowing 10 simultaneous users to search CD Plus. A computer lab was established in the Learning Center to train users, requiring significant staff time in consultation and training. End-user searching increased by 72 percent over the course of this year (to 3414 searches, as compared to 8,618 librarian-mediated searches that same year). Library staff was also beginning to investigate electronic access to journals and books and to consider the impact of the new "information highway" – the Internet. Little did we know!

A wide-area network (WAN) was created in 1993 to provide access to the CD Plus databases from several locations, including the nursing department, Phillips Eye Institute medical staff lounge, and areas at United Hospital that was part of the newly formed HealthSpan system. In 1994, Library staff worked with the Allina networking group to begin to provide Internet access. The Library Services Web page was developed in 1996. This was the first departmental page within Allina. It provided access to services and resources, including links to selected Internet sites. By this time, the Library had a full-time dedicated information technology staff member.

The Library suite of resources, known as Knowledge Quest, began as a joint venture with the Ramsey Medical Society. It consists of several Ovid databases (MEDLINE, CINAHL, ClinPsych, CancerLit), 30 full text journals, Micromedex, several online textbooks from Stat!Ref, Harrison's Internal Medicine, and Scientific American Medicine online. Most of these were hosted locally on a CD-ROM server, with regular upgrades. In 1998, the Library moved to a web-hosted version of Micromedex, as well as from dial-in to client/server access to the Knowledge Quest electronic resources. *The New England Journal of Medicine* became the Library's first publisher-hosted journal in 1995.

Mergers and Centralization

When HealthSpan formed in 1993, the library staffs of member hospitals (Abbott Northwestern, Mercy, United, and Unity) formed one department: Library/Media Systems and Services, with Donna Johnson as Director and Elaine Trzebiatowski as Library Manager. This saved costs and could provide consistent and high-quality service to all HealthSpan physicians and employees, regardless of their physical location. When Allina was formed in 1994, the merger was well underway. Also during that time, the Ramsey Medical Society ceased support for daily operations of its medical library, having entered into a joint operations agreement with the United Hospital library in 1976. Established in 1898, the Ramsey Medical Society Library had been most recently led by Mary S. Tarman.

Efforts in 1994 focused on bringing library staffs, policies, and procedures together, along with consolidation of vendors. Consideration of eliminating duplication in materials began, as journal subscription costs were beginning to rise (a constant ever since). Combined usage statistics for 1994 show 19,188 literature searches and a whopping 64,002 articles delivered. By 1995, a daily courier service was running between the four hospital library sites to deliver books, photocopied articles, and other materials. The combined library sites boasted a total of 72 PCs and 37 printers, not to mention numerous photocopiers and fax machines.

Many current or recently retired library staff came on board in the mid-90s, including Betsy Moore, Pam Barnard, Sharon Kambeitz, and Anita von Geldern. Cynthia Robinson took a brief stint as Library Manager, followed by Eileen Stanley.

The mid-90s also saw the rise of patient or consumer health resource centers throughout Allina, including one at the Virginia Piper Cancer Institute. Library Services provided key support to many of these in collection development, operational organization, and training in use of online information resources.

The merger of four hospital libraries into one reached its zenith in 1999, when Library Services moved most centralized services to 1801 Nicollet Avenue, a block away from the former Abbott Hospital site. The building housed Allina's archival journal collection, a "business reference" book collection, and the print Index Medicus dating back to the 1880s. But the intent was to create a more virtual library, which was not location-dependent. Inter-library loan, collection acquisition, Library Outreach, and some literature search functions operated out of this central location. Most of the Media Services staff was located there as well, with improved production suites for video and other services. With the opening of the Allina Commons in late 2005, the Nicollet Avenue Center was closed, and staff moved to the Commons. Throughout this time, library staff continued to operate at each of the four metro Allina hospital sites as well.

Library staff in 2000 numbered 23 employees, including eight Knowledge Consultants and ten Library Technicians. Media Services staff numbered 17 employees. This was the zenith of departmental staffing.

Children's Malkerson Library/ Wishing Well Show

With support and oversight from Abbott Northwestern Library/Media Services, the Malkerson Children's Library opened at Children's Minneapolis in the early 1980s. The Malkerson Library contained books and materials for all ages of pediatric patients, to educate, provide medical information, or simply entertain. Kathi Rokke was hired in 1985 and soon became the heart and soul of the Malkerson Library. Each day, Kathi did rounds to patients' rooms with a wagon loaded with books. By the late '90s, the library also contained computers where patients could play games or send e-mails.

Kathi was also the host for the hugely popular Wishing Well Show, the interactive TV program run on Children's closed circuit TV network, beginning in 1985 and running until 2006. Abbott Northwestern's Media Services staff produced the show, which starred the famous pig puppet, Porky Chops. The show provided a bright spot in the day for many patients. The format included call-in games for patients, stories, music, and jokes. Occasionally patients were the hosts. The guest list in 1999 included Patch Adams MD, Minnesota Viking

Robert Smith, Jim Fowler of Wild Kingdom (along with an arctic fox, timber wolf, and albino skunk), and the Minnesota Raptor Center (including a hawk, eagle, vulture, and owl).

The show encouraged children to participate and gave them a way to stay active during their hospital stay. One parent said this about the show: "Our 12-year-old daughter had four stays at Children's, three involving surgery. We truly believe 'The Wishing Well Show' was her incentive to recover." Unfortunately the show fell prey to budget concerns and was discontinued in 2006. It was later replaced by a different live show, produced by Children's employees. The Malkerson Library continues to serve patients and family members.

More Online Services

Library Services has always been quick to adapt to new technologies. In 2000, Library staff offered classes. Physicians and other employees were trained to use the Internet (e.g., what is a search engine, how is a URL structured, what websites are credible). Training in how to search MEDLINE or other online resources was also offered. This was a new and exciting time for all. The Library page was typically the eighth or ninth most-viewed page on the Allina Knowledge network – a rank held for several years. Soon new online knowledge resources were developed, piloted, and vetted by Library staff, including MD Consult, Natural Medicines, and InfoPOEMs – all making clinical content readily accessible to the provider.

The online journal collection began to grow substantially in the early 2000s. The shift from print to online had implications for library staffing. Tasks like shelving, photocopying, and journal check-in were replaced by "knowledge work" such as licensing and contracting negotiations, maintaining online access tools, and evaluating usage patterns.

Journal subscription costs began to climb significantly. From 1994 to 2004, the average print subscription cost grew from $160 to $400. Fortunately, the library was able to achieve some savings by eliminating duplication across the four Allina library sites. As subscriptions shifted from print to online, however, costs grew even more dramatically, as publishers scrambled to maintain revenue. By 2015, Allina's average cost per journal was $1,382, with many titles running as high as $7,000 – $8,000. As a result of these increases, cost-per-use has become a factor in journal purchasing decisions.

More Changes

For several years, Library Services had been part of Allina Information Services, which provided some advantages during the early days of rapid changes in technology. In 2001, Library Services began a new reporting relationship to Communications, Public Relations, and Marketing. Within a couple years, Media Services split off from the library function. Donna Johnson retired at that time, ending an amazing 32-year career with Allina Library Services. Eileen Stanley stepped up to the helm as Library Director.

In 2004, the reporting relationship changed again, now to Allina's Executive Vice President for Quality, Safety & Technology. In 2005, the Allina Commons site was established and the Nicollet Avenue Center closed, while active libraries remained at the four metro hospital sites.

2006 proved to be a challenging year for Library Services. Cost pressures within Allina led to major staff and materials reductions. The staff count dropped from 17 to 7 by December. The Library was able to work with some vendors to renegotiate prices, but nonetheless faced significant reductions in active journal subscriptions and online resources. Jim Bulger became Library Manager during this period.

Following these reductions, the decision was made to consolidate staff to the Abbott Northwestern library site. We ceased staffing sites at Mercy and Unity, as well as the Commons, and initiated part-time staffing at the United Hospital library on a rotating basis. Staff refocused efforts on core services: literature searches, document delivery, training, and support of Outreach Services. Needless to say, this was a painful and difficult period. However, the library staff proved to be resilient, and service to customers did not significantly suffer.

Perhaps a bit ironically, just prior to the layoffs, the Library staff were recipients of the Jean Williams Sayre Innovation Award from the Midwest Chapter/Medical Library Association for Library Services support to nurses. The award recognized staff efforts in the use of nursing evidence resources to improve access, ease of use, breadth of resources, and training in their use.

The next few years saw continued shifts in reporting relationships for Library Services. In 2007, we reported to Allina Human Resource Service Center and in 2009, to Clinical Decision Support. In 2013, reporting shifted to Allina Performance Resources, which led to a partnership with Health Catalyst in 2015. Each of these changes opened opportunities for reaching out at a system-wide level and creating greater synergies with Allina initiatives. Links to Library resources are now embedded in Excellian, the electronic medical record. Library staff has liaison roles with clinical service lines and other corporate structures.

The staff has acquired a reputation for being amazingly fast, often turning around article requests in less than an hour.

New Directions

Library Services continues to evolve. The shift from print to online was a huge paradigm shift, both for libraries and our users. Keeping up with new technologies (remember PDAs – Personal Digital Assistants?), designing systems to promote better access, training users, shifting staff resources and priorities, reallocating dollars for new resources – all have been a challenge. Library staff continues to provide mediated literature searches (an eight-year high of 1,740 in 2014), but the complexity of these has grown, as tools like UpToDate have become more ubiquitous and user-friendly. Online search sessions for Library-supported resources are now at 1.6 million per year, with 112,000 online journal articles viewed.

Surprisingly, document delivery by Library staff has shown modest growth over the past 10 years, despite ready access to over 2,000 online journals. The staff has acquired a reputation for being amazingly fast, often turning around article requests in less than an hour. The Library receives a fairly constant flow of thank-you notes from customers for the expertise, time-saving assistance, and cheerful service provided.

Although access to and delivery of information has changed radically since 1970, the core of our business has not. Library Services is about helping medical providers and staff to answer questions, gain knowledge, and make informed decisions using evidence-based research. Whether around a specific clinical question, performance improvement initiative, research, continuing education, or patient and family education, our role has always been to supply services, tools, and expertise to facilitate that process.

Medical Staff Support

Library Services has not gone it alone. We have been the grateful recipient of ongoing financial support from the Abbott Northwestern Hospital medical staff and the Abbott Northwestern Hospital Foundation. Grants have included $50,000 in 1986 for computer terminals and printer, along with a high-end color video camera package; $20,000 in 1987 for a new automated library system; $15,000 in 1990 for shelving, a printer, and new modem for online literature searching; new work stations in 1994. The Plus One Committee granted $15,000 in 2014-15 for e-books to replace MD Consult, a popular information resource being discontinued. The Bella R. Wyman Library Endowment contributes funds annually in support of nursing information resources.

Beyond the financial, the total support of medical and nursing staff, as well as hospital and Allina leadership has been a huge key to our success. We are grateful.

Beyond the financial [support from the Abbott Northwestern Hospital medical staff and the Abbott Northwestern Hospital Foundation], the total support of medical and nursing staff, as well as hospital and Allina leadership has been a huge key to our success.

Holst, R. Hospital libraries in perspective. *Bull Med Libr Assoc* 1991 Jan 79(1):1-9.

Wolfgram, PA. Hospital libraries in the United States: historical antecedents. *Bull Med Libr Assoc* 1985 Jan 73(1):32-38).

Kamman GR. Future aims of the hospital library. *Minn Med* 1983 Aug; 21(8):559-61.

Tague C. Chisholm. Personal correspondence. Apr 30, 1974.

MEDLINE. (2015, July 15). In Wikipedia, The Free Encyclopedia. Retrieved July 15, 2015, from https://en.wikipedia.org/w/index.php?title=MEDLINE&oldid=673069498

19

Medical Education Program
1960-2014
Dr. Claus Pierach and Dr. Laurel Drevlow,
Dr. Terry Rosborough

The Founding – 1960-1966
Dr. Claus Pierach and Dr. Laurel Drevlow

Northwestern Hospital was developing its medical staff with increasing specialization in the 1960s. As a result, the hospital developed an educational program and research facilities. In a meeting of the Board of Trustees in March 1961, Mrs. Hadlai Hull reported on an article in *Consumer Reports* of February 1961 concerning the quality of care administered in hospitals.

> One can go beyond the numerous accreditations in judging the quality of a hospital by asking a second question: Does it have a formal program for the training of medical personnel? The higher the level of teaching, the more likely the hospital is to provide good medical service. The best indication of a good teaching program is having an affiliation with a medical school. Hospitals with such affiliation are likely to have the services of qualified family doctors and specialists in all available fields as needed. They often had full-time physicians in charge of key departments. As a result they attracted many of the best

Virginia Piper and the Board raised three million dollars to endow the educational program.

young physicians who wanted residency training in the specialties. Such surroundings also were likely to bring out the best in practicing family doctors who were currently affiliated with the hospital. Only 229 hospitals in the whole country had such affiliations, however, and they were concentrated near the 85 medical schools. Consequently, most consumers did not have access to such a hospital. But they could get somewhat similar benefits from a hospital approved for residency training in at least four major specialties fields – Obstetrics and Gynecology, Internal Medicine, Surgery, and Pediatrics.

In 1962-63, Northwestern Hospital participated in the Matching Program, interviewing graduating medical students to obtain candidates to serve as interns and residents. However, the hospital had not received any candidates, which meant that in 1962 the hospital would have two residents and one intern. As a result, Dr. Mark Hanson stressed the need to establish a relationship with a medical school. Stan Nelson, the hospital administrator, contacted 12 medical schools in an attempt to understand just how such a program would work.

Dr. David Hickok and Virginia Piper visited Evanston Hospital in Chicago to look at its program with Northwestern University Medical School. It was obviously going to be expensive both to initiate and to maintain such a program: an estimated $200,000 for a research facility. A full-scale medical education program would cost $50,000 in 1964, $100,000 in 1965, and $137,000 in 1966. In order to have a relationship with the University of Minnesota Medical School, a Professorial Chair had to be funded at the Medical School at a cost of $500,000. (The professor would spend all of his or her time at Northwestern Hospital.) In July 1964, Archie Walker pledged $250,000 as an initial step to fund such a Chair. Mr. Walker requested that Northwestern Hospital contribute a matching amount, and this was accomplished by August 1965.

Virginia Piper and the Board raised $3 million to endow the educational program. This was accomplished with a team effort consisting of one Board member, one member of the Men's Advisory Committee, and a member of the Medical Staff calling on potential donors. This proved to be successful with such donors as Bertin Gamble of the Gamble-Skogmo Company. Mr. and Mrs.

Archie Walker gave an additional $100,000 in this effort. (Their gift apparently turned out eventually to be $250,000.) By the end of 1965, it was determined that the Medical Education Program would cost $300,000 annually. A third each would come from annual giving, hospital operating funds, and endowment income. The Medical Education and Research Facility, which was initially estimated to cost $200,000, eventually cost $850,000.

The University of Minnesota Medical School needed additional hospitals where it could send medical students for further training. As a result, the Board of Regents voted in January 1965 to approve the affiliation of Northwestern Hospital and the Medical School. Dr. Cecil J. Watson, the Chief of Medicine at the University of Minnesota Medical School, was scheduled to retire from the University. He was approached to be the Medical Director at Northwestern Hospital and was hired in July 1965 at a salary of $35,000. In addition, a Chief Resident, (Dr. Vince Fromke), an assistant, and a secretary were hired, and the program began.

Dr. Watson established the teaching program in July 1966. He had a national and international reputation in Internal Medicine and obtained initial accreditation from the American Medical Association. The program was scheduled to have six medical internships and six residents in Internal Medicine. The goal was to provide a teaching program that included continuous medical education for medical students, house staff, and practicing specialists. This required a free bed unit of 30 medical and 20 surgical beds plus outpatient facilities. In addition, an educational facility with office space for 20 faculty members, a seminar room for 25 people, an auditorium seating 250, laboratory space, a library, and a meeting room for in-service education was planned.

Cecil James Watson [was] "first and foremost a medical educator, whose boundless enthusiasm and insatiable intellectual curiosity stimulated countless medical students to search for the why of clinical phenomena observed at the bedside."

The Early Years of the Teaching Service – 1966-1982
Dr. Claus Pierach

"Sine doctrina est quasi mortis imago." ("Life without teaching would be just an image of death.") So begins Dr. Rudi Schmid's brief biography of Dr. Cecil J. Watson, citing a quotation found in one of Watson's laboratory notebooks. Schmid describes Cecil James Watson as "first and foremost a medical educator, whose boundless enthusiasm and insatiable intellectual curiosity stimulated

In 1966, Dr. Watson accepted the challenge of starting an academic medical unit at Northwestern Hospital... Virginia Piper, chair of the Northwestern Hospital Board of Trustees, saw the benefit of adding an academic branch to the already highly regarded hospital.

countless medical students to search for the why of clinical phenomena observed at the bedside."

Thus the history of medical education at Abbott Northwestern Hospital rightly begins with the history of its founder, Cecil J. Watson. Dr. Watson was born in Minneapolis in 1901 and was schooled there. While literary interests initially inclined him toward English and French literature in college, he ultimately graduated from the school of medicine at the University of Minnesota in 1925. In 1928, he received a Ph.D. for his studies of phagocytes in the spleen and accepted a position as pathologist, laboratory director, and clinician at a newly founded clinic in Minot, ND. He practiced there for two years before returning to Minneapolis, where he soon obtained a fellowship in the laboratory of the world-renowned researcher, Hans Fischer, in Munich, Germany.

Dr. Fischer was awarded the Nobel Prize for unraveling the pyrrole ring formulae of heme and of chlorophyll, two surprisingly similar structures that are fundamental in biology. In Munich, Dr. Watson started his lifelong work with heme, ultimately becoming one of the foremost authorities in bile pigments and porphyria. He learned to speak German fluently, to ski, and deepened his already profound cultural interests. Moreover, the laboratory of Hans Fischer at that time was a clinical-scientific hub, where, among others, Drs. Jan Walderström, Richard Duesberg, Irvine Page, and Alexander Pierach (father of Claus Pierach) worked. The laboratory was part of the clinic and hospital of Dr. Friedrich von Müller, who was considered by his peers to be "King of the Clinicians." Not surprisingly, von Müller was also a friend of a fellow King of Clinicians, Sir William Osler.

Upon his return to Minneapolis in 1932, Dr. Watson joined the staff at the Minneapolis General Hospital (now Hennepin County Medical Center) and the University Hospital. In 1942, he became the first full-time Chief of Medicine at the University Hospital. He held that position until 1966. During those years, Dr. Watson was deeply involved in both laboratory and clinical work as well as engaged in numerous academic committees. His many contributions to science were acknowledged when he was named a Regents Professor and elected to the National Academy of Science.

In 1966, Dr. Watson accepted the challenge of starting an academic medical unit at Northwestern Hospital, the leading private hospital in Minneapolis.

Virginia Piper, chair of the Northwestern Hospital Board of Trustees, saw the benefit of adding an academic branch to the already highly regarded hospital. A committee led by Dr. Mark Hanson recommended that Northwestern's Board of Trustees approach Dr. Watson to establish a medical residency program at Northwestern. Dr. Watson accepted the offer. In addition, Dr. Watson was able to transfer to Northwestern not only his laboratory but also his co-workers: Dr. Eugenia Davis and Dr. Zbyslaw Petryka, and his indispensable assistants, Irene Bossenmaier, Ruth Cardinal, and Mary Weimer. These three assistants were colloquially and affectionately known as "The Gifts." Ms. Lydia Johnson was the secretary.

Dr. Watson's scientific productivity continued to be impressive. During his career, he published more than 350 papers. Many were written in cooperation with the chemist Albert Moscowitz, Dr. Rudi Schmid, and especially Dr. Sam Schwartz. With Dr. Schwartz he devised the first biochemical test for porphyria, a chemical in the blood, known as the Watson-Schwartz test (1941). This diagnostic triumph was later crowned by his discovery of what is still considered the ultimate treatment for porphyric attacks: the infusion of hematin (1971). Hematin was the very first Orphan Drug (a drug for which there previously was no use) initially produced in Watson's laboratory at Abbott Northwestern Hospital. It is still commercially available. Research projects under the sponsorship of the National Institutes of Health, National Cancer Society, and National Science Foundation were actively pursued in the area of porphyria.

In addition to his abundant scientific work, Dr. Watson successfully launched the "University of Minnesota Professorial Unit for Teaching and Research in Internal Medicine" in 1966. Occasionally called Teaching and Research (T&R), it was a simple matter to demonstrate to patients that teaching and research were valuable supplements to superb clinical care. For his teaching staff at Northwestern Hospital, Dr. Watson brought with him Dr. Vincent Fromke from the University and soon added Dr. John Mork. With the teaching and research load continually expanding, Dr. Watson looked to his international scientific community of friends for additional support. Thus Dr. Waldenström referred Dr. Lars Almer from Lund, Sweden, and Dr. Eugen Frick from Zurich. He also sent Dr. Elizabeth Whurmann (who later married fellow resident, Dr. Earle Bennett) to the Northwestern Hospital residency program. Dr.

Claus Pierach received a one-year leave of absence from Dr. Duesberg in Mainz, Germany, and arrived April 1, 1968. That one year expanded into decades. At the time of this writing, Dr. Pierach is still regularly observed in the hallways of what is now Abbott Northwestern Hospital, ably educating students, residents, and colleagues about the art and science of medicine.

The early years of the residency program at Northwestern Hospital had a unique flavor, especially because of the international mix of the house staff. In addition to U.S. graduates, there were Chinese, Austrian, Indian, Swiss, and German residents, and even one from Iceland (Gudmundur Skullason). Exceptional students from across the globe eagerly sought out the chance to train with one of the foremost researchers and educators of the time. In this academically affluent and culturally rich community, friendships formed and endured. Since virtually everyone affiliated with the residency lived in close vicinity to the hospital, rich social networking relationships blossomed. There were frequent social gatherings. On one occasion, the fish tank of Dr. Käte Knopf (Switzerland) was not only admired at a party, but also treated to a jigger of gin, ostensibly to increase the happiness of the guppies. The fish turned their bellies upward and Käte cried. Lucas Guido (Switzerland) promised new fish. Not unlike some of the resident's patients, by the next morning the guppies had spontaneously recovered.

The Swiss connection in the residency was particularly strong. In addition to the previously mentioned Swiss residents, there were Drs. Hans Baur, Rudi Morant, Barbara Raflaub, Marco Roffi, and Hygo Saner. Many of these individuals were deeply engaged in scientific work, publishing superb scholarly papers, and ultimately pursuing clinical research in their remarkable academic careers.

The initial assignment of the residents was to the private services of the attending physicians of the hospital, many of whose names are woven into the history of Northwestern Hospital in multiple ways. Drs. Arnold, Blomberg, Dougan, Hanson, Kjellsen, McKinley, Plass, Rizer, Scott, and Weber were but a few of the physicians practicing at Northwestern Hospital at that time. Subsequently, rotations could be taken in-house or at other hospitals. The number of house staff had slowly but steadily increased from six to a dozen. The teaching efficacy was soon rewarded when the first resident, Dr. Michael Stenwick, passed the Board of Internal Medicine examination.

Dr. Watson presided over superb clinical conferences twice weekly, where a resident presented a patient's history and physical examination. The patient was wheeled in; Dr. Watson, whose bedside skills were truly extraordinary, then expertly demonstrated pertinent parts of the examination. On one occasion, the presenting resident blushed to admit that no rectal examination had been done because the patient had refused. In the most professional manner, Dr. Watson proceeded to ask the patient, who was covered by a bed sheet, if the necessary digital examination of his rectum could be performed. The patient nodded approvingly, whereupon Dr. Watson performed the exam with characteristic dignity.

The rigorous academic flavor of the program was further enhanced by frequent visiting professors, among them Dr. Peter Duesberg (San Francisco), Dr. Wolfgang Gerok (Germany), Dame Sheila Sherlock (London), Dr. Petr Skrabanek (Ireland), Dr. Jan Walderström (Sweden), and Dr. Horace Zinneman (Virginia). Weekly Grand Rounds always involved the presentation of a patient who was escorted into the meeting hall and examined by Dr. Watson on stage. The respect for Dr. Watson and his program made it quite an honor for patients to become a teaching subject for such an august assembly. The same could be said about the increasing number of medical students from the University of Minnesota and from abroad who appreciated the rich clinical material and erudite clinical instruction at their disposal on the wards.

An outpatient clinic allowed the residents to provide ongoing long-term care for many patients in the neighborhoods around the hospital. Medical care was also rendered to patients referred from the Salvation Army. A wonderful opportunity opened up in the early 1970s for senior residents to spend an afternoon once a week with the Neighborhood Involvement Program (NIP) on Hennepin Avenue. NIP featured a small laboratory, a dentist, free legal services, and a free clothing closet for community members in need. It was a profoundly holistic approach to patient care that deepened the clinical experience and level of responsibility for Northwestern trainees. NIP was started with substantial support from the hospital and provided highly productive hands-on education for residents. The reputation of the residency increased steadily over the years as well-trained graduates of the program began to enter primary care

Weekly Grand Rounds always involved the presentation of a patient who was escorted into the meeting hall and examined by Dr. Watson on stage. The respect for Dr. Watson and his program made it quite an honor for patients to become a teaching subject for such an august assembly.

[Dr. Howard's] progressive attitudes and forward thinking led him to make the Abbott Northwestern residency a highly coveted training program for exceptional women physicians coming from medical schools across the country.

and subspecialty practices as well as make contributions to research in the community and beyond.

In the early 1970s, Dr. Watson, still energetically pursuing his research and education, began gradually transitioning the program leadership to his former student, Dr. Robert Howard. Dr. Watson had been a mentor for Dr. Howard for much of his education, including his eventual entry into administrative endeavors. For a brief time, when Dr. Howard was serving as dean of the College of Medical Sciences at the University of Minnesota, (1958-1969), he was actually Dr. Watson's superior. Dr. Howard took a year off for sabbatical time in Zurich with Dr. Paul Frick. He was able to hone his clinical skills as well as his German language proficiency much as Dr. Watson had done earlier in his career. In 1971, Dr. Howard accepted the call to help coordinate the young program at Northwestern Hospital. He became the full-time program director a year later. Dr. Howard refused to consider himself a great teacher. He stated that, "I was fortunate to have Dr. Claus Pierach and a couple of other guys who were very good at the bedside." Dr. Howard helped develop the entire education program, adding a surgical residency training program during his tenure. In 1980, Abbott and Northwestern hospitals merged onto the Northwestern site, creating one of the largest hospitals in the Midwest. Dr. Howard took advantage of the expansion to provide opportunities for even wider clinical experiences.

Among his many contributions to the education program, Dr. Howard records the increased number of women in training as one of the most important. At that time, women in medicine still faced significant obstacles to obtaining high-quality, competitive residency positions. Dr. Howard made a determination that the Abbott Northwestern residency would welcome women candidates on an equal basis with men. His progressive attitudes and forward thinking led him to make the Abbott Northwestern residency a highly coveted training program for exceptional women physicians coming from medical schools across the country. He took fitting pride in the outstanding clinical and research work of the women in his training program. This achievement would surely have made the spirited and intrepid women who founded Northwestern Hospital in 1882 equally proud.

In 1984, a symposium was established in honor of Dr. Watson, who had died the year before. In apt homage to his legacy, national and international luminaries including Dr. Paul Berk of New York, Dr. Thomas Fuchs of Germany, Dr. Saul Krugman of New York, Dr. Michael Moore of Scotland, Dr. Hans Popper of New York, and Dr. Rudi Schmid of San Francisco presented their work. Local presenters added to the luster. These included Drs. Joseph Blomer, John Najarian, Terry Rosborough, Sam Schwartzm, William Swaim, and Leslie Zieve. An annual C.J. Watson Lecture is now delivered at the University of Minnesota in Dr. Watson's memory.

In 1975, the preeminent physician Dr. Howard Burchell, author of more than 400 articles and editor of the journal *Circulation* from 1965-1970, joined the program as a consultant. He had been Consulting Cardiologist at the Mayo Clinic as well as the inaugural Chief of Cardiology at the University of Minnesota in 1968. His reputation as the doyen in cardiology enhanced the reputation of the residency program still further.

Dr. Burchell's electrocardiography sessions were just as popular as his rounds on the wards. Residents took great pleasure and no doubt a sense of pride in seeing patients with him. The last question Dr. Burchell usually asked a patient was, "Is there anything else I can do for you?" That was remembered and reiterated by many a resident. Before leaving the bedside of a patient, Dr. Burchell would fluff up the patient's pillow or gently straighten out the bed linens. He possessed the skills born of decades of practice that could truly put patients at ease. More importantly, he willingly shared these skills with all of the residents under his tutelage. The annual Howard Burchell Lecture was established during the master's lifetime. It has been delivered at Abbott Northwestern Hospital by prominent cardiologists.

Throughout the years, the camaraderie of the small program and its very compatible education staff grew as well. Annual outings involved floating down the Apple River in Wisconsin and a boat ride on Lake Minnetonka. These outings were eagerly attended, not only by the residents, but also by their families. The lasting interpersonal relationships and collegiality created in the early years of the program have remained a constant of professional behavior that firmly defines the education system at Abbott Northwestern Hospital.

The last question Dr. Burchell usually asked a patient was, "Is there anything else I can do for you?" ...Before leaving the bedside of a patient, Dr. Burchell would fluff up the patient's pillow or gently straighten out the bed linens.

Internal Medicine Graduate Medical Education — 1982-2014
Dr. Terry Rosborough

For me, the past 32 years of Internal Medicine education at Abbott Northwestern Hospital are a blur of many people and events. I did not keep a regular journal and cannot create a detailed history of these years. I am left hoping that this memoir of important events and issues will suffice. Everything done was a group effort, and whoever started something was almost always standing on the shoulders of others. To attribute something to one individual would be neglecting others who made valuable contributions; I decided to minimize the use of names. Nevertheless, it was the people who recognized and responded to the events that created the success we have had.

In January 1980, Abbott and Northwestern hospitals came together on a mostly newly constructed campus now named Abbott Northwestern Hospital. This marked the beginning of rapid change for the institution, which coincided with rapid change within health care and medical education. Subspecialization in internal medicine was increasing, making community hospital internal medicine programs less attractive because they did not have direct access to subspecialty fellowships. The requirements for internal medicine residency programs were becoming more stringent and more programs were out of compliance. The Abbott Northwestern program found itself with fewer applicants and the possibility of being unaccredited.

Abbott Northwestern Hospital had a large endowment fund for the residency program, and the hospital leaders chose to find a way to strengthen the program rather than close it. The Director of Medical Education position at Abbott Northwestern was offered to Dr. George Sarosi, the Chief of Medicine at the Minneapolis VA hospital. George had strong relationships with some of the internists at Abbott Northwestern. He accepted the position and began his tenure in January 1982, bringing me with him.

Reaccreditation

There were two fundamental problems to be solved, one easier than the other. The easier problem was restructuring the residency to meet the accrediting agency requirements. Residents had been assigned as "apprentices" to small groups of physicians, but now Resident Services, to which a large group of physicians would admit patients, was introduced. Teaching rounds were restructured, facilitated by the generosity of a core group of independent internists. We implemented a new conference schedule with a structured curriculum. After a repeat accreditation site visit six months later, the program was fully accredited and has remained so for the past 32 years.

Having accomplished the reaccreditation of the program, Dr. Sarosi still had the desire to be a leader in a Department of Medicine in a medical school. When the opportunity came to be the Vice Chairman at the University of Texas in Houston, he had to go. I realized that I couldn't move to Texas, and I stayed at Abbott Northwestern.

The more difficult and long-term problem was making the residency program competitive for applicants. Abbott Northwestern was recognized as a strong private hospital. However, medical schools for residency training did not look upon such hospitals favorably because they did not offer easy access to fellowship programs or have enough "academic" infrastructure. The applicant pool for the Abbott Northwestern program in 1982 was small.

In July 1983, we decided that survival depended on building the structurally best program we could, with what we could control. Resident education and well-being were made the top priorities, which was a departure for the times. Fortunately, the Medical Education Endowment Fund and federal reimbursement for medical education provided ample resources to do what was necessary without a drain on hospital finances. Experimentation began.

Over the next four years, we did a number of things earlier than most programs, such as controlling work load and call schedules, integrating outpatient clinic and hospital schedules, and developing an optimized night float system. Many of these things eventually became requirements for all programs. We experimented with a number of teaching and curriculum approaches and developed a more extensive and integrated formal curriculum than existed in most programs. This included an extensive Bedside Diagnosis curriculum, including use of one of the earliest heart sound simulators, and a curriculum on the use of medical literature and diagnostic tests that we called Critical Appraisal. We also worked hard to involve the best Internists at the hospital. These changes bore fruit with an increased number of applicants and strong candidates.

In 1983, the government created the Diagnosis Related Groups (DRG)

*Abbott
Northwestern
was rapidly
growing as a
regional specialty
hospital, led by
the Cardiology
division, and our
residents and
students were
having a superior
educational
experience.*

system for hospital coding/charging to control costs. The residency program was questioned periodically about whether residents made care at Abbott Northwestern less efficient and more costly. Several non-published analyses of common diagnoses were performed, showing that care with residents was not less efficient or more costly. A published study (1990) showed that patients on the resident service had shorter lengths of stay and less resource use than comparable patients not on the resident service. Residents had an incentive to move patients efficiently through the hospital stay, and with good supervision, they were not wasteful of resources.

In 1987, the Abbott Northwestern residency was stable and successful, but around the country, interest in internal medicine as a career was decreasing, demonstrated by a big drop in the National Resident Matching program that year. Although Abbott Northwestern escaped trouble in 1987, within several years, we did not have enough applicants and had to cut the size of the entering resident class from 12 to 10. We had a brief conversation with the Hennepin County Medical Center residency program about a possible merger of the two programs, but both sides thought that a merger was difficult at that time.

The 25th anniversary of the residency program was in 1991. My notes from that time reflect some satisfaction with the overall state of things, but a continuing worry about applicants' fears that subspecialty fellowships would be harder to obtain if they came to our program. Abbott Northwestern was rapidly growing as a regional specialty hospital, led by the Cardiology division, and our residents and students were having a superior educational experience. However, these issues always limited our applicant pool and kept the program to 10 residents per year. At this size, we could continue to attract a pool of strong physicians.

In 1993, a group of internists approached us with the idea of taking over the inpatient care of their patients while they remained in the clinic. We decided that we had to try this new hospitalist concept and began a service. Within a few years, the service was expanding, and we recruited new faculty from our residency graduates. Over time, the Abbott Northwestern hospitalist program became one of the largest in the country and definitely enhanced the attractiveness of the residency program. A hospitalist career became popular with residency graduates both at Abbott Northwestern and around the country.

By 1998, the Medical Education Department had a high-quality outpatient continuity clinic for the residents that had expanded to involve residents in all three years of their training. We were in the process of designing new and better space for this clinic, which was completed several years later. However, we had no other general internal medicine outpatient experience to help residents consider a career in outpatient general medicine. When the opportunity came to adopt a well-functioning, existing Allina clinic into our department, we took it. This was the beginning of what we now call the Abbott Northwestern General Medical Associates (ANGMA) faculty group. With the formation of this group, we instituted a faculty compensation model based on time, not on units of service. This system has been important as a flexible and fair system for a faculty with multiple missions. ANGMA now serves the hospital and three different clinic sites with approximately 30 physicians.

Informational and Educational Technology

We can mark the beginning of the influence of information and educational technology on our programs as the year 2003. We became leaders in the early phase of adopting an electronic medical record (EMR) for Allina; the two ANGMA clinics were early adopters of the EMR in 2004. The EMR went live at Abbott Northwestern in 2005, again with the residency program and faculty in the lead of this important project. The residency program was one of the earliest hospitals in the country to have a full EMR. About that same time, we were also early adopters of hand-held computers for information access.

The EMR project would have been enough for us to handle in 2005/06, but at this time the University of Minnesota Internal Medicine residency program approached us with the proposal to merge the two programs. This was a compliment to the strength of our program, but it was also worrisome to think of all that could be lost with such a merger. After detailed discussions and explorations, we recognized that the benefits of the merger did not outweigh the costs. With this decision made, and a fresh view of our future, Bob Miner took over as the Program Director of the residency program.

In 2007, Abbott Northwestern explored becoming a key partner in a new medical school in the Twin Cities, and the Medical Education Department was the lead in these discussions. In retrospect, with the financial downturn on the

Over time, the Abbott Northwestern hospitalist program became one of the largest in the country and definitely enhanced the attractiveness of the residency program.

Many of the approximately 300 graduates of the program are now medical staff members of Abbott Northwestern Hospital or other Allina hospitals and clinics.

horizon, it was fortunate that these discussions ended with a negative decision. One positive outgrowth of this adventure was a complete revision and editing of the formal conference curriculum for the residency program.

Also in 2007, the hand-held computer project evolved into the full use of the iPhone to replace pagers and serve as the bridge to all sources of information. We were nationwide leaders in this undertaking. We developed a faculty/resident procedure team that improved the quality of bedside procedures in the hospital, with safety results that lead the nation. Importantly, the procedure team made heavy use of simulators for training. We then expanded to a full Simulation Center program, including the use of a full-body simulator for multidisciplinary training in emergency medical situations.

The procedure team made use of point-of-care ultrasound, and as the technology evolved, we became convinced that Internal Medicine needed a new and better physical exam for many situations. In 2011, we became a national leader in Internal Medicine point-of-care ultrasound physical examination, convinced that this was the path to improved quality of care with lower cost and better patient satisfaction. This innovation has improved our attractiveness as a residency program and contributed to better care for Abbott Northwestern patients.

Conclusion

The past 32 years of medical education at Abbott Northwestern have been challenging and rewarding. Many of the approximately 300 graduates of the program are now medical staff members of Abbott Northwestern Hospital or other Allina hospitals and clinics. We have an unusually high proportion of our graduates in generalist careers of primary care or hospital medicine. This has been important for the growth of many Abbott Northwestern and Allina clinical activities. I never knew what was coming during these 32 years, so I certainly have no idea what the near- or long-term looks like for medical education. I think that if the program focuses on resident education and well-being as top priorities, and continues to be an innovator in high-value patient care, Medical Education will continue to be a valuable asset.

20

Neurosurgery
1946-2014
Dr. John Larry Seymour

The history of Abbott Northwestern Hospital neurosurgery can be traced back to 1946 when Dr. Harold Buchstein began private practice in Minneapolis after serving in the Army in World War II as a neurosurgeon. Previously he had trained at the Mayo Clinic. He was the first neurosurgeon in practice in the Twin Cities and practiced alone initially but was later joined by Drs. Paul Blake, David Johnson, Leonard Titrud, and C. Kent Olson in turn. Each worked with him for a year or two before starting out by themselves. Dr. Erich Wisiol joined Harold in about 1964 and stayed on as a partner. I joined the two of them in 1969. After two years, we formed a corporation, Neurosurgical Associates, Ltd, which was the beginning of the larger group now at Abbott Northwestern Hospital.

Structure of the Practice

When I joined the practice, members of our group were on the staffs of many hospitals. Twin Cities hospitals at that time included Abbott Northwestern, Swedish, St. Barnabas, Fairview Southdale, Fairview, North Memorial, Mercy, St. Mary's, Lutheran Deaconess, Eitel, and of course, Hennepin County General. Initially our group served all except Mercy. I remember making rounds one day for six patients in six different hospitals. One of the other neurosurgeons in town had told me, "have good rubber on your tires." Not one of the hospitals had a neurosurgical call list. The hospital ER would just call around until they found one. The primary care physician would admit the patient to his/her hospital and then call for a consult. Each of us was on call essentially all the time.

With the growth of our practice, we were able to narrow the list of hospitals we served and the time on call. Each of us began to focus on one or two main hospitals. Initially, Dr. Erich Wisiol and Dr. Harold Buchstein worked mainly at Abbott and St. Barnabas hospitals. These were high-quality, small (200 or so beds) hospitals, and good places to practice with homogeneous medical staffs. However, the cost of the newer technologies was to make the small hospital obsolete.

During the early years of our practice, coverage for the neurosurgery residents and the other residents on the neurosurgery service at Hennepin County General was supplied on nights and weekends by the community neurosurgeons. We also made rounds one day a week with the residents. This was initially not reimbursed. Then the University supplied a staff neurosurgeon who was responsible on a daily basis. Dr. Gaylan Rockswold, the second staff neurosurgeon to take that position, joined our practice. With Dr. Rockswold spending half his clinical time in coverage for interns and residents, his time was at least in part recompensed. The responsibility of Neurosurgical Associates for resident teaching and supervision at Hennepin County Medical Center continues to this day. Since Dr. Rockswold's retirement, Dr. Tom Bergman and Dr. Walter Galich have filled this role.

Diagnostic Studies

In the 1960s, the main sources of intracranial information from the neurosurgical perspective were 1) Direct stick carotid angiogram, in which contrast material is injected into the carotid artery and 2) pneumoencephalograms, a procedure in which air is injected into the spinal fluid by lumbar puncture. Both were dreaded and miserable to go through. If we wanted a study of the vertebral arteries in the neck, this was achieved by a retrograde injection of contrast material under pressure into the brachial artery. The advent of transfemoral angiography of the cranial arteries (employing a catheter inserted through the groin to allow contrast material to reach the brain), was a major step forward. It quickly became apparent that it made sense for the radiologist to do all of the studies. As a result, we stopped doing the angiogram ourselves.

CT scanning was the next development and essentially did away with the pneumoencephalograms. The MRI followed in the mid-'80s. Now we had access to a positive image of the pathology in much greater detail, which also minimized bony artifacts that had been visible on the CT scans. The next, and I'm sure not the final, development was functional MRI imaging, which outlines fiber tracts in the brain, speech areas, and can even give readings for certain chemicals in the brain to help determine if a lesion is malignant. These studies have to be seen to be believed, especially by one who grew up in the era of the wire Gigli saws and hand-turned trephines for cutting a hole in the skull to reach the brain. Abbott Northwestern Hospital now has a dedicated MRI scanner in the operating room, mainly used in neurosurgical cases. It is useful in evaluating adequacy of tumor removal before ending an operation, and in detailing speech areas and white matter tracts displaced by tumors.

Neurosurgical Instrumentation

Neurosurgeons began using headlights in the 1950s and 1960s to get good light into the surgical wound since the standard OR lights were not focused lights. However, the headlights heated up the surface of the brain and had a parallax problem because the light source was above and not in the same plane as the eyes. They evolved in the early 1970s to a single ocular microscope that could be brought into the field. However, the microscope itself compromised the vision of an assistant, since we dealt with narrow, deep surgical sites.

Next came a binocular microscope with a binocular vision sidepiece for the assistant. Eventually the microscope came on a large, wheeled stand and had two pistol grips to allow aiming, as well as triggers on the grips. When the scope was properly positioned in the field, the triggers were released and the scope held its position exactly. These innovations were amazing and marvelous

The next... development was functional MRI imaging, which outlines fiber tracts in the brain, speech areas, and can even give readings for certain chemicals in the brain to help determine if a lesion is malignant.

At Abbott Northwestern Hospital, the neuroradiology experience is one of the largest in the world.

for the surgeon. Even though the cost for this tool was more than $100,000, no large hospital got along with just one of them.

To make a hole in the skull back in those days, we used a trephine. It looked like a carpenter's bit and brace, but was stainless steel. Its drill bit, adapted from a railroad drill, could stop as it got through the inner table of the skull, but required some touch, careful teaching, and experience. Power drills, which were quicker and safer for the patient, supplanted the trephine. The bits for the power drills eventually became single use only because the drill points could malfunction, sometimes with severe complications. They were quite complicated in design and certainly added a component to the surgical cost.

Changing surgical procedures

All of the many surgical procedures we used changed at least once during the 30 years of my practice. For example, both Tic Douloroux and Hemifacial Spasm (pain in the face related to the trigeminal nerve) were in most cases caused by aberrant loops of an artery pressing on the particular cranial nerve (fifth and seventh respectively) just as they exited the brain stem. A small piece of Teflon felt could be placed between artery and nerve for relief of the condition without the damaging effects of ablation of the nerve or part of it. This supplanted the long-standing percutaneous injection of alcohol into the trigeminal nerve, as well as other surgical approaches that in one way or another damaged the nerve thought to be the cause of the pain.

The surgery for ruptured cerebral aneurysms is difficult in its timing and complex in its demanding technique. Many aneurysms are dealt with now by the interventional radiologist who, by placing a catheter through the femoral artery and advancing it into the brain, can seal it by filling the aneurysm with a malleable wire. This potentially eliminates the need for a craniotomy. At Abbott Northwestern Hospital, the neuroradiology experience is one of the largest in the world. There remains some controversy and continuing discussion about which aneurysms are best treated one way or the other.

The most common tumor in the brain is the malignant glioma, and despite all the technical advances, results are still dismal. A lot of work is going into the genomics and immunology of these tumors, but so far there has been no breakthrough. It has been clear for decades that malignant glioma is not primarily a surgical disease. Surgery offers diagnosis and debulking, but it is rarely curative. In the last few years, genomics has led to the subclassification of glioblastoma multiform, a highly malignant tumor, into four groups, with a different course of treatment for each group, but the "silver bullet" is lacking.

Spine surgery for tumors of the spinal cord, for discs and for spinal stenosis (a result of degenerative arthritis of the joints of the spine) has long been a major part of neurosurgery. This has grown to include some very complicated approaches for conditions that cannot be safely treated through the standard laminectomy or laminotomy approach (the surgical removal of bone from the spinal cord or surrounding area). The microscope has played a huge role here as well.

Shunts have been used for years for hydrocephalus. However, their type and placement has changed over the years with improved outcomes from placing the outflow end of the shunt into the peritoneal cavity of the abdomen. Exact placement of the upper end is now aided by ultrasound. Newly developed in the last 15-20 years is a technique for implanting pumps in the abdominal wall, with a tube into the lumbar cerebral spinal fluid for delivery of pain and anti-spasm drugs.

Finally, a word about stereotaxis. This procedure was long used for accurate placement of an electrode or cutting instrument in the brain depths. It required placement of a frame on the patient's head with pins into the skull surface, followed by X-rays, and surgery using the x, y, z-axes of the frame to place the object. This allowed the surgeon to have exact measurements in order to insert tubes or wires into a tiny area of the brain. Abbott Northwestern Hospital was the beta site for a new procedure and apparatus that used marks attached to the scalp by glue. This greatly simplified the procedure, which could be done the day before surgery and required no anesthesia. As long as the surgery was done with the head in the same position at surgery as in the scanner, namely brow up, it was accurate.

This was a step forward. Its use has spread to the spine for accurate placement of pedicle screws during fusion procedures. Another use of stereotaxis has been the implantation of stimulating electrodes for relief of tremors of Parkinson's disease. It has also been used for the relief of some intention tremors,

Another use of stereotaxis has been the implantation of stimulating electrodes for relief of tremors of Parkinson's disease.

Neurosurgery is a story of increasing diagnostic accuracy and of increasing technical complexity. Better outcomes are due to both.

in which the amplitude of the tremor in the extremity increases as the motion nears completion. Some think that stereotaxis will soon provide relief for severe obsessive-compulsive disorder and perhaps chronic pain, although that is a very complex problem.

Neurosurgery is a story of increasing diagnostic accuracy and of increasing technical complexity. Better outcomes are due to both.

Administrative help is a major part of this story, particularly in financially supporting the development of neurosurgical and neuroradiologic specialties. This led to the ability to attract neurologists to a Neurologic Institute. We all have been fortunate to have the support of Gordon Sprenger, Bob Spinner, and many fine administrators who have followed their leads. Dr. Douglas Yock's leadership of the Neurologic Institute was invaluable.

21

Nursing
1882-2014
Carol Huttner MA, BSN, RN

Nursing Research – 1990-2002
Elaine Hogan Miller, Ph.D., RN

Part I - Nursing
Northwestern Hospital

Abbott Northwestern Hospital is the largest hospital in the Minneapolis/St. Paul area and a leading quaternary medical center. The organization has been delivering exceptional care to the community for 132 years.

It all began on a small scale when Harriet G. Walker, wife of the prominent businessman Thomas B. Walker, summoned a group of 44 women to an afternoon tea in November 1882. A compassionate person with a strong sense of responsibility to the community, she was appalled at the lack of attention that was being given to the health of women and children in the 1880s. Over tea, she convinced the women that they could work together to build a hospital for the poorest women and children in their community.

They would be astonished that the hospital they created not only survived but, more than a century later, is recognized nationally as a comprehensive, thriving hospital, leading the

Harriet G. Walker... summoned a group of 44 women to an afternoon tea in November 1882. A compassionate person with a strong sense of responsibility to the community, she was appalled at the lack of attention that was being given to the health of women and children in the 1880s.

country in new ways of providing compassionate care coupled with the latest technology.

In December 1882, the newly formed Northwestern Hospital for Women and Children moved into a small, rented house on 3½ Avenue South in Minneapolis and opened its doors. They began by opening a training school for nurses with the first class totaling two young women. Compensation for nurses in training during this era was known as "board and wash." Each trainee also received a dollar a week to pay for books and incidentals. Work was from seven o'clock in the morning to seven in the evening with time for "exercise and rest." The students were given part of Sunday off and occasionally, one afternoon during the week. The first four nursing students graduated in 1884.

The course of instruction for the nurses at the time "shall embody all that belongs to best methods of care for the sick – the dressing of wounds and sores, fomentation, friction, bathing, keeping of temperature records, cookery for the sick, care of the rooms, beds and utensils, and accurate observation and report to the effect of medicine and diet."

The Training School for Nurses on-the-job program made Northwestern Hospital function as well as it did in the early years. Actually, there was little difference between the physical work for a nurse and that of domestic help, except that the job had better hours and higher wages. Even with these demands, nursing was seen as a good job opportunity for young women.

As the patient census quickly increased, Mrs. Walker sold the house and moved into a new Northwestern Hospital at Chicago Avenue and 27th Street. The nurses were now paid $2 per day! The nursing school increased its enrollment from two students in 1882 to 21 in 1899 and 40 by 1912. Recognizing the strides nursing had made as a profession, Mrs. Walker addressed the graduates of the Nursing School of 1915.

Mrs. Walker said, "In the very early days of the life of this school, and when it was the only one in the city, we were hesitating about enlarging the number of pupils from two to four, for fear of overstocking the market. An elderly and somewhat old-fashioned physician, even for those times, remarked, 'you are spoiling them – utterly spoiling them. You are teaching them to use the thermometer, and to know the nature and effects of medicine, and to understand a patient's symptoms as well as a physician. All a nurse needs to know is how to make a bed, fill a hot water bottle, and wait for the doctor. That is all I want my nurses to know.'" Mrs. Walker added that, "The times have certainly changed."

Abbott Hospital

In 1902, Northwestern Hospital celebrated its 20th anniversary. Less than a mile away, Amos Abbott, M.D., opened his Hospital for Women at 10 East 17th Street. The yellow brick house seemed perfect for his work. It had room for 15 beds, an operating room and laboratory, as well as living quarters on the third floor for the five nurses-in-training, a cook, and a superintendent. Unlike Northwestern Hospital, Abbott Hospital was designated for the finest families in the city in addition to some of the poorest. Whatever their situation, Dr. Abbott treated every person as though their care was singularly important to him.

He hired Miss Susan Holmes in 1903 to be hospital superintendent and superintendent for the Nurse Training program. By some accounts, she wasn't easy to work for, but she was fair, and she made Abbott Hospital her home and her life for 42 years. She wore all hats with a compassionate determination that made the doctors and nurses grow to love her. It was said that the hospital didn't go to sleep at night until she had made her rounds. Doctors grew to trust her judgment and believed her to be one of the best examples of nursing excellence.

Many things in hospitals changed over the years. Nursing students took special pride in their assigned areas and began to specialize their interests along with the physicians. By 1939, in a move to expand the graduate nursing staff, Abbott Hospital hired Miss Margaret Amble, RN, as surgical supervisor, Miss Sybil Pitts, RN, as assistant surgical supervisor, and Miss Marian Chaladek, RN, as obstetrical supervisor. These three new "executives" were asked to make a "conscientious effort to organize their departments into efficient units of the hospital." The minutes of the hospital's executive committee for that year suggest that they did an excellent job, thus setting new professional goals for Abbott Hospital.

Within a few months, as World War II became a dreaded reality, a national push for medical help changed the role of nurses. The advent of new drug therapy coupled with ever-increasing new diagnostic technology significantly

They began by opening a training school for nurses with the first class totaling two young women.

By 1969, plans were made to combine the nursing schools and admit nursing students to the new school – Abbott Northwestern School of Nursing – beginning in September 1970.

effected the care of patients. Nursing was at the forefront of the change at both Abbott and Northwestern hospitals Schools of Nursing.

By 1951, both Abbott and Northwestern hospitals had joined with St. Barnabus Hospital in expanding and centralizing their nursing programs and had become affiliated with Macalester College in St. Paul. The Central Teaching Program allowed all three hospitals to offer a revised three-year teaching program for potential RNs, expand their faculty and improve their facilities. With only three semesters of additional work, nurses could also receive a Bachelor of Science degree from Macalester. Clearly, the "on-the-job" nurses' training had gone the way of the horse and buggy. By the 1950s, the science of nursing, as well as the art of nursing, had become an essential part of its course of study.

As hospitals expanded and grew to care for rapidly growing communities, nursing dormitories were built for both Abbott and Northwestern Schools of Nursing. In the mid-1960s, Diagnosis Related Groups (DRGs) came into being. There were 467 groups. This changed the way in which procedures were paid for. Previously the charge had been on a "cost-based" system and now it was changed to a "product." The modern age of health care meant not only better and bigger facilities for quality patient care but increased governmental regulation, higher medical costs, and a growing shortage of trained personnel to operate new equipment and to care for patients. Private hospitals were evolving into non-profit businesses on a large scale. People at both Abbott and Northwestern recognized that a significant change in health care administration was imminent. It became more important than ever to prepare both hospitals for what was to come.

While hospital administrators and lawyers were busy discussing the details of a merger between Abbott and Northwestern hospitals, the faculties of the two nursing schools were having complex conversations as well. By 1969, plans were made to combine the nursing schools and admit nursing students to the new school – Abbott Northwestern School of Nursing – beginning in September 1970. Both schools had spent the 1960s carefully reviewing their curricula in light of the great changes taking place in health care. Even though significant alterations had been made in courses, structure, presentation, and practical experience, the handwriting was on the wall. The days of the hospital-run nursing school were slipping away.

Just as medicine had become more complex, so had nursing. The students were seeking a broader-based education from colleges and universities. Many found it difficult to transfer credits from an accredited nursing school into the college of their choice and often ended up taking many more courses than would have been otherwise required.

In spite of all the revisions and excellent reputations of both schools of nursing and the combined program, eight years after the merger the school issued its last diploma.

When the schools closed, the door opened to a world of continuing education on a post-graduate basis. The completion of Continuing Education Units became as important to nurses as their nursing degrees or diploma. New seminars, workshops, and courses in specialties such as cardiovascular, oncology, and intensive care were offered to kick off the new Nursing Education Program in 1978. Continuing education became a requirement for state RN licensure in the late 1970s, so Nursing Education became an integral part of Abbott Northwestern Hospital. Carefully designed courses, workshops, and seminars were offered to comply with the new state Board of Nursing regulations.

The Director of Nursing at Northwestern Hospital from late 1950s to mid-1970s was Virginia Paulson, RN. She was well respected by all the nurses and also by the administrators, including Gordon Sprenger, who became CEO of Abbott Northwestern Hospital in 1971. Knowing that the organization needed a nursing leader who could bring Abbott and Northwestern nursing staff together in an orderly fashion, Mr. Sprenger conducted a search for a dynamic nursing leader who had extensive senior-level leadership experience and the ability to bring people together. He found that in Barbara Donaho, RN, MA, who had been the director of Nursing at the 1,000-bed Hartford Hospital in Hartford, Connecticut.

Abbott Northwestern Hospital

Ms. Donaho joined Abbott Northwestern Hospital in September 1975, during the period when the two hospitals were still physically separated. She was charged with providing leadership for a smooth integration of nursing as Abbott and Northwestern became one hospital on one campus. According to Mr.

Three hundred registered nurses were hired during the summer of 1980 to help staff the growing patient population.

Sprenger, she brought a broad background of leadership and management experience that enabled her to interact with physicians, nurses, and administrators to make the consolidation process progress smoothly. Ms. Donaho was an articulate leader who commanded respect from all who met her. Mr. Sprenger said she was an "excellent executive to work with as she was a strong nursing advocate but could bring a much larger perspective that included design of the new integrated campus as well as stewardship of the resources."

Ms. Donaho did an admirable job of integrating nursing and developing a new structure that supported the team going forward. She did all of this and served as President of the American Organization of Nurse Executives in 1976. Ms. Donaho was there that cold day, January 26, 1980, to provide leadership for the final transfer of patients from Abbott Hospital to Abbott Northwestern Hospital. That was truly the day it became Abbott Northwestern Hospital. It was a joyous time as she was an inspirational leader who made all proud to be nurses in such a great, new hospital!

With both hospitals located on one campus in 1980, integration of all hospital services was a key strategic initiative. Nursing was no exception. The Intensive Care Units were frequently filled to capacity. Three hundred registered nurses were hired during the summer of 1980 to help staff the growing patient population.

The Education Department was challenged with providing a comprehensive orientation for new employees. Yvonne Gorecki, MSN, RN, led the challenge along with clinical nurse specialists and education specialists from the expanding Nursing Department. As technology was rapidly changing, Clinical Nurse Specialists (CNS) were hired to fill the clinical education needed in cardiovascular, pulmonary, neuroscience, gerontology, medical surgical, and mental health departments. The enterostomal therapy school was also part of the expansion as the needs increased.

New units opened for neuroscience patients, eye patients, and a new medical surgical ICU as open heart surgery expanded and needed a dedicated unit. The first interventional cardiology unit in the U.S. opened in the early 1980s at Abbott Northwestern Hospital to provide service for patients undergoing angiography and percutaneous transluminal angioplasty.

Once the integration of services was completed and stabilized, Barbara

Donaho resigned her position following a job exceptionally well done. Nancy Higgerson, MA, RN, joined Abbott Northwestern in the early 1980s. As a strong nursing advocate, she reorganized nursing leadership, positioning directors over the various medical, surgical, and specialty areas of care. Higgerson was challenged to provide leadership for the largest group of nurses in the Minneapolis/St. Paul area.

Ms. Higgerson worked tirelessly to advance nursing and was at the bargaining table in 1984 for the citywide nursing negotiations between the hospitals and the Minnesota Nurses Association. Ultimately, negotiations were unsuccessful, and what followed was the biggest nursing strike of its kind in years, lasting for six weeks. In the days of preparation before the strike, nurses were laid off as the census decreased. During the strike, nurses who crossed the picket line and nurses who were not in the union, such as clinical managers, CNSs, and educators, staffed the hospital. Nurses from agencies were also flown in to cover patient care.

Once the strike was settled, the long healing process began. It took weeks to bring the nurses back to work as all positions had to be reposted. Nurses came in to select open positions based on seniority. Out of necessity, new ways of providing service for patients were introduced during the strike. Outpatient angiography was implemented, which led to the development of new types of care delivery. Patients requiring eye surgery no longer needed inpatient hospital stays. Some of the units nurses had previously worked were no longer needed.

Higgerson did her best to support leaders in focusing all their efforts on patient care. She did all of this and was also president of the American Organization of Nurse Executives (AONE) at the same time! To this end, she charged Marjean Leary, BSN, RN; Mary Koloroutis, MSN, RN; Cel Dahlmeyer and Ginger Malone, MSNs, RNs, with drafting the Department of Nursing Philosophy. They drafted and edited Advocacy Through Caring, and processed it through several nursing staff and leadership focus groups for discussion and revision. The Nursing Council approved the final statement.

In Nursing Perspectives, the communiqué from Higgerson, stated, "We are what we believe. Our professional practice, our personal goals, our lifestyles are the actualization of what we individually believe. The collection of our beliefs has been translated into the Nursing Department Philosophy – Advocacy

"We are what we believe. Our professional practice, our personal goals, our lifestyles are the actualization of what we individually believe. The collection of our beliefs has been translated into the Nursing Department Philosophy – Advocacy Through Caring. The Department Standards and activities transform our philosophy into action and outcomes."
–Nancy Higgerson, MA, RN

The cornerstone of the philosophy statement was "Advocacy Through Caring," which emphasized that patients are the reason we exist as a profession. By caring acts, critical thinking and clinical competency, we displayed a fundamental respect for the patient as a person with experience, knowledge, and values that were unique.

Through Caring. The Department Standards and activities transform our philosophy into action and outcomes."

Marjean Leary, director of Nursing, Mental Health/Chemical Dependency, and Mary Koloroutis, director of Nursing at Women's Hospital, submitted the following to Nursing Perspectives to reach all nurses within this growing department.

"The current health care environment, nationally and here at Abbott Northwestern, bears one constant fact – and that constant is change." This included changes in technology, delivery of care, reimbursement, and relocation of nursing units. All these elements included the different pulses of the environment, changes in the rhythm and intensity, which were on a daily basis.

In light of today's tumultuous environment, it was clear that we, as a Department, had to move into the future with a clear direction established. The foundation of this direction, the how and why we deliver nursing services to patients and their families was the focus of the newly revised philosophy statement.

A task force was established by the Nursing Council to revise our philosophy statement. This task force worked in concert with a focus group of unit staffs – RNs, LPNs, and MHYCs, head nurses, clinical specialists and Communications/Public Relations staff. After much input and many revisions, the writing of the document was complete. Sharing the Philosophy with unit nursing staff, physicians, management staff and the patients and their families would be the next step in the process.

The cornerstone of the philosophy statement was "Advocacy Through Caring," which emphasized that patients are the reason we exist as a profession. By caring acts, critical thinking and clinical competency, we displayed a fundamental respect for the patient as a person with experience, knowledge, and values that were unique. The statement emphasized the importance of the role of the nurse as integrator of patient care: that nursing is one element in the delivery of care as a whole, but also pivotal in keeping the whole complete.

Our hope was this philosophy would be a "living" document versus a paper to be filed in the dusty annals of time. We realize there were gaps between who we were as a department now and what the philosophy described. The philosophy and actions which will support its words would serve as our guide for decisions and changes necessary to move into the future from a perspective of unity and central purpose.

This Nursing Philosophy created in the 1980s is as relevant today as it was when it was created. It is still proudly displayed on all patient care units and in the entrance of the hospital. Indeed patients are the reason we exist; people are the reason we excel, and systems support our work!

Nancy Higgerson left Abbott Northwestern Hospital in the late 1980s and Julianne Morath, MS, RN, became Vice President of Patient Care. A new era was born, with the focus on living out the philosophy of nursing. Ms. Morath was a strong, thoughtful leader.

Nursing in the 1990s - Innovation

The 1990s was an era of massive change within health care and at Abbott Northwestern Hospital. Mergers of hospitals occurred as they closed and/or re-aligned. LifeSpan, Abbott Northwestern's parent company, became HealthSpan. HealthSpan merged with Medica to become the Allina Health System in 1993.

As all of these changes were occurring, Abbott Northwestern's Nursing Department was focused on the principles established in the Nursing Department Philosophy: Patients are the reason we exist, people are the reason we excel, and systems support our work. These three principles that emerged in 1989 were foundational to Abbott Northwestern Hospital receiving a planning grant from the Robert Wood Johnson Foundation/Pew Charitable Trusts for Strengthening Hospital Nursing: A Program to Improve Patient Care. In 1990, the hospital was one of 20 in the United States to receive a $1 million, five-year implementation grant.

While this was a nursing-focused grant, the entire patient care team needed to be included to achieve the desired outcomes. This was the beginning of clinical "silos" coming together and learning how they could be stronger as an integrated team. Ginger Malone, RN, was charged with leading the team for the five-year grant. The work of the grant became known as "Innovation." The project was integrated with the hospital's overall total quality management efforts that focused on improving quality for all patients, specifically appropriateness, efficiency, and effectiveness.

Abbott Northwestern's Nursing Department was focused on the principles established in the Nursing Department Philosophy: Patients are the reason we exist, people are the reason we excel, and systems support our work.

Two corporate mergers enabled Abbott Northwestern to become part of the second largest not-for-profit health care delivery system in the country.

Innovation was based on having a shared vision, focusing on the patient, creating a new design and improving the systems that existed at the hospital. Innovation depended on learning as a team, creating visions, designing new systems, and mastering change. The teams called themselves EPIC – Employees Promoting Improved Care. The goals the teams set forth were:

- Increased patient/family satisfaction
- Increased clinical effectiveness
- Increased organizational efficiency and effectiveness
- Reduced costs
- More meaningful work

Innovation efforts were sponsored in three patient care areas: rehabilitation, cardiovascular, and an intensive care unit. As the years went by, efforts spun off from the original design teams, creating further changes. Once the changes were deemed successful, they were expanded to other parts of the hospital. In addition to the work in-house, the teams determined that they needed to have former patients and families join the interdisciplinary teams. They also reached out to six Minnesota and North Dakota planning grant recipients to share ideas, barriers, and strategies.

The beginning of the work was difficult. Each discipline was entrenched in its own silo, and not everyone liked change. Half the group was working top down and the other half bottom up. Together they learned to get beyond processing to get the work done. The six years of the grant, from planning to doing, saw two Nursing/Patient Care vice presidents leave and two Minnesota Nurses Association contracts ratified. Abbott Northwestern absorbed most of Metropolitan Mount Sinai Medical Center when it closed. Two corporate mergers enabled Abbott Northwestern to become part of the second largest not-for-profit health care delivery system in the country.

Patient Satisfaction

The first goal of the Innovation was increased patient satisfaction. "Patients are the reason we exist."

The experience: The teams came together with the idea that the work needed to be patient-centered not discipline- or department-driven – a huge shift in thinking! This goal stated that services should be brought to the patient as much as possible. Through extensive use of patient/family focus groups and the involvement of patients and their families on the design teams, staff members developed specific measures of patient satisfaction. Patients clearly identified those elements that affected their experience: comfort, control, communication, coordination, and continuity. In response, team members made real improvements, ranging from small but meaningful changes to the construction of a new unit designed around patients' needs.

Clinical Effectiveness

The second goal was increased clinical effectiveness.

The experience: Teamwork was at the root of increasing clinical effectiveness. Defining each professional's scope of practice and continuous quality improvement methods were key to the improvements made.

By working together to make measurable, standards-based changes with clearly defined outcomes, the staff was able to increase the use of care pathways, clinical progressions, increase the use of physicians' standing orders, reduce patients' length of stay, and, for example, decrease the length of time patients were intubated – changes that improved patients' experiences while increasing clinical effectiveness.

Organizational Efficiency and Effectiveness

The third goal was increased organizational efficiency and effectiveness.

The experience: The people closest to the work easily identified what needed to get done and what was unnecessarily complicated. They were able to identify wasted time and activities. By identifying "non-value-added" activities and suggesting improvements, the staff made dramatic reductions in the number of unnecessary patient transfers. This meant a dramatic reduction in the miles patients traveled from one area of the hospital to another, which also decreased patients' aggravation around particular system problems. We were able to reduce staff without a layoff. In the end, these changes created communities of patient care units with similar services and reorganized the hospital's leadership.

"Innovation" was the key to employees making dramatic changes, working as a team toward their vision for change.

Cost of Care

The fourth goal was reducing costs of care.

The experience: Allowing employee teams to make substantial contributions to cost reduction is difficult because it demands that employees have access to financial information that many administrators do not want to disclose to the employees. In the grant process, it was readily apparent that when employees were given the financial information they needed, they made intelligent monetary decisions and thus reduced cost. The team became wise stewards of the resources and were able to make dramatic cost reductions. Administration was very supportive of providing the Innovation teams with the information they needed to achieve the goals. As a result, millions of dollars were saved. The Innovation grant that started out in nursing united the entire hospital around patients!

Meaningful Work

The fifth goal was more meaningful work for employees.

The experience: The real benefit of the improvements made through Innovation was a marked improvement in meaningful work for employees. By the end of the grant, every employee was affected in some way. The work of Innovation highlighted the fact that, when an individual's values and the values of the organization for which they work are in sync, then the employee's commitment is deeper and the work improves. This increased commitment in turn created a greater capacity for change and an interest in expanding individual skills.

"Innovation" was the key to employees making dramatic changes, working as a team toward their vision for change.

The first phase of the grant focused on three key areas: the cardiovascular redesign with Pam Van Hazinga, BSN, RN, as nurse leader; rehabilitation with Sue Durkin, MS, RN, as nurse leader; the new medical/surgical/neurologic ICU with Ann Watkins, BSN, RN, as nurse leader. By the end of 1993 the team accomplishments were:

Cardiovascular Care – Stations 41 and 45
- Tested a regional care management model using community/tertiary partnerships

- Developed a clinical progression that spanned the continuum of care over one year

- Developed core concepts for new therapeutic and diagnostic processes

- Used collaborative governance and management partnering to establish a cardiovascular community

- Developed a model for forecasting cardiovascular admissions and testing to allow more responsive service

Intensive Care – Station 20

- Opened a new Intensive Care Unit (ICU) designed by patients, families, and caregivers on which all aspects of the unit design promoted healing

- Designed new work processes that streamlined systems, simplified work, and promoted healing relationships

- Tested care management of long-term ICU patients to improve resource management, improve caregiver communication, and better meet patient needs

Rehabilitation – Sister Kenny Institute

- Redesigned rehabilitation care delivery model

- Streamlined management structure

- Created caregiver continuity throughout the continuum of care

- Created 24-hour therapeutic environment

- Designed environment to support team interaction

In addition to these three models, nursing staff members from a variety of clinical areas were involved in formal groups and teams charged with considering new designs to support the work of patient care. Team efforts were underway in Behavioral Health Services, Scheduling/Staffing Resources, Nursing Education/Professional Development, and WomenCare. In Surgical Services, councils and task forces examined the Operating Room expansion, renovation, and reorganization. The Nursing Intravenous Team reviewed the IV Therapy Program and made changes that took out waste and benefited the patient.

The entire organization was involved in creating the best possible environment for the care of patients. All care providers determined what each

The entire organization was involved in creating the best possible environment for the care of patients.

discipline had as their scope of practice and how best to integrate a plan that would provide the best outcomes for patients.

Restructuring to Meet the Needs of Patients

In health care, rapid change was key in this era. Health care institutions strived to keep a balance between doing the work and keeping costs under control. One of the primary strategies to effect this balance was to more fully utilize the knowledge, ingenuity, and creativity of nurses. The Structure Committee of Abbott Northwestern's Nursing Department met for 15 months to draft a plan aimed at restructuring the department to more fully tap the knowledge nurses possess, as decision-making is moved closer to the bedside.

Communities of Care were created, which included Medical/Surgical, WomanCare, Neuroscience, Orthopedics and Rehabilitation, Cardiovascular, Mental Health, Emergency/Outpatient, and finally Perioperative and Surgical Services. The Nursing Education Department became the Center for Clinical and Professional Development. Directors of Nursing were assigned responsibility over the various areas and, along with the Vice President for Patient Care, Julianne M. Morath, formed the Nurse Executive Council. Each of these clinical areas had a council, and staffs were asked to join and to provide input. The councils fed into their Communities of Care Committee and then to the Nursing Board, which was chaired by Ms. Morath.

The common tenets were:

- Increased participation in the development and monitoring of nursing practice standards
- Ability to influence, contribute to, and support professional development and education
- Recognition of the commitment and investment nurses hold regarding their Practice
- Greater opportunity to maximize each individual nurse's work

Clinical Practice Model

In 1993, the new Nursing Department structure worked collaboratively to design and implement the Clinical Practice Model (CPM). The model is a system that supports the effective, individualized delivery of nursing care to patients based on their holistic care requirements and the art and science of professional nursing practice. The goal of the model is to define consistency in practice, assure appropriateness of care, and decrease costs of care through increased efficiency, focus, and comprehensiveness. The CPM:

- Provides a framework for addressing the appropriateness, efficiency and effectiveness of practice
- Aligns all the activities in the department in a way that makes sense and strengthens nursing care delivery
- Reflects the Nursing Department philosophy and standards
- Ties nursing to the work of Abbott Northwestern Hospital and the managed care environment in which we work
- Creates greater avenues for interdisciplinary, patient-focused collaboration

Implementation of the CPM began when more than 80 nurses attended presentations about three professional practice models under consideration. Individual staff nurses shared their views about the models with Professional Practice and Nursing Patient Care Council and committee members. The committee members analyzed the responses of the nurses and forwarded the summary to the Nursing Board. The Nursing Board approved the selection of the CPM, originating out of the Clinical Practice Model Resource Center in Grand Rapids, Michigan, if the model could be responsive to the interdisciplinary and managed care environment at Abbott Northwestern. The contract was signed with Bonnie Wesorick, MSN, RN, FAAN, founder and president of the Clinical Practice Model Resource Center, to consult in the implementation of CPM.

By January 1994, more than 1,000 staff nurses attended sessions with Bonnie Wesorick. A contact person on each patient care unit was identified through whom information would be channeled. More than 250 nurses participated to determine how to manage the implementation, and the CPM model was gradually implemented on all patient care areas. By the end of 1995, the following had been completed.

- More than 93 percent of all nurses on patient care units validated their competency in the use of functional health patterns, nursing diagnosis,

In 1993, the new Nursing Department structure worked collaboratively to design and implement the Clinical Practice Model (CPM). The model is a system that supports the effective, individualized delivery of nursing care to patients based on their holistic care requirements and the art and science of professional nursing practice.

and guidelines of care. These components were the foundations for the consistent provision of holistic patient assessment and care planning.

- Four new documentation tools were piloted to provide a more holistic picture of patients, standardize communication about patients across the hospital, and streamline the documentation system.

- The first quarterly meeting of CPM unit contacts provided an opportunity for unit contacts to discuss the progress of the implementation.

- Abbott Northwestern nursing staff presented five of the 11 concurrent sessions and four poster/roundtable dialogues at a CPM National Meeting.

- Members of Nursing Leadership participated in a Scope of Practice session to address the role of leadership in support of patient care.

- A professional exchange report was drafted and implemented by key nursing staff.

Advanced Practice Nurse Group

The clinical nurse specialists (CNS) were advanced practitioners and educators through the Nursing Education Department. With all the changes with the CPM and patient needs becoming the main focus, the CNS Group Practice emerged in 1993. The focus of their work was to:

- Enhance managed care strategies through the development of 28 new or revised clinical progressions that were used as pathways of care

- Set up a consultation service to facilitate changes in clinical practice and care delivery and assist in the plan of care for complex patients

- Provide a Geriatric Nurse Resource Team as part of a coordinated effort to enhance the quality and cost effectiveness of care provided to geriatric patients

- Provide leadership for more than 50 nursing research studies that directly improved patient outcomes

By 1997, they became known as the Advanced Practice Nurse Group. They provided primary services for nursing case management and consultation, working strategically across the organization and within specific communities to improve patient outcomes.

Center for Professional and Clinical Development

To support the Nursing Philosophy, "Advocacy through Caring," the Department of Nursing implemented a one-day workshop in 1992. Participants discussed the vision for the Department of Nursing, the impact of collaborative governance, the importance of caring, and how each nurse could put the department's philosophy into proactive use every day. In addition, "Person Mastery: The Nurse as a Person, Colleague and Integrator of Care" began as a three-day workshop. The purpose was to let nurses reflect on the art of nursing and define strategies to move their personal vision into daily practice. Mae McWeeny, MSN, RN, and Mary Koloroutis, MSN, RN, were instrumental in designing the program and implementing it.

The role of the clinical education specialist changed, after the creation of the Center for Professional and Clinical Development, emphasizing clinical and professional practice and cost reduction. The Center provided education, leadership, and consultation for individuals, nursing units and groups through these services:

- Professional Development: Clinical practice model, managed care, leadership, innovation, individual consultation, and practice support
- Clinical Development: Orientation, competency-based practice, in-services, mandatory education requirements, individual consultation, and practice support
- Learning Services: Conferences, recognition programs, outreach, writing and publishing, career guidance, academic alliances, individual consultation, and practice support
- Self and peer review process
- Operations consultations team

When Allina was formed in the mid-1990s through the merger of HealthSpan with Medica, an insurance company, Abbott Northwestern's leadership went through significant change. In addition, Abbott Northwestern

Participants [in a one-day workshop] discussed the vision for the Department of Nursing, the impact of collaborative governance, the importance of caring, and how each nurse could put the department's philosophy into proactive use every day.

transitioned to roles at Allina. Julianne M. Morath left her position as Vice President of Patient Care Services and became the Allina Quality Vice President responsible for the entire system of hospitals and clinics.

Carol Huttner, MA, BSN, RN, was charged with taking on the role of Vice President for Patient Care Services at Abbott Northwestern. Ms. Huttner joined Abbott Northwestern in 1980 and, until her promotion to vice president, served as director of Cardiovascular Services. She was well known to the organization and could provide leadership at this crucial time of change. In her new role, she expanded accountabilities for Women Care and Surgical Services at Abbott Northwestern. She was also named "sponsor" of Obstetrics and Gynecology across the metro Allina hospitals.

As Ms. Huttner worked with members of the Nursing Board and the Nurse Executive Committee, problems with existing structure were identified, including poor attendance at meetings, ineffective communication, and perceptions of minimal outcomes. A new structure was created to respond to these problems, which would ensure a strong collaborative governance model and participation for the future.

The changes included replacing the three department-wide committees and the nursing board with a single Nursing Practice Board that was linked directly to the seven community councils. The structure was designed to simplify and clarify the Nursing Department's process for setting priorities, making decisions, and communicating practice issues. Unit-based work groups and task forces supported the community councils. The work of multidisciplinary patient care councils, which developed as part of the Innovation Grant, was linked directly to the community councils.

The Nursing Practice Board consisted of the chairpersons of each community council, the Patient Care Vice President, nurse leaders and consultants, the chairpersons of the clinical nurse manager group, the assistant nurse manager group and the advance nurse practice group, the Center for Professional and Clinical Development practice specialists, the nurse researcher, and an administrative representative. This council was linked to the President's Council and other professional practice boards throughout the organization.

As a result of the new structure, nurses from each of the communities became integrated in hospital-wide section meetings. Nurses and physicians could now have a formal channel to discuss and improve patient outcomes. In order to have all staff hear a common message, Ms. Huttner worked with Media Services to tape a five-minute monthly video for all the communities of care. The Abbott Northwestern Hospital Foundation funded this effort.

During this era, the key theme was "Patients are the reason we exist," "People are the reason we excel," and "Systems support our work." To this end, Ms. Huttner worked with Bob Spinner, president of Abbott Northwestern Hospital, and the senior leadership team to make these statements meaningful. While the Patient Care Vice President made daily rounds, weekly rounds were made by the Patient Care Vice President and senior executive leadership team on patient care units and other departments. Each administrator would share the experience at the weekly executive meeting. The act of connecting with staff, patients and families, physicians, and multidisciplinary team members increased the engagement staff felt with people who led the organization. Through this process, people on the units were empowered to identify issues that impeded their ability to deliver the best possible patient care.

For the first time, a chief financial officer was able to go to the Medical and Surgical ICU and hear incredibly moving patient stories as told by dedicated nursing staff. They also met with families in the waiting rooms and heard the stories of human suffering and the toll it takes on families. This fostered greater understanding about how resources are allocated to improve outcomes. It was also an opportunity to inspect the facilities where care was provided. Many issues were identified, and people talked in real time about how to fix a specific area in need of repair. By empowering the staff to get the job done locally, they knew that senior leaders better understood the needs of patients, staff, and the facility.

By empowering the staff to get the job done locally, they knew that senior leaders better understood the needs of patients, staff, and the facility.

Care Coordination in the late 1990s

During the late1990s, a key strategic initiative was to increase nursing skill in advancing the patient's plan of care. Though most of the hospital's resources were concentrated on a small number of complex patients, all patients could benefit from case management efforts. In some forums, the perception was that this was an effort to move patients through the system too quickly and back

When done in the way intended, care coordination is a way of focusing – not limiting – the care patients receive.

into their homes without sufficient support. That is not true care coordination. When done in the way intended, care coordination is a way of focusing – not limiting – the care patients receive. It is not just about getting the patients out of the hospital quickly. It is about moving them smoothly through the system and making sure they have the necessary support when they are ready to return home.

Abbott Northwestern's Case Management Design Team, made up of multidisciplinary leaders as well as physicians and nurses, worked with the communities of care to design plans of care. The first area was in the Medical Surgical patient community with an eye toward achieving measurable outcomes. Efforts on this project received widespread support since they reinforced the belief in the importance of those who work directly with patients being active in the coordination of their patients' care.

Another area of remarkable process improvement was in the cardiovascular surgical patient population. By the late 1990s, the heart transplant program was in full swing, and the number of open heart cases increased to about 1,300 annually. Jody Portu, MSN, RN, CV, clinical nurse specialist, worked creatively with a multidisciplinary team to use evidence-based literature to improve cardiovascular patient care. She led the team in developing clinical progressions with input from all staff. She worked with anesthesia staff, surgeons, and respiratory therapy staff to implement early extubation.

Previously patients had been intubated overnight, but using evidence-based findings, some patients who met criteria were safely extubated the evening of surgery. The patients were also encouraged to sit on the side of the bed with assistance the evening of surgery. Portu and the team had to revise pre-operative patient teaching so patients and their families would know what to expect and why. All of this was revolutionary practice for the time and fit into Dr. Donald Berwick's strategies from the Institute for Health Care Improvement. Members of the Abbott Northwestern team, including Ms. Portu, Dr. Frazier Eales and Dr. Richard Nelson, Carol Huttner, RN, and Mark Dixon, Vice President of Cardiovascular Services, were part of the process improvement effort.

Ms. Portu worked with process improvement team members as well as Finance to develop baseline measurements and identify trends. Ms. Portu used this information to meet with surgeons one-to-one to share data. She also shared surgeons' information on their patient cohort in an overall "blinded" manner. Gradually, each surgeon looked at best practices and determined how to replicate what was being achieved by others. This was no easy process, but Ms. Portu was a well-respected clinical nurse specialist who possessed exceptional relationship skills. While there were many more pieces to the puzzle, this was important in improving outcomes for patients and reducing expenses. "More" was now seen as not necessarily "better" care.

The process that began at Abbott Northwestern was brought to other parts of the Allina system. Care for patients improved because of the combined, focused efforts of a multidisciplinary team. The Cardiovascular team presented nationally more than 25 times in one year, sharing the process improvement outcomes they attained.

A New Millennium

Those of us who were there remember the incredible effort put into Y2K planning, even though it proved to be a non-issue in most locations across the country and at Allina. It was a new time and a new leader was brought in after Carol Huttner retired as Vice President of Patient Care. Sharon Dudley, MS, RN, joined Abbott Northwestern in April 2000. As Patient Care Vice President, she had an expanded role as administrator over the Virginia Piper Cancer Institute. In this role, she worked with physicians and other team members to elevate the cancer program to a Center of Excellence. She also worked closely with a team to open and expand the work of the Penny George Institute for Health and Healing.

During this time, the Collaborative Governance model for nurses was restructured to meet demands of the changing times. Ms. Dudley also engaged Jody Portu MS, CCNS, RN, to begin the lengthy process of applying for Magnet® status. The American Nurses Credentialing Center's Magnet Recognition Program, "recognizes health care organizations for quality patient care, nursing excellence and innovations in professional nursing practice." It is the highest level of recognition of its kind for nursing. The Magnet Recognition is awarded to about 5 percent of the hospitals in the nation.

Ms. Dudley also worked with key executives planning the implementation

Abbott Northwestern's Case Management Design Team, made up of multidisciplinary leaders as well as physicians and nurses, worked with the communities of care to design plans of care.

of Excellian, the patient electronic medical record. The original proposal for nursing documentation went to the Abbott Northwestern board in 1994 at a cost of $8 million. The complexity of creating a patient electronic medical record has been overwhelming and has cost hundreds of millions of dollars thus far. It is, to this day, a work in progress.

Ms. Dudley led the change in the Collaborative Governance Structure to reflect the needs of the times. The Nursing Board's purpose was identified as assuring consistency and integration of practice standards across the organization. In addition to overseeing the Nursing Department and representing its interests within the organization, the Nursing Board worked closely with the Nurse Practice Council (NPC), the Professional Development and Education Council, and the Quality and Research Council. Each council's chairperson was asked to serve on the Nursing Board. In addition, patient care communities and staff nurses had direct representation on the Board through clinical practice coordinators, a Minnesota Nurses Association representative, and staff nurses from the NPC.

The Nursing Board provided a formal structure to ensure that the department's goals and activities were communicated effectively. It also provided a forum to evaluate and address the needs of nurses and the issues facing patient care communities as part of the Board's ongoing goal-setting and decision-making processes.

Before the new structure was in place, nurse managers and educators made most decisions about nursing practice. In the revised structure, NPC membership included significant numbers of staff nurses, which enhanced communication and promoted a better understanding of the needs and practice issues on each unit. By the end of 2004, the Board identified the 2005 goals as follows:

- Helping nurses maintain quality care as they participate in key organizational transitions (including implementing the electronic medical record called Excellian)
- Moving to the Heart Hospital
- Achieving Magnet® status

By the end of 2004, Jody Portu led the Magnet Steering Committee through the completion of the first phase. The goals of the Magnet Recognition Program® at the time of that application were to:

- Promote quality in a milieu that supports professional practice
- Identify excellence in the delivery of nursing services to patients
- Provide a mechanism for the dissemination of "best practices" in nursing services

The Magnet Steering Committee developed documentation that explained how Abbott Northwestern would meet the Magnet® selection criteria called the "Forces of Magnetism."

In addition, unit-based Magnet champions worked with the steering committee to prepare for the appraiser site visit. The Magnet champions served as liaisons between the steering committee and direct care providers, helping to communicate Magnet news and provide feedback from staff to the steering committee.

In 2005, Sharon Dudley resigned her position, and Terry Graner, DNP, RN, NEA-BC, CENP, became the Vice President of Patient Care Services. Ms. Graner came to the position with deep roots in Abbott Northwestern. She started in the early 1980s when Eitel Hospital closed and folded into Abbott Northwestern. Graner had a strong nursing presence as staff nurse, clinical manager, and director of Medical Surgical services. She was well respected by all team members, and the perfect person to lead the organization into the challenges facing it in 2005.

While no era in health care is without its challenges, many staff members at Abbott Northwestern remember 2005 as a year defined by challenges. Patients, staff, and programs moved into the new Heart Hospital and Excellian was implemented, making the year the most challenging yet! This all happened with extraordinary creativity, collaboration, dedication, and patience. This was all done while maintaining the excellent care for which Abbott Northwestern Hospital is known. Nurses were at the forefront in helping the hospital plan and implement the changes.

To prepare for the Excellian implementation, nurses from throughout the hospital led key initiatives, assisted in workflow planning, and supported

This new era of overwhelming amounts of data led to more information available for patient care team members to do process improvement. Nursing was at the forefront of all this work.

training efforts. More than 500 nurses were trained as "super users" who provided critical support during the go-live period.

In addition, nurses continued to support the Excellian implementation at Abbott Northwestern and within the Allina system by participating in the Patient Care Excellian Workgroup. Over the years, Excellian has had frequent updates for all aspects of care documentation. This new era of overwhelming amounts of data led to more information available for patient care team members to do process improvement. Nursing was at the forefront of all this work.

Nursing Excellence: Achieving Magnet® Status

Jody Portu provided all the support work and documentation of the application for Magnet® status in 2005. Abbott Northwestern nursing representatives presented a request to the American Nurses Credentialing Center Commission on Magnet® for an exception to their rule regarding applicants and unfair labor practices. In April 2006, the hospital received formal documentation stating that the request had been denied. Abbott Northwestern would not be able to apply again until late 2007.

Magnet® recognition efforts continued under the leadership of Tonya Montesinos, MS, BS, RN-BC, NE-BC, PHN, director of Nursing Professional Practice and Magnet Coordinator. Ms. Montesinos worked with the Magnet Steering Committee to write the formal documents for submission in late 2008. These documents told the story of nursing at Abbott Northwestern through the scope of the 14 Forces of Magnetism.

After a week-long site visit by Magnet® appraisers in December 2008, Abbott Northwestern received the long-awaited Magnet® designation in early 2009. A celebration was held in the hospital foyer to mark this momentous achievement for which so many worked relentlessly to pursue! Under Ms. Montesinos' guidance, the hospital was redesignated in 2014.

Magnet® status would not have been achieved without significant leadership from Ms. Graner, who earned a doctorate in nursing during the time Magnet® status was being sought. She, along with a strong nursing leadership team and dedicated nursing staff, was able to achieve what only two other hospitals in Minnesota have done.

Foundational to the process of achieving Magnet® status is the nursing practice model that grew out of our evolving nursing vision and core beliefs:

1. Advocacy
2. Caring
3. Continuous improvement
4. Cultural awareness and recognition
5. Ethics
6. Leadership
7. Relationships
8. Stewardship

This model arises from the Nursing Department Strategic plan for 2014-2017 and is in line with the first of five Magnet® goals. The five Magnet® goals are:

1. Transformational Leadership

This plan is synchronized with the hospital's strategic plan and outlines objectives and goals at a high level, leaving flexibility for the changing priorities and objectives that come with annual goal setting done at the Allina Health level.

The plan was developed with input from 25 staff nurses and nurse leaders. The group did the following:

- Reviewed the existing strategic plan
- Reviewed the Abbott Northwestern strategic plan
- Analyzed the department's strengths and weaknesses, opportunities and threats
- Narrowed the plan's scope and language
- Created a 2014-2017 plan that is user-friendly and attainable

2. Structural Empowerment

This is demonstrated by the development of strong relationships and partnerships that provide an environment where professional practice flourishes

Abbott Northwestern received the long-awaited Magnet® designation in early 2009.

and where nurses are empowered to find the best way to accomplish organizational goals and achieve desired outcomes.

An example of this goal is found in the work led by Faith Pollock, RN, ACNS-BC, CDE, a diabetes clinical nurse specialist. Ms. Pollock is known throughout the hospital as the go-to resource for diabetes, pre-diabetes, hyperglycemia, and hypoglycemia care. Her clinical expertise and strong problem-solving skills have helped shape a comprehensive, patient-centered approach to diabetes care. The growing incidence of diabetes poses a significant challenge for hospitals. (Approximately 23 percent of Allina Health inpatients have diabetes.)

Ms. Pollock leads the house-wide glycemic control team and collaborates with multidisciplinary team members daily. She has led efforts to better understand how diabetic care can be improved and has developed diabetes-related tools, resources, and education. Most importantly, Pollock has cultivated strong relationships with medical and nursing staff, earning their respect as a trusted resource.

3. Exemplary Professional Practice

This is commitment to the highest standards of professionalism and sustains a culture of safety, compassion, and quality in the delivery of patient care. The hospital is replete with exceptional stories of exemplary professional practice. The best example of this is found in the multidisciplinary rounds that were begun as a pilot project in 2013 and then expanded to the Heart Hospital in 2014. This new approach to patient rounding is helping the hospital prevent fragmentation and delays in health care delivery while enhancing the patient experience.

Multidisciplinary rounding is a new process with these key elements:

- Geographically dedicated staff: hospitalist, care coordinator, social service scribe to assist the care team with documentation and communication

- Common note template and discrete fields for discharge plan to the electronic medical record

- Rapid rounds meeting at 8 a.m. to highlight major progression of care issues and discharge needs

- Multidisciplinary rounds at the bedside with the patient/family that involve the hospitalist, bedside nurse, scribe, and others as appropriate

According to Autumn Gode, RN, ACNS-BC, a clinical nurse specialist who helped to plan and launch the multidisciplinary rounding at Abbott Northwestern, "If the nurse and hospitalist did not connect to discuss the plan that day, he or she would rely on the hospitalist's note in Excellian. This means the nurse may have cared for a patient for a period of time after the physician visit without knowledge of the plan. This does not support taking care of the patient as a team."

She goes on to say, "Multidisciplinary rounding creates a stronger sense of cohesiveness on the unit, with everyone working together to anticipate obstacles and prevent delays in care. The end result is a more clearly articulated care plan, better communication, and a better patient experience."

The impact of multidisciplinary rounding is measured using a variety of metrics. These metrics lead to team understanding of opportunities to continually plan, do, study, and act (PDSA).

4. New Knowledge and Innovation

Nurses contribute to patient care, to Abbott Northwestern, and to the profession by identifying new models of care, improving existing protocols, assessing new evidence, and developing more effective practices.

The finest example of this goal is the St. Catherine University partnership with Abbott Northwestern in the Evidence-based Practice Fellowship Program (EBP). This is a 12-month program in which a staff nurse is partnered with an advanced-practice registered nurse to address a relevant practice question.

The partnership provides collaboration between clinical staff, faculty, and students with expertise to help answer the nurses' clinical question. It augments Abbott Northwestern's EBP Fellowship by bringing faculty expertise in research and EBP, support for grant applications, and additional disciplines to partner with nurses. In addition, it provides support for education of EBP Fellows and clinical mentors, and lessens the work load through project sharing.

Teams conduct and complete a clinical question to address hospital organizational priorities related to improving patient outcomes. At the end of eight modules, staff at Abbott Northwestern and faculty and students at St. Catherine University demonstrate greater knowledge and stronger attitudes supporting

"The Evidence-Based Practice Fellowship has expanded my nursing practice. I now ask about or look for the research to back up the interventions implemented at the bedside. The whole direction of my career has changed because of the fellowship..."
—*Laura Genzler, BSN, RN, PB2000*

evidence-based practice. At the close of the project, fellows will disseminate results to colleagues at Abbott Northwestern, the annual Inter-professional Summit at St. Catherine University, and submit for a poster, oral presentation, and/or publication at a local and or national nursing conference.

Here is the response from Laura Genzler, BSN, RN, PB2000, one of the fellows who completed the program: "The Evidence-Based Practice Fellowship has expanded my nursing practice. I now ask about or look for the research to back up the interventions implemented at the bedside. The whole direction of my career has changed because of the fellowship. Initially, I was totally ignorant about EBP and nursing research. I have now completed a research study, presented the results at the University of Minnesota and the National Teaching Institute, and have been accepted into a PhD nursing program to begin this fall. Two years prior to the fellowship, I would have never envisioned these opportunities occurring."

Sue Sendelbach, PhD, RN, CCNS, FAHA, Director of Nursing Research at Abbott Northwestern, leads this collaborative program. Ms. Sendelbach also provides leadership around use of evidence-based knowledge that supports changes in nursing practice. She is integrally involved with process improvement at the bedside.

5. Empirical Outcomes

Nursing at Abbott Northwestern focuses annually on determining the key areas for improvement in patient outcomes and addressing how the evidence-based process is used to improve practice. Each community of care is involved in the process and focuses on areas of significance such as pressure ulcer prevention, patient fall prevention, improved nursing communication, or improved inter-professional communication. Each study is followed for improvement. The data is posted so that patient care providers can use it to continually improve outcomes.

The benefits of the Magnet® program to Abbott Northwestern Hospital are:

- Attract and retain top talent
- Improve patient care, safety, and satisfaction
- Foster a collaborative culture
- Advance nursing standards and practice

- Grow the hospital business and financial success

Abbott Northwestern Hospital leadership is very supportive of nursing and the need to invest in the Magnet® program to ensure patients receive the highest quality of care.

Recognition, Awards, and the Power of Philanthropy

Abbott Northwestern has a long history of recognizing nurses for the excellent care they provide. For more than 30 years, Nursing has sponsored a luncheon recognizing nurses for their outstanding achievements. The events are hosted during National Nurses Week in May, coinciding with the birthday of Florence Nightingale on May 12. While the Nursing Department sponsors the luncheon, the generosity of the Abbott Northwestern physicians, who contribute financially through the Plus One Program, provides $5,000 annually for a gift in recognition of excellence.

Since the early 2000s, a Nursing Excellence in Practice luncheon has been held to honor all the nurses who have worked at Abbott Northwestern for 25 years or more. In 2015, 405 nurses were invited to attend the luncheon. Some of the awards are for scholarships for nurses to complete Bachelor of Science in Nursing requirements, advanced nursing practice degrees, or Doctorate of Nursing Practice programs. The following is a list of the awards given annually, with new additions for 2015.

- The Irene Briggs Award given to a nurse in The Mother Baby Center
- The Mae McWeeny Nursing Mentorship Award
- The Compassionate Care Award
- The Marguerite S. Richards Nursing Preceptorship Award
- The Jane Wachtler Becker Award given to a nurse to pursue degree completion or a MSN degree
- Abbott Northwestern Community Service Award
- The Judy Edin Excellence in Nursing Practice Award given to a nurse in cardiovascular (CV)

- The Carol Huttner Nursing Excellence in Practice Awards given to 10 recipients
- The Dee and Gordon Sprenger Scholarship Award, a $15,000 award
- The William Petersen Award, a $10,000 award given to a nurse annually

None of these awards would be possible without the generous support of Abbott Northwestern senior leaders, dedicated physicians on the medical staff, grateful patients, and families and nurses paying it forward. To this end, Nursing Champions of Care was established in 2014, a collective, compassionate philanthropy among nurses, for nurses, and for the health of the nursing profession at Abbott Northwestern. The program was created to address an urgent need to enrich the hospital's Nursing Excellence Fund with appeals to actively employed and retired nurses and Abbott, Northwestern, and Abbott Northwestern nursing school alumni. Establishing a robust Nursing Excellence Fund allows more nurses to receive the advanced training and continuing education they need to provide the highest level of patient care.

The Nursing Champions of Care program honors Dr. Bill and Mary Petersen for their support of nurses and for providing the seed funding to launch this program. Dr. Petersen received the lifelong, honorary title of Abbott Northwestern Nurse for his passionate and unwavering devotion to Abbott Northwestern nurses. We are forever grateful to Bill and Mary.

We are also grateful to Gordon and Dee Sprenger for the generous support they provide annually through the Sprenger Scholarship Award, which supports one nurse who is pursuing an advanced degree in nursing.

We are grateful to Anita Thompson, RN, a retired Abbott Northwestern obstetrics and gynecology nurse who has generously donated a significant legacy gift. Thompson says, "This gift is about my love of the hospital and my love of nursing. I loved being a nurse. I think it's important to support nursing and I want to help others further their education in nursing."

Judy Edin, RN, was so inspired by Anita's generous gift that she donated a $30,000 gift to be given in $10,000 increments over the next three years to nurses working in the cardiovascular service area to complete a BSN degree. Ms. Edin spent her career at Abbott Northwestern working the cardiovascular ICUs, and in the cardiovascular lab prior to her retirement.

A great deal of thanks goes to the nurses, past and present, for compassionate care and compassionate giving. We are grateful to all who contribute to advance excellence in nursing practice, which will be reflected in the exceptional outcomes of patients cared for at Abbott Northwestern Hospital.

Part II
Nursing Research – 1990-2002
Elaine Hogan Miller, Ph.D., RN

Prologue
What institution, in addition to the University of Iowa, would have a patient care/nurse researcher on staff in the 1990s? Turns out it would be a place with visionary leadership. Abbott Northwestern had the leadership to support the vision of evidence-based patient care by supporting the work of a clinical researcher.

Nurse leaders saw the opportunity to incorporate a patient care nursing researcher, resulting in patient care improvement projects and strong interdisciplinary participation and growth. In this section, I include the major studies conducted during this period, with emphasis on patient care results and their incorporation into practice, interdisciplinary participation, growth of staff, publications in peer-reviewed journals, presentations at conferences, and grants obtained. I've included citations for those interested in reviewing the exact patient care improvements achieved. Other studies of less magnitude completed during the period are not described here.

The Birth of the Clinical Researcher Role – The Angiogram Study
As a nursing faculty member from Mankato State University, I practiced summers on an interventional cardiovascular unit at Abbott Northwestern to maintain relevant clinical practice. While there, astute leadership, committed clinical nurse specialists, engaged physicians, interested staff nurses, and most importantly a relevant patient care problem helped create my role of patient care nurse researcher.

Clinical nurse specialist Debra Rustad noted complaints of post-operative

Abbott Northwestern had the leadership to support the vision of evidence-based patient care by supporting the work of a clinical researcher.

Brenda Kerschbaum... championed a study... to regularly move high-risk patients in bed, place pillows to protect protrusions, use special rotating mattresses, and use nutrition and wound care to reduce pressure ulcer development and improve wound healing. Pressure ulcers at Abbott Northwestern were reduced by 40 percent as a result of the study.

discomfort by patients undergoing the common procedure of coronary angiogram. The discomfort arose from immobilization of the groin angiogram site with a 10-pound sandbag for six hours after the procedure. The research tested the differing effects of the sandbag, a sheet tucked over the affected leg, or advice to lie still in bed, all for six hours. There was no significant difference between the sandbag and the sheet tucked over the leg (Hogan-Miller, E., Rustad, D., Sendelbach, S., Goldenberg, I., 1995).

As a result of the study, patients no longer had the heavy sandbag at the potential bleeding site, but rather a sheet tucked over the leg. This resulted in greater reported comfort for patients and eventually shorter length of hospital stays. Dr. Irv Goldenberg was the necessary physician researcher on the project. This study was presented at six research conferences (references below), most notably to a standing-room-only audience at the American Heart Association Meeting in New Orleans. Soon, $13,800 in grant monies was obtained for the study.

This study resulted in a major practice change for the patient and opportunity for collaborative nursing and medical research.

Pressure Ulcer Guidelines and Study

The Agency for Health Care Policy and Research established guidelines for the prevention of pressure ulcers. Brenda Kerschbaum, director of enterostomal nursing at Abbott Northwestern Hospital, championed a study that used the guidelines to regularly move high-risk patients in bed, place pillows to protect protrusions, use special rotating mattresses, and use nutrition and wound care to reduce pressure ulcer development and improve wound healing. Pressure ulcers at Abbott Northwestern were reduced by 40 percent as a result of the study. A practice change was implemented Abbott Northwestern-wide, and two presentations made at national conferences (references below). Grant funding for the project totaled $6,189.

Pain Management

The pain management studies resulted in the greatest breadth and depth to patient care improvement. A pre-test/post-test design was used to assess the effect of modified medical order sets that reflected evidence-based pain drugs, route of administration, and plans of care. Results of the study included reduced length of stay, increased use of recommended drugs and route of administration, better education of providers, improved patient response with decreased pain intensity, and increased satisfaction with pain management. Implementation was methodically introduced to cardiovascular, surgical, and oncology patient units. Interdisciplinary work was diligent: Dr. Miles Belgrade, director of the Pain Management Clinic at Abbott Northwestern, was our tireless medical champion; pharmacists Shelley Shepherd and Mary Cook were vital to the study of drug components; and clinical nurse specialists Jody Portu and Jennifer Neitzel orchestrated the changes into patient care practices.

The project resulted in several publications (Hogan Miller, E., Belgrade, M., Cook, Portu, J., Shepherd, M., & Sierzant, T., Sallmen, P, & Fraki, S., 1999), (Sierzant, T., Portu, J. B., Belgrade, M., Cook, M., Shepherd, M., Rogness, E., Hogan-Miller, E., Cassibo, L., & Neitzel, J., 1999) , and seven presentations (references below), with grant monies totaling $82,100. A CD-ROM was created to educate providers both within and outside of Abbott Northwestern. This study, spanning seven years, reaped hospital-wide improved patient pain management, ability to influence national trends in pain management, stellar and committed interdisciplinary work, and promotion of professional growth by opportunities for publishing and presentations.

Bladder Ultrasound Accuracy and Effectiveness

The purpose of this study was to determine the effect ultrasound assessment of urinary bladder volume had on patients and cost outcomes for patients needing postoperative catheterization. Patients who had routine, timed urinary catheterization were compared with those having ultrasound assessment only when prescribed volumes were met. There was no difference in numbers of catheterizations during hospitalization; however, there were significantly more urinary infections for patients in the routine catheterization group. Both patients and nurses had high satisfaction levels with the bladder ultrasound technology. The Bladder Ultrasound Technology was purchased for patient use. Martha Frederickson, nurse manager, Jennifer Neitzel, CNS, and John Heller, MD, were process owners for this study. The study resulted in one publication (Frederickson, M., Neitzel, J., Hogan-Miller, E., Reuter, S., Heller, J. Graner, T.,

2000), two presentations (references below) at national conferences, and grants totaling $10,188.

Enteral Feedings

Hospital policy advanced the use of blue dye assessment with enteral feedings to prevent aspiration. As a result of an evidence-based literature review, X-rays were used to verify placement, rules about tube placement and residual volumes, head elevation, and the care of the artificial airway. Policy and practice change in this instance were the result of existing studies. Linda Fellows, CNS, and Patricia Felt, RN, were the process owners of this practice change. One publication resulted from this study (Fellows, L., Hogan Miller, E., Frederickson, M., Bly, B. & Felt, P., 2000).

Daily Weights

A staff nurse, Katie Simonson, RN, working the night shift on a post-operative cardiac unit, identified that waking patients early in the morning for a body weight disturbed patient rest. Body weight is important in medication dosing of patients with cardiac disease. The literature was reviewed, and one research study was identified: weight before bed and weight at 5 a.m. the next morning did not differ. The study in the literature was replicated, and again there was no difference. This result was undoubtedly because patients in the hospital are recumbent and do not experience dependent edema. Physicians did not support a practice change based on these data. One presentation resulted from this study (references below).

Music Therapy

A randomized clinical trial was conducted to test the effects of music therapy (easy listening, classical, and jazz) – versus a quiet, uninterrupted rest period – on pain intensity, anxiety, blood pressure and pulse, and opioids consumed. The patients had undergone coronary bypass graft or heart valve surgery. Patients having the music therapy had a significant reduction in reported pain and anxiety. There was, however, no difference in blood pressure, pulse rate, or opioid amounts. The process owner for the study was Susan Sendelbach, CNS.

The patient care study was noteworthy for the rigorous experimental design in a clinical environment and for the multiple hospital sites involved. Nurses learning of the study results utilized music as a pain care intervention, but the intervention was not incorporated into post-operative order sets. One publication (Sendelbach, S., Doran, K., Halm, M. & Hogan Miller, E., 2006) and one presentation (references below) resulted from the study. Grant monies totaled $24,900. This study generated much academic interest and represents a progression from studies with a physiological emphasis to one of the patients' response to illness.

Patients having the music therapy had a significant reduction in reported pain and anxiety.

Summary

In summary, seven consequential studies were conducted, five practice changes occurred; health care professionals (clinical nurse specialists, pharmacists, physicians, dieticians, enterostomal nurses, staff nurses, nurse managers) were intimately involved and professionally changed by the projects. The research, with leadership support, emphasized patient-centered research questions, strong research methods and statistical analysis, and interdisciplinary research teams. Experimental designs were used if possible (angiogram and music studies), descriptive designs when necessary (pain studies). Strong research design was upheld so that patient care improvements could be implemented.

The history would be incomplete without noting that having a researcher/academic role in a clinical agency was not without controversy. Directors of Operations did not always see the value of the role. Physicians, accustomed to medical research, warmed slowly but surely when they viewed the academic, evidence-based, patient-centered projects. Staff nurses got bogged down in the methods and drudgery of data collection. In retrospect, I might have worked more to interpret the work internally, rather than to methodically complete the work.

One important inroad was that I became a member of the Abbott Northwestern Institutional Review Board (Research Review Board), as patient care nurse researcher. This was the first time that nursing was represented on that important research board.

The clinical nurse patient care researcher role at Abbott Northwestern and

The researcher embodies, espouses, and effectuates evidence-based care. The patient care research ideas and hard work came from clinical nurse specialists, pharmacists, physicians, enterostomal nurses, staff nurses, and dietitians.

consequent patient care and professional effects are a result of the visionary leadership of two nurse leaders: Carol Huttner and Julianne Morath. Huttner, an always practical, hardworking and patient care-centered director of Cardiovascular Services, recognized the potential for the role once she viewed the power of the Angiogram Study. On the day the order sets arrived to the Interventional Cardiology Unit with "sandbag to site" removed, I can still see Huttner at the unit entrance mouthing quietly, "No more sandbags, no more sandbags." She promoted the clinical research role by finding finances to present the Angiogram Study at the American Heart Association. She assured that nurses in all roles, from staff nurse to researcher, were able to attend. She then advocated for the role of patient care nurse researcher to then Vice President of Patient Care, Julianne Morath. Vice President Morath, who was cognitive, warm and articulate, obtained administrative approval for the role. She was a consistently erudite yet egalitarian advocate for the role into its future.

The history of Abbott Northwestern Hospital from 1990-2002, especially its patient care, was enhanced by the presence of a clinical researcher on site. The researcher embodies, espouses, and effectuates evidence-based care. The patient care research ideas and hard work came from clinical nurse specialists, pharmacists, physicians, enterostomal nurses, staff nurses, and dietitians. In addition, several masters theses were completed as a result of the studies. Most prominent is the focus on and improvement to patient care at Abbott Northwestern that resulted from this role.

Patient care research outcomes at Abbott Northwestern during 1990-2002 were the result of visionary leadership, a focus on patient care, a passion for evidence-based care among health care disciplines, and the respected glue of research.

References – Part II
Angiogram Study
Hogan Miller, E. (1993). The effects of three methods of femoral site immobilization on bleeding and comfort post cardiac angiogram: A randomized clinical trial presented on Critical Care Nurses, a television presentation supported by Sigma Theta Tau's Nursing Approach. Sundays, June, July, and August 1993.

Hogan-Miller, E. (1993). The effects of three methods of femoral site immobilization on bleeding and comfort post-cardiac angiogram: A randomized clinical trial. 17th Annual Research Conference of The Midwest Nursing Research Society, Cleveland, OH, March 1993.

Hogan-Miller, E., Rustad, D. (1993) The effect of anxiety, coping strategies, and gender on discomfort of patients post-cardiac angiogram. 10th Annual Nursing Research Conference: Coping with Illness, Marquette University, Milwaukee, WI, March,1993.

Hogan-Miller, E., Rustad, D., Sendelbach, S., Guthrie, S., Hood, J., Ismert, A, Rudebeck, R., Goldenberg, I. (1992). The effects of three methods of femoral site immobilization on bleeding and comfort post-cardiac angiogram: A randomized clinical trial. The 65th Scientific Session of the American Heart Association, New Orleans, LA, November 16-19, 1992.

Hogan-Miller, E., Rustad, D., Sendelbach, S., Goldenberg, I. (1995). The effects of three methods of femoral site immobilization on bleeding and comfort post-cardiac angiogram. *The American Journal of Critical Care* 4(2), 143-148.

Rustad, D. & Hogan Miller, E. (1992). The effect of anxiety, coping strategies, and gender on discomfort of patients post-cardiac angiogram. The 5th Annual Clinical Research Conference. Iowa City, Iowa, February 18, 1993.

Sendelbach, S. & Hogan-Miller, E. (1993). The effects of three methods of femoral site immobilization on bleeding and comfort post-cardiac angiogram: A randomized clinical trial. AACN National Teaching Institute, Anaheim, CA, May 23-27.

Pressure Ulcer Study
Hogan-Miller, E. (1994). Abbott Northwestern Hospital Nurses Find Large Cost Savings in Bed Sore Prevention. Invited presentation to the Washington Press Corp at the presentation of the 15th AHCPR Guideline, "Treatment of Pressure Ulcers." Department of Health and Human Services, Washington, D.C., December 21, 1994.

Hogan-Miller, E. (1995). The Effect of Implementation of the AHCPR Pressure Ulcer Guidelines on Patient and Provider Outcomes in a Tertiary Care Setting. Invited presentation at the Midwest Nursing Research Society

"Nursing Research: Driving Health Care Outcomes," Kansas City, Missouri, April 3, 1995.

Pain Study

Belgrade, M.J., Hogan Miller, E., Portu, J., Shepherd, S. (1999). Implementation of the agency for health care policy and research (AHCPR), acute pain guidelines in a population of coronary artery bypass graft recipients. 8th World Congress of Pain, Vancouver, BC, Canada, August 17-22.

Frederickson, M., Cook, M., Belgrade, M., Hogan-Miller, E. (1997). Use of Evidenced-based Practices to Improve Patient Pain Management after Hysterectomy: Strategies and Outcomes. Abstract presentation at the Fourth National Research Utilization Conference, The University of Iowa Hospitals and Clinics Department of Nursing, Iowa City, IA, April 25, 1997.

Hogan Miller, E., Belgrade, M., Cook, Portu, J., Shepherd, M., & Sierzant, T., Sallmen, P, & Fraki, S. (1999). Institution-wide pain management improvement through the use of evidence-based content, strategies, resources, and outcomes. Quality Management in Health Care, 2, (7), 28-40.

Hogan-Miller, E. Sierzant, T., Shepherd, S., Portu, J., Cook, M., Belgrade, M. (1998). Use of Evidence-based Practices to Improve Patient Pain Management in Surgical Patient Populations: Strategies and Outcomes. Poster presentation at the Midwest Nursing Research Society, Columbus, OH. March 28-31.

Neitzel, J., Hogan-Miller, E. (1997). Implementation of the Agency for Health Care Policy and Research Acute Pain Guidelines with an Orthopedic Surgical Population. Abstract presentation at the National Association of Orthopedic Nurses "Make a Difference," Philadelphia, PA, May 18-21, 1997.

Neitzel, J., Hogan Miller, E., Shepherd, M., Belgrade, M. (1999). Improving Pain Management after Total Joint Replacement Surgery. Orthopedic Nursing, 18(4), 37-45, 64.

Sierzant, T., Portu, J., Hogan-Miller, E. (1997). Implementation of the Agency for Health Care Policy and Research (AHCPR) Clinical Practice Guidelines for Acute and Cancer Pain Management: Process and Outcomes in a Tertiary Care Hospital. Poster presentation at the American Society of Pain Management Nurses Seventh Annual Meeting, Seattle, WA, March 9-12, 1997.

Sierzant, T., Portu, J. B., Belgrade, M., Cook, M., Shepherd, M., Rogness, E., Hogan-Miller, E., Cassibo, L., & Neitzel, J. (1999) Pain Management: A Comprehensive Approach (CD-ROM, V.1.0). Aspen Publishing: Chicago, IL. 1,800 CDs sold on 12/2001.

Thompson, A., Hogan-Miller, E. (1997). Implementation of the Agency for Health Care Policy and Research (AHCPR) Acute Pain Guidelines for the Hysterectomy Patient: Effects on Patient and Provider Outcomes. Poster presentation at the Association of Women's Health Obstetric and Neonatal Nurses AWHONIN 1997 Convention, Washington, D.C., June 15-18, 1997.

Bladder Ultrasound Study
Frederickson, M., Reuter, S., Neitzel, J., Hogan-Miller, E., & Heller, J. (1999). The Implementation of Bedside Bladder Ultrasound Technology: Effects on Patient and Cost Postoperative Outcomes in Tertiary Care. Poster presentation at the Academy of Medical-Surgical Nurses 8th Annual Convention, Phoenix, AZ, September 23-26, 1999.

Frederickson, M., Neitzel, J., Hogan-Miller, E., Reuter, S., Heller, J. Graner, T. (2000). The Implementation of Bedside Bladder Ultrasound Technology: Effects on Patient and Cost Postoperative Outcomes in Tertiary Care. *Orthopaedic Nursing*, 19(2), 79-87.

Neitzel, J.,Frederickson, M., Hogan-Miller, E., Cassibo, L. (1999). The Effects of Bedside Ultrasound Assessment of Bladder Bolume vs. Intermittent Catheterization on Postoperative Patient Outcomes. Abstract presentation at The Sixth National Research Utilization Conference "Diffusion of Practice Innovations," The University of Iowa Hospitals & Clinics, Iowa City, IA, April 25-26, 1999.

Enteral Feeding Study
Fellows, L., Hogan Miller, E., Frederickson, M., Bly, B. & Felt, P. (2000).

Evidence-based practice for enteral feedings: Aspiration prevention strategies, bedside detection, and practice change. *Medical Surgical Nursing*, May, 2000.

Weight Study
Simonton, K., Hogan-Miller, E., Cassibo, L. (1999). Difference in weights obtained in the evening and during the night for patients hospitalized post-open heart surgery or for congestive heart failure. Abstract presentation at The Sixth National Research Utilization Conference "Diffusion of Practice Innovations," The University of Iowa Hospitals & Clinics, Iowa City, IA, April 25-26, 1999.

Music Therapy Study
Hogan Miller, E., Sendelbach, S., Doran, K., & Halm, M. (2000). The effects of music therapy on physiological and psychological outcomes for adult patients having cardiac surgery. 24th Annual Midwest Nursing Research Society Conference: Millennium Milestones: Looking Back, Moving Forward. Dearborn, MI, March 31-April 3.

Sendelbach, S., Doran, K., Halm, M. & Hogan Miller, E. (2006). The Effects of Music Therapy on Psychological and Physiological Outcomes for Adult Patients Having Cardiac Surgery. *Journal of Cardiovascular Nursing*, May/June.

22

Obstetrics and Neonatal Care
1880-2014
Dr. Emanuel P. Gaziano, FACOG
Dr. Ron Peterson, FACOG

Northwestern Hospital was founded in 1882, and its first mission was the care of women and children. Dr. Mary Hood patterned the hospital after Woman's Medical College of Pennsylvania and provided nurse education from the beginning. It is likely that obstetrics was always a part of Northwestern Hospital care since the original endowment specified providing obstetrical beds. Abbott Hospital, founded in the first decade of the twentieth century, also provided maternal and obstetrical care.

As the hospitals grew, peripheral medical services were enhanced, and the great transformation in obstetrical care resulted in decreased maternal and fetal mortality. The treatment of the major contributors to maternal mortality, such as eclampsia, hemorrhage, and sepsis, improved outcomes and progressively led to more births conducted within hospitals. The use of magnesium sulphate for eclampsia improved blood transfusion techniques, and the advent of antibiotics also led to the decline of maternal deaths.

It is likely that obstetrics was always a part of Northwestern Hospital care since the original endowment specified providing obstetrical beds.

Modern Obstetrics

By the 1950s and 60s, both Abbott Hospital and Northwestern Hospital were served predominantly by obstetrician/gynecologists. The post-World War II increase in births facilitated the development of private obstetrician/gynecologists groups, and large private practices thrived in Minneapolis and St. Paul. The Leonard Lang group at St. Mary's Hospital attended hundreds of births per month in the 1950s. Drs. Paul Larson, John Haugen, and Mancel Mitchell led other predominant groups. Among nationally recognized practitioners, Dr. William Stromme, a Northwestern Hospital practitioner from Cornell in New York, co-authored the popular textbook, *Operative Vaginal Delivery*.

Consolidation of Obstetrical Units

In the 1960s and 1970s, priority concerns included consolidation of obstetrical units and the development of tertiary obstetrical care.

By 1967, the formation of a single obstetrical department was considered, to be located at the new Children's Hospital adjacent to Northwestern Hospital. Other discussions for consolidations with Lutheran Deaconess Hospital and Mount Sinai Hospital did not succeed. In 1973, discussions were held with the University of Minnesota Department of OB/GYN to consider a consolidation on the Abbott Northwestern campus. No consolidation agreement was ever reached with the University, but in the 1990s, residents and fellows rotated from the University onto the Perinatology service at Abbott Northwestern.

On May 15, 1969, the OB/GYN Department agreed unanimously to support a merger between Northwestern and Abbott. It was not until 1976 that the two obstetrical campuses were combined at the Northwestern Hospital site. The merger of the two obstetrical units initiated a fusion of cultures. The nursing staffs were joined, and tension remained for a number of years regarding differences in the approach to nursing care. Abbott Hospital had a smaller obstetrical unit and stressed patient inclusivity and birth choices, while Northwestern remained a specialist obstetrics unit.

Development of a Tertiary Care Obstetrical Unit

In the late 1960s, world-class obstetrical investigators from Montevideo, Uruguay participated in the obstetrics program at the University of Minnesota Medical School and at Hennepin County General Hospital under Dr. Donald W. Freeman's direction. These physicians introduced fetal monitoring and fetal physiology concepts that influenced a generation of obstetricians in-training.

On June 17, 1971, Gordon Sprenger, the Northwestern Hospital administrator, reported a meeting of four pediatricians from Children's Hospital regarding the establishment of a high-risk maternity center at Abbott Northwestern Hospital. The adjacent Children's Hospital, with its neonatal intensive care unit, and the proposed high-risk obstetrical unit at Abbott Northwestern would fuse to form the tertiary care unit.

Mr. Sprenger and Dr. David Hill, representing the Abbott Northwestern obstetrical committee, were the driving forces and vision for the creation of Abbott Northwestern's Perinatal Center. Dr. Hill attended the Great Plains Perinatal Association meeting in the fall of 1971. He met with Dr. Roger Freeman, an early national figure in perinatal medicine. The Great Plains organization encouraged the formation of perinatal centers and exchanged conceptual ideas and organizational trends for such centers. The creation of these centers was based upon data demonstrating better outcomes for premature infants delivered at tertiary care centers compared to local hospitals.

Dr. Hill formed a committee of neonatal intensive care physicians and obstetricians to propose criteria for the Perinatal Center. In February of 1973, the Abbott Northwestern Hospital Executive Committee recommended the development of an obstetrical high-risk unit. Other recommendations included specialization and development of cardiac surgery, therapeutic radiology, as well as medical-surgical specialty services. By mid-July 1973, a permanent neonatologist (Dr. David Klein) was on the staff at the adjacent Children's Hospital.

On September 19, 1974, Dr. Hill presented a draft discussion regarding development of a high-risk perinatal unit. Key components included a registered nurse with special training to coordinate services to include:

- Genetic counseling by referral
- Amniocentesis and amnioscopy

The adjacent Children's Hospital, with its neonatal intensive care unit, and the proposed high-risk obstetrical unit at Abbott Northwestern would fuse to form the tertiary care unit.

- Special testing of blood, urine, and amniotic fluid
- Stress testing
- Fetal scalp sampling
- Electronic fetal monitoring
- Emergency operative delivery capabilities

While there was some opposition to the development of the high-risk program, the Department of Ob/Gyn agreed to proceed with planning at their October 14, 1975 meeting. In 1976, Marlene Fondrick was hired as the clinical nursing director for Obstetrics and Gynecology. She remained instrumental in further development.

Approval by the Metropolitan Health Board and recruitment of a perinatologist were critical to the formation of the Perinatal Center. From 1976 until July 1978, the Perinatal Center structure was defined, through meetings with local obstetrical committees, visits to successful perinatal centers around the country, and the formation of a call system to cover transfers of high-risk patients.

Abbott Northwestern Perinatal Center

Dr. Eric Knox became Medical Director of the Perinatal Center in July 1968. Abbott Northwestern and Children's Hospital coordinated outreach activities, neonatologists, perinatologists, and nursing care. In furthering this development, Dr. Knox's role included education, perinatal conferences, staff development, seminars, outreach education, and affiliation with medical school programs. He served as the primary resource for the practice of high-risk care. He developed an outreach program and set the tone for relationships with referring physicians and patients. As a result, obstetrical volume progressively increased. Given the reputation of the two hospitals, low-risk patients also chose to give birth at the facility. Dr. Knox continued to publish and contribute to the medical literature.

In the summer of 1980, the Minnesota Board of Health designated Abbott Northwestern and Children's Hospital as a level III Perinatal Center. Other designated centers in the Twin Cities included Hennepin County Medical Center, the University of Minnesota, and St. Paul's Children's Hospital.

Minneapolis Children's Neonatology Intensive Care Unit (NICU)

Neonatologists were permanently in place at Minneapolis Children's Hospital by July 1973. A transition in neonatal care occurred in 1979 with neonatologists Dr. John Fangman and Dr. Ron Hoekstra. A philosophy developed that differentiated the neonatologists by their decision to be in attendance at high-risk pregnancy deliveries. The group developed an effective outreach strategy and also attended deliveries at outreach hospitals. The neonatal program participated in research, including surfactant and the one-on-one care. The results, as measured by the Vermont Oxford, consistently demonstrated superior outcomes.

Growth of Tertiary Care

By 1985, four perinatologists on the staff took call every fourth night. The Perinatal Center developed a clinic whose services included high-risk consultations, amniocentesis, and prenatal care for high-risk patients. A full-time genetic counselor was on the staff, and a nurse specialist performed in-service education. These individuals were active in monitoring patients, as well as developing quality improvement activities. A formal fetal testing program was also developed.

The neonatal NICU program grew simultaneously. Additional neonatologists were added to the staff, and by 1981, eight neonatal nurse practitioners had been trained. Weekly perinatal conferences were held with local hospitals, which included Fairview Southdale, Unity, Buffalo, and Shakopee.

Growth in Low-risk Births

The growth in low-risk births paralleled the increase in tertiary center activities. Surveys suggested that patient choice for birth included nearness to neonatal

A philosophy developed that differentiated the neonatologists by their decision to be in attendance at high-risk pregnancy deliveries. The group developed an effective outreach strategy and also attended deliveries at outreach hospitals.

In October 1982, the Obstetrical Homecare Program was established. This became one of the largest such program in the United States.

facilities. New groups formed, including those initiated by Dr. Penny Wheeler and Dr. Beth Kilburg (Women's Health Consultants). Existing groups expanded, including John A. Haugen and Associates; Diamond, Hill, and Haislet at Diamond Women's Center; and Associates in Women's Health. Later Health-Partners added Abbott Northwestern as a delivery site for their patients.

Trends in Care

By 1970, all requests for sterilization were submitted to a sterilization committee. The committee modified its criteria by discontinuing the approval process for patients older than 21, but kept in existence all requests for therapeutic abortions. The committee was eventually disbanded.

By the early 1960s, patients sought increased family participation in the birth experience. The presence of fathers in the delivery room at Northwestern was first discussed on October 20, 1965. Due to pressure from other local hospitals, fathers were increasingly admitted to the birthing suite. By 1972, formal classes were offered for expectant parents. A candlelight dinner was offered for obstetrical patients and a guest of their choice prior to discharge. By April 1978, the department approved the presence of fathers in the caesarean section delivery room. Dr. Ronald Peterson led an effort to increase pain relief and anesthesia options, resulting in 24-hour anesthesia coverage with a 24-hour epidural service.

In February 1981, a grief support group was proposed for women and their families with perinatal losses. In October 1982, the Obstetrical Homecare Program was established. This became one of the largest such programs in the United States.

In 1980, the average length of stay for a vaginal delivery was 4.09 days, and for a caesarean section 7.05 days. These lengths of stay have declined to about two days or less for vaginal delivery and three days or less for a caesarean section.

Expansion of Tertiary Care Services

By 1989, five perinatologists staffed the Perinatal Center. Dr. Manny Gaziano was named Medical Director (1989-2006). Dr. Eric Knox (1978-1999) remained as a partner in the management of the center. Dr. Gaziano and Dr. Bruce Ferrara (neonatology) took the strategic lead in developing an outreach program, as well as visiting hospitals within the region. Dr. Gaziano led the expansion to Park Nicollet. He established outreach clinics in Minnesota at Fairview Southdale, Fairview Ridges, St. Cloud, HealthPartners-St. Paul, University of Minnesota, and North Memorial, as well as in Mason City, Iowa.

In 1991, he established a second tertiary care unit with a clinic at United Hospital in St. Paul. Clinical volume markedly increased, and by 2005, 15 perinatologists were on the staff. A similar number of neonatologists were hired. This made Allina's combined prenatal centers at Abbott and United Hospitals one of the largest in the United States. Care and specialization expanded to include chorionic villus sampling, fetal blood sampling, fetal transfusions, pre-natal sonography of malformations, and consultations. Perinatologists and neonatologists provided consistent contributions to the medical literature, and perinatologists covered call at the tertiary care centers and staffed the outpatient clinics.

This cooperative relationship between perinatologists and neonatologists expanded the range and breadth of clinical care. Nursing services at both sites became stronger. Given the patient volume and acuity, the obstetrical and neonatal nurses were achieving elevated skills.

The sonographers and genetic counselors were also expanding their knowledge and skills. In addition, both programs achieved greater financial stability. This allowed the programs to grow. Children's Hospital continued to expand and attract a wide range of subspecialists.

Dr. Gaziano transitioned from Medical Director of the perinatal program to clinical staff in 2006. He retired from service at Abbott Northwestern Hospital in 2012. Dr. Bruce Ferrara continued in a strong leadership role for the Neonatal program.

Administrative Support

In 1981, Venetia Kudrle was an administrative resident at Abbott Northwestern. In 1982, she became the administrator for Perinatal Services. She was key

Mother Baby Center services include low- and high-risk deliveries, breast feeding and lactation support, high-risk pregnancy and genetic counseling, neonatal care, post-partum services, reproductive medicine, and social services.

in supporting a cooperative association with the University. From 1996 to 1999, Carol Huttner, RN, served as Vice President for Patient Care and sponsor for obstetrics at four metropolitan hospitals. Gordon Sprenger, CEO of Allina, continued to support the program with Bob Spinner as administrator at Abbott Northwestern. Other critical administrative support included Dr. Penny Wheeler, Dr. Ben Bache-Wiig, and Dr. Robert Weiland. Ken Paulus, CEO from 2005 to 2014, was also a key supporter.

Tertiary Care Services: 2006 to Present

Increased competition from the University of Minnesota perinatology group significantly reduced the number of outreach perinatal clinics and high-risk deliveries. At the same time, Allina clinics were added in Woodbury and North Dakota.

Allina Health and Children's Hospitals and Clinics of Minnesota formed The Mother Baby Center. After years of planning, the center opened in 2012 with a new facility on the Children's campus in Minneapolis. Dr. Lisa Saul is the lead physician. Mother Baby Center services include low- and high-risk deliveries, breast feeding and lactation support, high-risk pregnancy and genetic counseling, neonatal care, post-partum services, reproductive medicine, and social services.

The Midwest Fetal Care Center provides maternal fetal therapies including fetal invasive procedures and neonatal care. The team is composed of maternal fetal medicine (MFM) specialists with specialized training and neonatal surgeons. Dr. Bill Block (MFM) and Dr. Brad Feltis (Pediatric Surgeon) have led the effort. Supporting specialists include those in ultrasound, cardiology, neurosurgery, pediatric surgery, genetics, obstetrics/perinatology, radiology, nursing, and neonatal medicine. Nursing coordination of care is emphasized.

As a result of The Mother Baby Center, low-risk volumes have increased. An extension of the concept is planned for Mercy Hospital in July 2015.

A transition in the care model for perinatology was developed and pursued by the perinatology group with Dr. Donald D. Wothe as Medical Director. Perinatology care is transitioning increasingly to consultation only, with fewer staffed outpatient clinics. OB/GYN laborists at Abbott Northwestern and United Hospitals will perform high-risk deliveries predominantly. The care model change has resulted in fewer staff perinatologists.

REFERENCES

1. http://en.wikipedia.org/wiki/Abbott_Northwestern_Hospital

2. Dr. Paul Larson, Northwestern OB/GYN minutes, May 20, 1965

3. Ob/GYN minutes, and NW, 5/16/1963

4. Ob/GYN Minutes, NW 5/20/1965

5. Ob/GYN Minutes, NW 10/19/1967

6. Ob/GYN Minutes, ANW 8/30/1973

7. Ob/GYN Minutes, ANW 5/15/1969

8. Nancy Sawyer, RN, interview, May 22, 2014

9. Ob/GYN Minutes, ANW 6/17/1971

10. ANW Executive Committee Meeting February 13, 1973

11. Ob/GYN Minutes, ANW 9/19/1974

12. Ob/GYN Minutes, ANW 10/14/1975

13. Ob/GYN Minutes, ANW 1976 to 1978

14. Ob/GYN Minutes, ANW 11/21/1977

15. Ob/GYN Minutes, ANW 4/19/1973

16. Dr. John Fangman, Interview, June 27, 2014

17. Ob/GYN Minutes, ANW 7/6/1970

18, Ob/GYN Minutes, ANW 10/20/1965

19. Ob/GYN Minutes, ANW 4/20/1972

20. Ob/GYN Minutes, ANW 4/25/1978

21. Ob/GYN Minutes, ANW 2/23/1982

22. Ob/GYN Minutes, ANW 2/24/1981

23. Ob/GYN Minutes, ANW 10/1982

24. Ob/GYN Minutes, ANW 1/27/1981

25. Ob/GYN Minutes, ANW 1/26/1982

26. Ob/GYN Minutes, ANW 3/4/1980

27. http://www.specialtycare.net/bio/carol-huttner-rn/

28. http://themotherbabycenter.org/

29. http://themotherbabycenter.org/services/midwest-fetal-care-center/meet-team/

30. http://themotherbabycenter.org/mother-baby-center/coon-rapids/

23

Ophthalmology
1970-2014
Dr. Donald P. LeWin

More strides have occurred in ophthalmology at Abbott Northwestern Hospital in the past 40 years than in the previous several centuries. It would be impossible to consider each individual who served as a staff ophthalmologist during these years. Rather, this history will read like a highlight reel of those individuals whose innovation and expertise allowed major surgical techniques and treatment modalities to be brought to Abbott Northwestern. Our thanks to the many ophthalmologists on staff during these years who simply could not all be mentioned in this brief history.

The huge strides made in ophthalmology were not a result of efforts by the ophthalmic community alone. The support of a medical staff that cared for our patients and an administration that provided the machinery needed to deliver these technologies was essential. We are especially thankful to Dr. Robert Scott and Dr. Richard Sturgeon, and their partners, for medical support, and to Gordon Sprenger, CEO of Abbott Northwestern Hospital, for his administrative support.

Cataract Surgery

Ophthalmology traces its origins as a surgical specialty to 2000 B.C. with the first description of cataract couching. This procedure dislocates a cataract into the vitreous space (the space between the lens and the retina) so that light might reach the retina. Slowly, improvements in safely removing cataracts appeared right through to the 1950s. But restoring vision for an individual required either a contact lens or thick cataract glasses. Fortunately, innovations by some brilliant entrepreneurs in 1965-1975 improved the functional outcome for the cataract patient.

The first motorized operating microscope was introduced in 1965; the first intra-ocular lens implant was performed in 1969. Phako-emulcification was introduced in 1967, allowing for a cataract to be removed in small fragments through a micro incision, leaving a capsular membrane behind for supporting lens implants. New suction cutter instruments for the removal of abnormalities in the vitreous gel and complicated cataract removal were introduced (Dr. Robert Machemer, the VISC, 1972; Dr. Nicholas Douvas, the Roto-extractor, 1973). These instruments could be inserted through needle-sized openings and the intra ocular pressure maintained at a normal range with infusion cannulas (small tubes for injecting medication).

Lens implants fell out of favor for almost two decades until the early 1970s because of their tendency to dislocate from the pupillary space into the vitreous space. When I arrived in 1970, Abbott Hospital already had a motorized operating microscope, while many other institutions did not. This was almost entirely due to the influence of Dr. Malcolm McCannel, a leader in the ophthalmic community at that time. Malcolm was a giant of a figure, whose keen interest in new procedures and treatments led him to visit ophthalmic centers all over the world to bring new techniques home to Abbott Hospital.

He was especially intrigued with intra ocular lens implants. In 1972, Dr. McCannel performed the first cataract surgery with intra ocular lens implantation in Minnesota. These early lens implants were not without their problems. Large corneal incisions required sutures and hospital stays of three or more days. Abbott Northwestern even had an eye wing at this time, Station 54, with Ms. Jensen as head nurse.

Over the next few years, many surgeons at Abbott Northwestern adopted Phako-emulcification techniques. Dr. Brooks Poley's interest and surgical expertise in lens implantation and small incision surgery was important in refining these new technologies. Because of the micro incisions now possible in cataract surgery, companies began to develop lens implants that could be folded and injected through a needle and then positioned within the capsular bag for proper support. This technique is still used today with minor changes. Sutures are no longer required, and it has become outpatient surgery, with most patients able to resume normal activities within days, and with excellent vision. The principles and technology of small incision surgery would soon be adopted and modified by other surgical specialties. Gall bladders could be removed and knees endoscopically repaired with only a small incision.

Vitreo-Retinal Surgery

When I first arrived in Minneapolis in 1970, there were only four fellowship-trained retinal surgeons in Minnesota. Some patients with retinal detachments were still being referred to Philadelphia and Boston for surgical repair. The success rate with newer techniques for retinal detachment repair had risen from 15 percent to almost 90 percent. Laser surgery had just been introduced in the U.S., and Abbott Hospital received one of the first Argon Lasers in Minnesota, thanks again to a supportive hospital administration.

This new technology allowed us to treat retinal tears, diabetic retinopathy, macular degeneration, and other types of retinal vascular diseases in a non-invasive and effective manner. Retinal surgery at Abbott Northwestern Hospital had its beginnings at this time, and Abbott Northwestern became a referral center for treating retinal disease in patients from all parts of Minnesota. Over the next decade, new lasers were developed so that:

- Membranes within the eye could be treated non-invasively (YAG Lasers)
- Glaucoma patients could be treated (Argon lasers for trabeculoplasty and iridotomy)
- Corneal refractive surgery could be performed (Eximer laser for PTK, PRK, LASIK, and LASEK)

Because of the micro incisions now possible in cataract surgery, companies began to develop lens implants that could be folded and injected through a needle and then positioned within the capsular bag for proper support.

Retinal surgery at Abbott Northwestern Hospital had its beginnings at this time, and Abbott Northwestern became a referral center for treating retinal disease in patients from all parts of Minnesota.

Soon, interest from other surgical specialties for laser applications within their areas of focus began to bubble. In 1984, the hospital administration asked Mary Balzar, R.N., Nursing Director of the operating rooms, and me to visit several new laser centers in the U.S. We were to evaluate their designs and approaches and recommend a model for a laser center at Abbott Northwestern. In 1985, we opened the first multi-specialty laser center in Minnesota with many types of lasers available for use by all of the surgical subspecialties.

Vitreous Surgery was the next frontier in ophthalmic surgery to come to Abbott Northwestern. New technology allowed retinal surgeons to safely remove blood from the vitreous space in diabetics and laser the retina with good visualization, all through needle-size openings for suction cutters, infusion cannulas, illuminating ports, and endo laser probes. Difficult retinal detachments with dense constricting membranes that could not be successfully treated by routine buckling procedures could be approached for the first time. Intra ocular gases and liquid silicone were added in certain cases to "blow" the retina back into position, allowing laser or cryopexy (surgery to attach a detached retina) to be delivered for adequate adhesion between the retina and underlying structures.

We spent time with Dr. Bob Machemer, the VISC (vitreous infusion suction cutter) inventor, and Dr. Nicolas Douvas, the inventor of the Roto-extractor, and acquired both types of machinery to begin vitreous service. Cataract problems that could not be addressed with routine cataract technology could now be addressed safely. We treated dozens of patients with dislocated cataracts from Marfan's Syndrome and other conditions because we could remove the lens and the surrounding vitreous through a needle-sized opening.

The need to train other ophthalmologists in this technology led me to work with the Storz company to develop a hands-on training seminar in the use of the Ocutome in vitreo-retinal surgery and complicated cataract procedures. Storz designated Abbott Northwestern as the Midwestern center for training ophthalmologists in vitrectomy technology and procedures using their Ocutome machinery. Ophthalmologists from across the United States, Europe, and the Philippines attended. The course was limited to 30 participants because of the hands-on lab that provided machines, animal eyes, and supervision for each of the attendees.

I offered this course in 1982 and 1983 and was asked by Storz to continue it in 1984, but declined because of other commitments. I can remember taking Thursday off before the course registrants arrived and traveling to the South St. Paul stockyards where, with the help of workers on the trimming line, we would remove 160 or so pigs' eyes. They were placed in a plastic bag with ice, before refrigeration and use in the Friday and Saturday afternoon surgical practice sessions. I am grateful to Dr. Thomas Aaberg from Atlanta, as well as Drs. Dennis Robertson and Helmut Buettner from the Mayo Clinic for helping with the morning lectures and the afternoon practice surgical sessions. I am also grateful to Nancy Peterson, from the Medical Staff office at Abbott Northwestern, for the many hours that she spent with paperwork and arrangements for these meetings. These were indeed very exciting times for Ophthalmology at Abbott Northwestern.

Oculo Plastic Surgery

As with other subspecialties within ophthalmology, fellowship-trained, oculoplastic surgeons arrived in Minneapolis in the 1970s. Dr. Thomas Purcell joined our group and the Abbott Northwestern staff. He offered refined approaches to commonplace lid and orbital problems. He enlisted two surgeons from other specialties to form a multidisciplinary team to address congenital cranio-facial deformities in infants not previously treatable. Along with Dr. Erich Wisiol, a respected neurosurgeon, and Dr. Bruce Schilling, a plastic surgeon, Purcell performed these complex surgeries at Abbott Northwestern or at nearby Children's Hospital.

Corneal Surgery

The introduction of new therapies and the increased understanding of new corneal diseases required additional fellowship training for the corneal surgeon. Dr. Todd Zwickey brought this extra knowledge and surgical expertise to Abbott Northwestern when he joined the staff. Not only has his expertise increased the success rate with corneal transplantation, but also he is a busy practitioner of laser corneal refractive surgery. Hundreds of thousands, if not millions, of eye patients have been able to give up their glasses or contact lenses with the new vision that this type of surgery provides.

Glaucoma

During this same time, new or newly refined procedures were developed to treat glaucoma patients where topical and systemic medications had not controlled their disease. Dr. James Mitchell, Dr. Thomas Sanderson, and others used laser and filtering procedures to address difficult cases. Dr. Mitchell is also a fellowship-trained neuro ophthalmologist, one of the few doctors in Minnesota to have this expertise.

Additional History

In 1993, several downtown hospitals merged and became part of Allina. Among them was Phillips Eye Hospital, an independent eye center several blocks from the Abbott Northwestern campus. Because Abbott Northwestern and Phillips Eye were now both part of Allina, the eye equipment and Eye Department of Abbott Northwestern was moved to the Phillips site. PhillipsEye Institute is currently one of the busiest eye centers in the United States and has nearly all of the eye surgeons in the Twin Cities as part of its staff.

Among those who have made significant contributions to new technology and treatment at Phillips are: Dr. Howard Gilbert and his associates; Dr. Robert Ramsay and his Retinal group; Dr. Richard Lindstrom and his associates; Dr. Irving Shapiro and Dr. Emmett Carpel, who both have had significant roles as Medical Directors at Phillips Eye. Of course, many others have made significant contributions to ophthalmic care at Phillips Eye, and we are grateful for their involvement.

Summary

The past 40 years have brought great improvements in the understanding and treatment of eye disease at Abbott Northwestern Hospital. The success rate for treating ophthalmic maladies utilizing new technologies has markedly increased. We are grateful to all who have contributed, and to the physicians on staff at Abbott Northwestern Hospital and Phillips Eye Institute who were part of this remarkable story.

Phillips is currently one of the busiest eye centers in the United States and has nearly all of the eye surgeons in the Twin Cities as part of its staff.

24

Orthopaedics
1940-2014
Dr. James R. Larson

Go into orthopaedics? Don't. You will be wasting your surgical talent. Flat feet, crooked backs, and a few cases of joint tuberculosis. —Advice given in 1910, *The Story of Orthopaedics*, Mercer Rang

The word orthopaedics was first used by Nicholas Andry in the mid-1700s. It is derived from the Latin word meaning "straight child." The first Orthopaedic Hospital was founded in 1780. The early orthopaedic surgeons were considered "strap and buckle doctors." Most of the treatments evolved around traction, splints, braces, and plaster casts. Not until the late 1800s, when anesthesia and aseptic techniques improved and X-ray was available, did the practice of orthopaedics expand into surgery.

The American Orthopaedic Association, dedicated to the science of orthopaedics, was founded in 1887. In the first decade, however, the Association spent most of its time and resources on tuberculosis, club feet, and dysplasia of the hip, with very little interest in expanding the surgical practice of orthopaedics. It was not until World War I that surgery became critical in the training and practice of orthopaedics. After the war, surgery became less relevant, and most orthopaedic surgeons went back to the practice of bracing and casting. However, the

Not until the late 1800s, when anesthesia and aseptic techniques improved and X-ray was available, did the practice of orthopaedics expand into surgery.

education and formal training was dramatically advanced in 1931 with the formation of the American Academy of Orthopaedic Surgeons. The organization was brought together to promote and teach new techniques and procedures.

As World War II started, United States medical professionals again realized that the surgical orthopaedist was a vital and necessary part of the team in the war effort. At this time, the surgical advancement in orthopaedics became the main driver in the education of the young trainees. Along with these advancements, Dr. Marius N. Smith-Peterson published results of the first series of 500 successful hip arthroplasties using a vitallium (metal) cup. This success helped to expand a rapid growth in the surgical techniques in all of orthopaedics.

Minnesota, and especially Northwestern Hospital, also became famous during this period. In 1940, Sister Elizabeth Kenny left Australia and moved to Minneapolis. She brought new techniques in the treatment of polio. The treatments at that time consisted only of casting and immobilization. It was her feeling that polio was not irreversible but was a result of spasm and muscle tightness with shortening of the muscle groups. Her treatments consisted of increasing activity with physical therapy and hot packs.

The Sister Kenny Institute was founded at Minneapolis General Hospital with Dr. John Pohl as the pediatric orthopaedic consultant. Initially, the treatments were not well accepted but with the support of Dr. Pohl as the consultant, the treatments eventually became the standard treatment protocol. The Sister Kenny Institute was later moved to Northwestern Hospital and resides today on the Abbott Northwestern Hospital campus. It is now known as the Courage Kenny Rehabilitation Institute, following its merger with the Courage Center in 2014. (See Chapter 8 on Courage Kenny Rehabilitation Institute.)

During the 1950s and '60s, both Abbott and Northwestern grew as separate hospitals. Abbott Hospital, with Dr. John Pohl as its Chief Surgeon, played a strong role in the orthopaedic community. Dr. Elmer Salovich led the core with his subspecialty training in hand, spine, and hip surgery. He joined with Dr. A. Bruce Sundberg and Dr. Rodney Peterson in a group practice.

Northwestern Hospital also had a strong core of orthopaedic surgeons. Dr. Keith Millett brought his University of Minnesota practice to Northwestern Hospital to join with Dr. I. J. Schaffhausen. Drs. Fred Rosendahl, Richard Jones, and later Frank Trost also were based at Northwestern Hospital. Dr. Dick Jones, with his special interest in bracing after amputations, was considered one of the top orthopaedic surgeons in the country. Aside from practicing orthopaedics, Dr. Fred Rosendahl delighted the hospital staff by playing his trombone at hospital parties and celebrations. In the late '70s, Drs. A. Bruce Sundberg, Rodney Peterson, and Elmer Salovich gradually brought more of their practice from Abbott to Northwestern Hospital. Drs. John Kearns, James Larson, and later, Douglas Drake, joined their practice in the early 1980s.

By October 1970, the Northwestern Orthopaedic Section had progressed enough to have its first educational program. It was largely limited to the treatment of hip fractures with massie nails and the need for anticoagulation after surgery. The 1970s brought major advancements in orthopaedics with the introduction of fiberoptics. Arthroscopy could now be used to access most any joint in the body. Now the orthopaedic surgeon could repair extremity injuries through small holes using minimally invasive techniques. In 1982, Abbott Northwestern Hospital bought their first video camera for use in arthroscopic surgery. The rest is history.

On September 17, 1981, the first Orthopaedic Section was formed at Abbott Northwestern Hospital. There were 23 surgeons in the section, but only four attended the meetings on a regular basis, according to the meeting minutes. When the nurses went on strike May 31, 1984, the practice of orthopaedics changed dramatically. Previously, most orthopaedic surgeries were done as inpatient procedures. With the shortage of personnel during the nursing strike, many of the cases shifted to the outpatient facilities. The patients did extremely well, and the surgical outcomes were not adversely affected. The new era of outpatient orthopaedic surgery had its debut and never looked back.

Subspecialty practice became more common by the mid-1980s. Although hand surgery had always been a separate entity, now surgeons were starting to focus on areas such as foot and ankle, total joint replacement, spine and sports medicine practice, with a focus on the knee and shoulder. The laser center was formed in the late 1980s and was directed by Dr. James Larson. Initially, there was great interest in use of the laser in spine and knee surgery. Although the laser is still used today, it became evident that it had only limited value.

A review of the sectional meeting minutes shows that, by the late 1980s, the sectional meetings became more political. The surgeons felt that it was time

Aside from practicing orthopaedics, Dr. Fred Rosendahl delighted the hospital staff by playing his trombone at hospital parties and celebrations.

The 1980s also brought a period of rapid growth in the orthopaedic educational program at Abbott Northwestern Hospital.

for orthopaedics to become a separate department. The biggest objection to being a department was that the group would have to meet monthly rather than quarterly. After many long discussions, the Department of Orthopaedics was formed in January 1989. The new department approved the then radical idea that the operating surgeon would mark the surgical site before the operation. Some surgeons felt that this would give the patients the impression that the surgeon was confused about the location of the surgical site. However, marking the site was finally passed and soon became the standard of care for the orthopaedic patient.

The 1980s also brought a period of rapid growth in the orthopaedic educational program at Abbott Northwestern Hospital. One of the largest areas of growth was spine surgery. In 1986, Dr. David Bradford was selected to direct the University of Minnesota/Fairview Spine Service. One of his responsibilities was to move the spine and general orthopaedic rotations for residents to Abbott Northwestern Hospital under the guidance of Dr. Gordon Aamoth. The spine program continued to grow, and in 1992, Dr. Ensor Transfeldt joined the spine practice at Abbott Northwestern Hospital. Later, Drs. Francis Denis, John Lonstein, Joseph Perra, Manual Pinto, and James Schwender joined the staff. This created the core that remains today as one of the finest spine programs in the country.

On May 25, 1989, the Orthopaedic Department meeting focused on blood transfusions. In the VMH (Volunteer Hospital Association) network of hospitals, Abbott Northwestern had the highest transfusion rate for total joint surgery. It was common for a total hip replacement patient to receive five units of blood, and for a total knee replacement patient to receive four units. By the end of 1989, the Orthopaedic Department had brought the transfusion rate down to 1.29 units per total joint replacement through improvements in surgical techniques. Aside from dropping the rate of transfusions, there was great concern that 1.5-2 percent of adult patients and 13 percent of pediatric patients could have received blood transmitting the HIV virus that causes AIDS. Today, with the use of the cell saver and tranexamic acid (an antifibrinolytic medication, which prevents excessive blood loss and helps clear the surgical field), the transfusion rates have plummeted.

By the early '90s, the Orthopaedic Department had grown to 41 surgeons on staff. In 1991, with the Emergency Department volume increasing, the group decided it was the duty of the surgeon to accept unassigned patients. In a lighter moment, the group also decided that no one could smoke in the hospital except in the mental health and chemical dependency units.

The March 26, 1992 department meeting was filled with discussion on operating block times (time put aside for a particular surgeon). The surgeon was required to use his/her block 75 percent of the requested time in order to maintain this privilege. In looking at the numbers, no one qualified. By 1993, the surgical volumes had dropped significantly. This required the operating department to close four rooms. However, by the end of the year, the orthopaedic volumes had risen to 2,561 cases, and everything was in a growth mode.

In early 1994, blood transfusions again became a hot topic and big concern. Sixty percent of the blood that had been donated by patients prior to their total joint surgery had been discarded, and patients no longer were asked to donate blood preoperatively. Also, in that year, endoscopic carpal tunnel surgery of the wrist had become the rage, with 22 percent of the carpal tunnel surgeries performed with the scope. With an increase in time to perform the procedure and the appreciation of the difficulty of this technique, the use of the endoscope for carpal tunnel surgery soon lost favor.

Starting in the mid-90s and continuing into the present day, the cost of a surgical procedure became the main topic of discussion. To help control costs for hip and knee joint replacement, Abbott Northwestern Hospital selected three vendors who supplied the devices. The orthopaedic surgeon could select one of the three prostheses for the surgery. This dramatically helped control the cost of joint replacement since the hospital was able to purchase surgical implants in larger quantities at lower prices. The average hospital stay for total joint surgery was brought down from five to three days. Today with advancements in the practice of anesthesia and pain management, the goal of one-to two-day hospital stays following total joint replacement looks like a reachable goal.

Along with the spine program, the Orthopaedic Department has been recognized as a Center of Excellence. In 2013-14, *US News and World Report* rated Abbott Northwestern Hospital's Department of Orthopaedics as the 13th best hospital program in the nation. The Joint Replacement Center under the leadership of Dr. Scott Anseth and Stephanie Eller, RN, has become second to none. The program received the first award in Minnesota of the Joint Commission Gold Seal of Approval for hip and knee replacement for quality and safety. This program also received the Blue Distinction Award for Knee and Hip Replacement from Blue Cross and Blue Shield.

Other programs underway are the shoulder program led by Dr. Frank Norberg and Dr. L. Pierce McCarty III, the hip fracture program led by Dr. Robert Tuttle, and the Women's Health Program led by Dr. Aimee Klapach. With these physicians and the leadership teams, the future looks bright for orthopaedics at Abbott Northwestern Hospital.

25

Pulmonology

Dr. Paul R. Hamann

And the Lord God formed man...and breathed into his nostrils the breath of life.
—Genesis 2:7

What's in a Name?

By the mid-1970s many "ologys" had emerged as medical and surgical subspecialties. Not so with the Internal Medicine physicians interested in diseases of the lung and chest. The Minneapolis VA had a Pulmonary Disease Service. Many internists with an interest in lung diseases, echoing their surgical colleagues, would refer to themselves as Chest Medicine or Thoracic Medicine Specialists.

About that time, an editorial appeared in the American Review of Respiratory Diseases. The author raised the question, "What should we call ourselves?" The editorial contained a picture of the entrance sign to the Pulmonary Medicine Section at the Gainesville Veterans Administration Medical Center. The sign, in the format of a multiple-choice question, listed Pulmonary Medicine, Pulmonology, Pulmology, and "other" as four choices. The author asked for feedback from the journal's readers. The writer of this chapter responded, and was quoted in a follow-up editorial, that "Pulmonology did not trip lightly off the tongue." However, a consensus of respondents chose pulmonology, so another "ology" was approved by its practitioners.

...effective bronchodilator therapy was just beginning to be developed for the treatment of outpatients with chronic obstructive lung disease and asthma. The development of new technology helped spur the growth of pulmonology and other medical subspecialties.

The Early Years

Until the 1950s and 60s, physicians interested in chest diseases spent much of their time dealing with tuberculosis. In some locations, these physicians were known as phthisists. They treated tuberculosis with rest, therapeutic pneumothorax (the induced collapse of a lung), along with the aid of thoracic surgeons.

Plombage was a surgical procedure to treat cavitary tuberculosis. Patients were isolated, many in special hospital wards or at facilities known as sanatoriums. Glen Lake Sanatorium, founded in 1916 in western Hennepin County, housed up to 700 patients by the mid-1930s. Effective anti-tuberculosis medications, Isoniazid and Ethambutol, became available in the 1960s. Coupled with a better understanding of the impact medication has on the infectiousness of the TB bacillus, early patient discharge became possible. The need for TB specialists declined.

What to Do Now?

The number of cases of tuberculosis in Minnesota declined, and most TB patients could be treated in clinics. Chest Physicians had less to do. However, effective bronchodilator therapy was just beginning to be developed for the treatment of outpatients with chronic obstructive lung disease and asthma. The development of new technology helped spur the growth of pulmonology and other medical subspecialties. For Gastroenterology, it was endoscopy; for Cardiology, cardiac catheterization; for Nephrology, dialysis. Pulmonology's growth came with the development and availability of the Flexible Fiberoptic Bronchoscope and the Volume Limited Ventilator.

Fiberoptic Bronchoscopy

Fiberoptic bronchoscopy provided vastly improved airway visualization over the rigid bronchoscopy technique. Performed with topical anesthesia and sedation, the procedure was easy for patients, could be performed at a lower total cost, and often available as outpatient surgery.

Pulmonologists could visualize all airways in all lobes of the lung, down to the sub-segmental level. They could make tissue diagnoses in places impossible to reach with a rigid bronchoscope. Brushings for cytology and biopsies using forceps under direct vision or with fluoroscopic guidance created this expanded ability. In addition, the flexible bronchoscope provided a well-tolerated way to retrieve foreign bodies in the airways and remove mucous plugs to treat partial or total lung collapse. Patients on ventilator support could be scoped in the intensive care unit.

Other uses of the flexible bronchoscope soon followed. In the 1980s, NdY-AG laser treatment for obstructing lung tumors was demonstrated to be effective. Dr. Paul Hamann and Dr. A. Stuart Hanson introduced it into use at Abbott Northwestern Hospital. This procedure required general anesthesia but was well tolerated by patients. Brachytherapy beads, used in the treatment of lung tumors, could be accurately placed with the bronchoscope. Trans-tracheal needle biopsy provided tissue samples for staging of bronchogenic cancers. The airways could be better prepped for bronchography. Subsequently, a vascular guidewire was introduced through the bronchoscope's operating channel as a guide to place the bronchogram catheter into the distal airways. Over time, the radiological technique using thin section CT scans replaced bronchography.

More recently, severe obstructive lung disease has been treated by placing stents in more central airways, with encouraging results. Thermal central airway ablation (using targeted ultrasound to destroy cells) appears to offer patients with refractory asthma another effective treatment modality. (Refractory asthma is a severe form of the disease, which has not responded to treatment.) Endobronchial ultrasound can better guide trans-tracheal or trans-bronchial biopsies. Sophisticated CT programs are available to better guide placement of biopsy and brush catheters peripherally.

Mechanical Ventilation

By 1955, Dr. Forrest Bird had perfected the Bird Universal Medical Respirator for acute or chronic cardiopulmonary care. It was the first universal mass-produced medical respirator and was sold under the trade name of the Bird Mark 7 Respirator. The Bird Respirator was pressure limited and did not provide information about the effective tidal volume generated. (The tidal volume is the volume of air in one breath.) The development of Volume Limited ventilators was a significant advance in mechanical ventilation support. One of the first was the Bennet MA 1. Volume ventilators allowed for modulation of flow rate, percent of oxygen delivered and, most helpfully, the ability to deliver a preset tidal volume.

The ventilator could also be set to deliver a predetermined number of breaths. This is most helpful for sedated or unconscious patients. The assist control mode delivers the predetermined number of breaths, but inhalation efforts by the patient can trigger additional breaths to meet the patient's ventilatory or respiratory demands. Other modifications to the ventilator's capabilities soon followed. Sophisticated weaning methods were developed, including Intermittent Mandatory Ventilation (IMV) and Pressure Support Ventilation (PSV). Both of these were an improvement over the traditional "t-Tube" trials, which required the patient to abruptly assume all the work of breathing.

The importance of adequate inspiratory muscle strength when weaning a patient from the respirator led to the measurement of Weaning Parameters. These include Inspiratory Muscle Force, Spontaneous Tidal Volume, and Spontaneous Respiratory Rate.

Another major improvement in ventilator support was Positive End Expiratory Pressure (PEEP). This modality maintained elevated airway pressures at the end of ventilation. The physiological effect of this modality was to hold open the alveoli, which are the small air cells at the end of the bronchial tree. This improved the oxygenation in patients with Adult Respiratory Disease Syndrome (ARDS). While on ventilator support, bronchodilators, if indicated, could be delivered by in-line nebulizers. More recently, patients with severe cases of ARDS are treated with Extracorporeal Membrane Oxygenation (supplying oxygen to the patient outside the body).

The Modern Era of Pulmonary Consulting Practice

In 1971, Dr. A. Stuart Hanson joined three other pulmonologists in the Pulmonary Department of the St. Louis Park Medical Center. Having received training in Flexible Fiberoptic Bronchoscopy, he started a fiberoptic program at Methodist Hospital the next year. This skill became known throughout the Minneapolis medical community, and he performed bronchoscopies at

Northwestern Hospital among others. Previously, physicians had provided only generally non-invasive pulmonary consultation, including thoracentesis (a procedure that removes fluid or air existing between the lung and chest wall through a needle or tube).

In addition, Dr. James Lillehei started a chest medicine consulting practice near Fairview-Southdale Hospital. He also provided consultations at hospitals around the Twin Cities. Dr. Herb Lauretsen was practicing pulmonary and allergy medicine at the Nicollet Clinic and Eitel Hospital, while Dr. Sumner Cohen had an office in downtown Minneapolis and used Mount Sinai Hospital. Dr. Tom Mulrooney replaced Dr. Tom Lowry on the teaching/attending staff at Hennepin County General Hospital.

The nature of pulmonology practice changed at Abbott and Northwestern hospitals in the fall of 1974. Dr. Wayne Stern and Dr. Paul Hamann opened their practice, Respiratory Disease Associates (RDA), at their office at 2545 Chicago Avenue South near Northwestern Hospital. Dr. Hamann also became the Medical Director of the Respiratory Care Department at Abbott Hospital. With these two actions, RDA signaled its commitment to practice at both campuses of the Abbott Northwestern Hospital Corporation. With the pulmonologist's new tools – the bronchoscope and the volume ventilator – convenient diagnostic and therapeutic interventions and advanced Pulmonology consultations became readily available. In addition, thoracic surgeons had previously provided thoracentesis, pleural biopsy, and chest tube placement for pneumothorax and pleural effusion. Now these procedures were available at Abbott and Northwestern.

Several factors contributed to the early success of RDA. Both physicians had trained at University of Minnesota-affiliated hospitals. A number of younger Abbott and Northwestern staff internists were acquainted with them. Their ability to interpret pulmonary function tests helped to identify them in the community. The Minnesota Thoracic Group (MTG), which included Drs. Frank Johnson, Ted Peterson, and Joe Kiser, also provided support. Dr. Johnson regularly attended a chest conference at the Minneapolis VA Hospital. Shortly before the opening of RDA's office, Dr. Johnson told Dr. Hamann, "You'll do well."

The MTG physicians supported RDA by sending referrals and obtaining

The need to study sleep issues led Abbott Northwestern to establish a sleep lab.

consultations when needed. After the consolidation of Abbott Hospital to the Northwestern campus in 1980, Dr. Hamann became the director of the combined Respiratory Care Departments, further integrating the practice into the Abbott Northwestern Hospital community.

As the practice grew in the 1980s, RDA relocated to the Minneapolis Heart Institute building on the Abbott Northwestern campus. Drs. Ieva Grundmanis, Ralph Steele, Will Corson, and Mitchell Kaye joined the practice. Outreach programs were established in Faribault, New Prague, and Waconia. With the assistance of the Continuing Medical Education Department at Abbott Northwestern, the programs were organized and successfully promoted. The topics of Obstructive Lung Disease and Cardiopulmonary Stress Testing attracted attendees from across the Upper Midwest. Speaking engagements at rural hospitals, county medical societies, and the Minnesota Academy of Family Practice helped promote Pulmonology at Abbott Northwestern.

Continued Growth

As the Cardiology and Cardiovascular Surgical programs grew in the 1990s, Pulmonology needed additional coverage and more space. During this time, Drs. Michael Bowen, Ted Berman, Kathy Gromer, Patrick Wright, and Mark Stang joined the practice. In 1993, the Minneapolis Heart Institute® added three floors to the top of its building. RDA moved to the top floor (where it remains today) and changed its name to the Minnesota Lung Center. Other practices also provided Pulmonology service at Abbott Northwestern. Dr. Kay Hale of Respiratory Disease Consultants practiced at Abbott Northwestern for several years before returning to her native state of Texas. For a period of time, the St. Paul Lung Clinic (founded a year after RDA by Dr. Mike Neren and Dr. David Bonham) had a presence.

To sleep, perchance to dream – William Shakespeare

In the late 1980s, the importance of sleep apnea in producing illness and daytime somnolence became widely recognized. Drs. Will Corson, Ted Berman, and Ralph Steele of RDA developed expertise in evaluating and treating sleep apnea. The need to study sleep issues led Abbott Northwestern to establish a sleep lab. In the mid 1990s, Dr. Corson, of the Minnesota Lung Center, assumed oversight of the lab, a management relationship that continues to the present time.

Pulmonologists at Abbott Northwestern Hospital

The Medical Staff office kindly provided a list of the names of those who have held Pulmonology privileges at Abbott Northwestern. They include: Drs. Kathryn Hale, Robert Colbert, Theodore Berman, R. Michael Bowen, Michael Alter, Susan Burton, Wilfred Corson, Joan Fox, Joseph Graif, Kathy Gromer, Ieva Grundmanis, Paul Hamann, Jay Hudson, Mitchell Kaye, Shelley Lennox, Jeanne Nelson, Mark Stang, Ralph Steele, Wayne Stern, Patrick Wright, John "Jack" Shronts, and A. Stuart Hanson.

Many of these physicians are still practicing. Further testimony to the youth of the specialty.

Valued Colleagues

The history of Pulmonology at Abbott Northwestern Hospital is not complete without acknowledging the valuable contributions of the Respiratory Therapists. Many names and/faces come to mind, but rather than slight some by forgetting to list all, the author wishes to honor the whole cohort. These capable professionals assisted with ventilator management, pulmonary function testing, bedside patient treatment, sleep studies, and bronchoscopy.

Dr. A. Stuart Hanson provided hitherto unknown history and reminded the author of the names of early pulmonologists.

Mitchell Kaye provided clarification and content.

Wayne Stern provided information related to Sleep Medicine.

The history of Pulmonology at Abbott Northwestern Hospital is not complete without acknowledging the valuable contributions of the Respiratory Therapists.

26

Spiritual Care
and Pastoral Education

1971-2012
Rev. Max R. Maguire and Rev. Richard D. Sellers

On September 1, 1971, before the two campuses were consolidated, Abbott Northwestern Hospital established a Chaplaincy Department. The two hospitals had different histories regarding the role of religion in their respective institutions. Abbott Hospital had been owned and operated by Westminster Presbyterian Church. Northwestern Hospital had been a community-based, non-sectarian hospital. Hospital Administrator, Gordon Sprenger, felt that the concept of a faith-based hospital philosophy would be important to bring into the merger. Mr. Sprenger was also aware of the growing influence of spirituality in the field of health care. Consequently, the Board of Abbott Northwestern Hospital hired a full-time staff chaplain.

The hospital administration, in keeping with its overall commitment to medical and allied health education, wanted to establish a clinical pastoral education center to be accredited by The Association for Clinical Pastoral Education, a national accrediting body. Most Twin Cities hospitals already had this program. Rev. Max R. Maguire, a certified chaplain and clinical pastoral educator, was hired as Director of the department. He prepared the necessary documents for an onsite accreditation visit. Provisional accreditation was granted with final accreditation occurring a year later. The training center was approved for all three levels of clinical pastoral education: Basic, Advanced, and Supervisory training.

Initially, hospital Board members, members of Westminster Presbyterian Church, and the Presbyterian Synod of Minnesota raised funding for the chaplaincy service and clinical pastoral education program. After the first year, funding was built into the hospital budget.

The department and the Clinical Pastoral Education center were ecumenical from their inception, admitting seminarians and clergy of all faiths to function as chaplains in a supervised experience with patients, families, and staff. Each group consisted of four to five students and met daily in group seminars, as well as in weekly individual meetings with the supervisor. These intensive, full-time programs were either three months (primarily for seminary students) or a full-year residency (primarily for clergy training to become health care chaplains).

The first students arrived in June 1972 for the summer unit and consisted of three Protestant ministers and two Roman Catholic nuns. The first year-long residents arrived in September 1972 and consisted of four Protestant ministers. In the ensuing years, the education program developed a national reputation for excellence. Consequently, over the years it attracted international students from countries including Norway (largest number of students), Iceland, Germany, Egypt, Kenya, Nigeria, Zambia, South Africa, Sri Lanka, Philippines, and Viet Nam. The center also gained recognition for its exceptional supervisory education program. For many years, most of the clinical pastoral education supervisors in the Twin Cities received part or all of their supervisory education at Abbott Northwestern.

With the expansion of hospital services and the increased demand for clinical pastoral education, the department needed more staff. The first staff addition was Sister Leslie Brancheau, a Roman Catholic nun. She remained three years and left to go into another field. Rev. Richard Sellers succeeded her. In the years following, the staff included Rev. Susan Thornton, Rev. Wilys Claire Nelson, Rev. Timothy Thorstenson, Rev. Steve Daniel, Rev. Paula Bidle,

Rev. Denise Dunbar-Perkins, Rev. Mary Albing, Rev. Judith Roska, Rev. Kyle Vlach, Rev. Kimberly Goodman, Rev. Ken Burg, and Eva Rogness.

In 1976, the department established an outpatient pastoral counseling service. Rev. John Martinson, a pastor with a Master's degree in counseling, was hired to direct the program. Dr. Scott McNary, a psychiatric consultant, met with the counseling staff once a week.

The Counseling Center program was located in the Abbott Northwestern Medical Office Building, and satellite programs were established at Wayzata Community Church and Westminster Presbyterian Church, staffed by Certified Pastoral Counselors. Dr. Sandra Brown and Rev. Robert Hurlbut staffed the center at Westminster Presbyterian Church. Rev. Steven Tate and Rev. Marilyn Beckstrom staffed Wayzata Community Church.

There were part-time programs in other churches staffed by part-time counselors. In addition, the center provided pastoral counseling training for clergy and laypersons. In 1991, the satellite centers were transferred to their respective churches for operation, and the outpatient program at Abbott Northwestern was discontinued. At this writing, the Westminster Counseling Center continues as an important referral resource to the Twin Cities community. To accommodate the broader role of both inpatient and outpatient services, the department changed its name to Health Care Ministries. The inpatient Chaplaincy Department was renamed Pastoral Care and Education. The inpatient staff continued to carry the title of Chaplain.

The need for a biomedical ethics committee became apparent with the development of new medical technologies, new treatment protocols, and opportunities to extend life and end-of-life issues. The hospital administration authorized the Pastoral Care Department to spearhead the establishment of the committee. The Committee on Ethical and Moral Issues in Health Care held its first meeting in December 1981. The minutes of that meeting state that the Committee ". . . originated in response to critical care nurses' requests for answers to their concerns regarding ethical issues – such as decisions to treat or not to treat." The committee included a physician, social worker, chaplain, nurse, director of the hospice program, and a representative from the community.

One of the first actions of the Committee was to establish a monthly hospital

The Committee on Ethical and Moral Issues in Health Care ". . . originated in response to critical care nurses' requests for answers to their concerns regarding ethical issues – such as decisions to treat or not to treat."

...the Committee's objectives included reviewing policies and procedures having ethical implications (e.g., Do Not Resuscitate /DNR), developing ethics position papers, and providing ethical consultation to medical and hospital staff, as well as to patients and family members.

interdisciplinary education forum for the purpose of presenting and discussing clinical case material that raised ethical issues. In addition to promoting hospital and community education, the Committee's objectives included reviewing policies and procedures having ethical implications (e.g., Do Not Resuscitate /DNR), developing ethics position papers, and providing ethical consultation to medical and hospital staff, as well as to patients and family members. The Committee began providing concurrent case consultations in 1986, and the consultation service has continued to be well utilized and to grow and develop.

Rev. Max Maguire was the Committee's first Chairperson, followed by Rev. Richard Sellers (1987-94; 2008-12), Rev. Timothy Thorstenson (1994-2004), Dr. Hallie Richards (2004-2010), and Rev. Verlyn Hemmen (2012-). Among the physicians who have played a significant role in the committee's development and overall impact are Drs. Todd Miller, Ray Scallon, Tom Flynn, Hallie Richards, Warren Kearney, and Mark Arnesen.

In 2010, in response to a similar need felt in the hospital community for a forum to reflect on complicated and distressing cases, the department initiated the Schwartz Center Rounds. A Boston attorney, who was dying of cancer in his 40s, developed this format that enables caregivers to discuss the ethical issues they encounter. More than 350 health care facilities in 33 states have adopted the approach. Dr. Ben Bache-Wiig and Rev. Richard Sellers led the initiative to bring the Schwartz Center Rounds to Abbott Northwestern. Key members of the interdisciplinary team present challenging and complex cases that have generated distress for caregivers to an audience also made up of interdisciplinary caregivers. This program has been extremely well attended and has given a much-appreciated forum for caregivers to share their concerns and seek best practices regarding communication, respect, and support among team members.

The physical presence of the department experienced increasing visibility over the years, and perhaps symbolic of that visibility is the location of the chapel. A small chapel at Abbott Hospital was located near the front entrance around a corner from the lobby. Given the religious connection of the hospital, there was a stained glass window in the chapel with many Christian symbols. Northwestern Hospital, in keeping with its non-sectarian tradition, had a small meditation room without any symbolism, on the fourth floor of the hospital.

In 1980, at the time of the consolidation of the two hospitals on the Northwestern campus, a new all-faith chapel was built near the front lobby. Caroline Ewe, a member of Westminster Presbyterian Church, funded the all-faith chapel. It was designed for both private meditation and public worship. There continues to be widespread appreciation for and use of the chapel, not only by patients and their families but also by employees of all faiths. In addition to individual prayer and meditation, the chapel has been used for worship services, weddings, and memorial services.

Rev. Max Maguire retired in 1993, after 22 years as Director and was succeeded by Rev. Richard Sellers. In 1999, the department broadened its focus and became the Allina Spiritual Care and Pastoral Education Department, with responsibility for providing spiritual care not only at Abbott Northwestern but also at United, Mercy, and Unity hospitals. A significant outcome of this transition was the establishment of clinical pastoral education programs at each of the other hospitals. This greatly enhanced the quality and amount of spiritual care coverage provided at each site. Rev. Sellers retired in 2012 after 35 years at Abbott Northwestern. Rev. Verlyn Hemmen, who had been Chaplain Manager and Center for Pastoral Education Supervisor at United Hospital in St. Paul, succeeded him as Director.

27

Urology
1970-2014
Dr. Thomas A. Rivers

Although I have been a physician for 50 years, I've been a urologist for the last 40, and have practiced Urology in Minneapolis for 38 years.

I started my career June 1, 1976 at Abbott Hospital. I showed up at 7:30 a.m. to meet my new partners. However, at the time, I was experiencing severe right upper quadrant abdominal pain. I thought I had an ulcer. Being originally from Indiana, Minneapolis was new to me, and I was stressed because I was having trouble finding the hospital. Later, Dr. Bruce Linderholm said it looked to him like I had a kidney stone. I went to the Emergency Room and eventually had an X-ray of the kidney. It showed a small stone in the distal right ureter, the muscular tube that moves urine from the kidney to the bladder. I spent the night in the hospital. I didn't eat, didn't drink, but slept all night and all day. I went to work on June 2, 1976. Three days later I passed my stone. My new partners realized that it was not because I was a narcotic addict that I could function through that pain, but that I had a low pain threshold.

My new partners were Dr. Bruce Linderholm, Dr. Roger Lundblad, and Dr. William Engel. At this time our group, Urology Associates, provided most of the Urology services at Abbott Northwestern Hospital. Dr. John Cooper was an independent urologist at Abbott Hospital at

There was a great deal of communication between the primary doctors and the doctors practicing in various specialties.

that time, and Dr. Richard Rodgers had just retired in the group. I was to take his place working at Abbott Hospital.

Nancy Peterson was the Medical Staff Secretary. I got to know her very quickly because I parked my car in her spot in the parking lot that first day on the job when I was having all that kidney stone pain. She was a little upset with the new urologist.

In the 1970s and 1980s, working at Abbott Hospital was wonderful for several reasons. There was a great deal of communication between the primary doctors and the doctors practicing in various specialties. All the physicians were making hospital rounds at the same time. If you didn't see the primary doctor on your rounds, you would probably see him at lunch in the Doctors' Lounge. The verbal communication between the doctors and nurses, between doctors and doctors, as well as doctors and ward secretaries was all very good. You knew the names of the head nurses of each floor. You knew the names of the ward secretaries. There were no computers, and there were no electronic medical records. There were no hospitalists. There were no physician assistants. The patient saw the primary doctor and also saw the urologist every day.

While this way of providing patient care may not have been efficient, the patients seemed to like it. When the health care system acquired physician assistants and the electronic medical records, everybody became concerned about entering data into the computer, and had less time to spend with the patient.

Evaluation and Treatment Methods

Patient evaluations in the 1970s were terribly different than how we do them today. At that time, cytoscopies (examining the bladder using a thin, lighted tube) were done in the hospital under general anesthesia. The patient went home the next day. We also did many transurethral resections of the prostate (surgery to relieve urinary symptoms caused by an enlarged prostate). Those patients frequently needed a blood transfusion and stayed in the hospital for 3-5 days. We made incisions for almost any type of problem, including kidney tumors, ureteral stones, kidney stones, the removal of the bladder, and cystectomies. Surgery to remove lymph nodes involved with spreading testicular cancer required exploration of the lymph system behind the intestines and major blood vessels in the abdomen. We also performed radical surgery for prostate cancer. In these cases, the patient stayed in the hospital for several days.

We would use cystoscopy to retrieve stones in the distal ureter by inserting, blindly, a basket to retrieve the stone. If the stone was large, we would leave the ureteral stone basket attached to the stone, apply traction for a day or two and then manipulate that device with the patient in bed. This would last for 1-2 days. It allowed the ureter to dilate, and we could usually get the stone and stone basket device out by using this procedure.

We could have 30-40 patients in the hospital on a weekend because we would do so many cystoscopies on Fridays. The patients all stayed until they were released on Saturday. Many of these patients had cystoscopies where nothing was found. The procedures were done because the patient had been found to have small amounts of blood in the urine or benign microscopic hematuria. Being on call on the weekends meant seeing a lot of patients and doing a lot of discharges.

Technological Change

With the tremendous advancement in instrument technology over the past 50 years, hospital stays have reduced dramatically. Many of these hospital procedures are now done in the office or in one-day surgery. Even when done in the hospital, the stay is only one or two days for nephrectomies (the total removal of a kidney), prostatectomies (partial removal of the prostate), as well as for the removal of the bladder and cystectomies.

When I started at Abbott Hospital, all patients who were to have a transurethral resection of the prostate were given a bilateral partial vasectomy, which is the removal of a small tube next to the testicle, so they would not get an infection of the epididymis postoperatively. After I started my practice, an antibiotic called Gentamycin was given preoperatively in these situations, and as a result, preoperative partial vasectomies were no longer needed. This ended the complaints from these patients about being sterilized.

By the mid-1970s, we had also moved from incandescent light bulbs in our scopes to fiberoptic instruments, and we could see much better. All the scopes today use digital optics, which are even better.

With the tremendous advancement in instrument technology over the past 50 years, hospital stays have reduced dramatically. Many of these hospital procedures are now done in the office or in one-day surgery.

Today, we no longer have to make incisions in order to remove ureteral or kidney stones. We have ureteroscopy (scoping of the ureter) and nephroscopy (scoping of the kidney) to remove stones. We have lasers, ultrasounds, and instruments to break up kidney stones.

Originally, all scopes were rigid and of large caliber. Scopes have gotten smaller, thinner, and more flexible. In the 1980s, ureteral stents were introduced, which kept the ureter open and allowed it to dilate. These were used either short or long term.

Today, we no longer have to make incisions in order to remove ureteral or kidney stones. We have ureteroscopy (scoping of the ureter) and nephroscopy (scoping of the kidney) to remove stones. We have lasers, ultrasounds, and instruments to break up kidney stones. In the 1980s, we also developed an electro shock wave called lithotripsy. This is a non-invasive procedure to break stones into powder so the fragments can pass. This is done in one-day surgery.

We have developed better urethral catheters with balloons that don't fail as frequently and are made of better materials. This results in much less irritation to the cells that line the urethra, called the mucosa.

When we obtained a CT scan at Abbott Hospital in the late 1970s, the imaging improved significantly. Later we were able to obtain bone scans, allowing us to see metastatic cancer more accurately. Today we have PET scans.

Laparoscopes were first used to remove pelvic lymph nodes. Later, the laparoscopes were used to remove kidneys either completely or partially. Today, we are starting to use robotic surgery in these cases. Robotics are also used to remove the bladder and the prostate. Now patients stay 1-3 days in the hospital with very little blood loss and much less morbidity.

Treatment of Prostate Cancer

In the 1970s and 1980s, diagnosis of cancer of the prostate was done with digital examination. In the late 1980s, we were given prostatic-specific antigen (PSA) as a blood test that greatly increased our ability to detect cancer of the prostate early. This test is also excellent for following patients who have been treated for cancer of the prostate, and is widely used today.

In the 1970s, at Abbott Hospital we commonly used ampicillin and gentamycin as the intravenous antibiotics of choice. The oral antibiotics we used for infections of the urinary tract were sulfa, usually Gantanol or Gantricin, macrodantin, and trimethoprin. Today we use a lot of Cipro and Levaquin.

In the 1970s, surgery was the primary treatment for cancer of the prostate for men under 70. The surgical procedure started out as an incision between the scrotum and the anus, called a perineal prostatectomy. Even in the late '70s, the surgery was a radical retropubic prostatectomy with the incision behind the pubic bone plus a bilateral partial lymph adenectomy (removal of the gland). We still do that procedure today, but it is done with robotic technique.

Patients with prostate cancers that were older than 70 were usually treated with some type of radiation. In the 1970s, it was external beam radiation. In the 1980s, seeds were implanted to deliver the radiation. In the 1990s, cryotherapy was introduced, which is the therapeutic use of low temperatures.

Now we are seeing observation with follow-up PSAs, and biopsies and re-biopsies of patients for what we consider a moderate or low-grade cancer of the prostate. The tumor is given a score called a Gleason grade 6 cancer. Some focal therapy for cancer of the prostate using cryotherapy is also used today.

A Changing Field

In the 1970s-1980s, the urologist did everything in Urology. We did pediatric urology, adult urology, female urology, oncology urology, impotence, infertility, kidney and ureteral stones, and took care of neurogenic bladders.

Today, the American Urologic Association identifies seven subspecialty areas:

- Pediatric Urology, which now has a fellowship training program
- Urologic Oncology
- Renal Transplantation
- Male Infertility
- Calculi (urinary tract stones)
- Female Urology, which now has a fellowship training program
- Neuro Urology (voiding disorders and erectile disorders)

By the time a urologist is ready to retire today, he or she is practicing very little of the full range of areas learned in a residency program.

The only constant in urology over the past 50 years is CHANGE in how we treat the same urologic diseases. This is due to improved instrument technology and new treatments, which include chemotherapy, immunotherapy, tools for testing, and tools for diagnosing. This change is occurring faster and faster because knowledge can be so rapidly disseminated.

Urology Associates

The doctors who primarily worked at Abbott Hospital in the 1960s-1970s for our group were Dr. Richard Rodgers and Dr. Bruce Linderholm. I'd like to give a little history of these two doctors, and the others who were part of Urology Associates at that time.

Dr. Richard Rodgers

Dr. Richard Rodgers founded Urology Associates in 1947. Dr. Rodgers attended Carleton College in Northfield, Minnesota and completed his urology training at Massachusetts General Hospital in Boston. Dick Rodgers retired at age 72 and lived to be 100 years old. Dick was originally from Chippewa Falls, Wisconsin, and he started out as a general practitioner and surgeon. He actually even pinned hips at one time. He adopted four children while living in Chippewa Falls, and eventually moved to the Minneapolis area and settled in Hopkins where he had a farm and a horse. Dick also was a musician and played the drums.

Dr. Bruce Linderholm

In 1957, Dr. Bruce Linderholm became Dick's first partner. Dr. Linderholm was from Belle Plaine, Minnesota, and graduated from Carleton College. He went to medical school at the University of Michigan and stayed for his urology training, training under Dr. Nesbitt. Bruce was very active in several areas besides urology. He received the Thirlby Award for the most interesting paper presented to the North Central Section of the American Urological Association in 1965. He also served as Chief of Staff at Methodist Hospital in 1966. Bruce was President of the Hennepin County Medical Society 1973-1974. He and Dr. Alex Cass were co-chiefs of the Urology service at the Hennepin County Medical Center. Dr. Linderholm died of multiple myeloma at the age of 63 in 1988.

I also want to mention that Dr. Linderholm was a founding father to Medica Insurance Company and to United Health Care. Dr. Linderholm was one of three doctors who helped start and were the directors of the HMO called Physicians Health Plan. GroupHealth had come to town and was gaining patients, which was perceived as a threat to all independent physicians. The private physicians in town all joined the Physicians Health Plan. This was painful because each physician was paid 20 percent of his fee through the health plan. At the end of the year, if monies were left over, partial refunds were given to the physicians.

Eventually, PHP grew so large that the doctors could not run the financial end of the business. Therefore, the PHP Board hired Mr. Richard Burke, who had left Park Nicollet Clinic. Mr. Burke convinced the doctors who were Board directors (Dr. Bruce Linderholm, Dr. Louis Lick, and Dr. Alfred Anderegg) to let him set up a financial corporation outside of PHP. This eventually became the Medica health insurance company. Mr. Burke and the Board named this company United Health Care.

Doctors were not allowed to invest in United Health Care. Mr. Burke also made a deal that United Health Care would have a 25-year contract with Medica. Mr. Richard Burke became a very wealthy man, quit his job, bought a National Hockey League team, and moved to Arizona with the team.

Dr. Linderholm regretted ever having hired Mr. Burke to his dying day.

Dr. Roger Lundblad

Dr. Roger Lundblad became a third partner to Urology Associates in 1967. Dr. Lundblad attended Gustavus Adolphus College in St. Peter, Minnesota. He went to the University of Minnesota Medical School and continued his urology training under Dr. Donald Creevy. He pursued additional training in pediatric urology in Columbus, Ohio and retired at the age of 63, in 1995.

Dr. William Engel

Dr. William Engel joined the group in 1969. He went to college at the University of South Dakota and attended medical school at the University of Washington in Seattle. His urology training was at Hennepin County General Hospital for two years, at the University of Minnesota under Dr. Creevy for one year, and at the VA Hospital for six months. He joined Urology Associates in 1969 and retired at the age of 67 in 2003.

I was the fifth partner to join Urology Associates. I started that strange day in June 1, 1976 and retired June 30, 2013 at the age of 72.

28

Penny George Institute
for Health and Healing
Integrative Health

When psychologist and philanthropist Penny George went through treatment for breast cancer, she realized that at the end of the twentieth century there was still a major gap in U.S. health care. "There wasn't a lot of attention to the mental and spiritual issues or the quality of life issues going through treatment, and I thought, *we can do better than that*. When I started looking into it for myself to see what else was out there, I realized there were options that could make the experience better." Penny gained a sense of empowerment in taking charge of her own return to wellness during her breast cancer journey by choosing to utilize therapies such as acupuncture, energy healing, and massage, which not only helped her healing process but aligned with her values.

She started thinking about the concept of integrative health: combining leading medical practice with ancient healing wisdom (acupuncture, aromatherapy, acupressure, etc.) to optimize health and wellness in the whole person—mind, body, and spirit. Integrative medicine is rooted in a belief of the healing potential of the body and the importance of the relationship

Integrative medicine is rooted in a belief of the healing potential of the body and the importance of the relationship between patient and caregiver.

between patient and caregiver. It considers healing to be the focus of medical efforts, whether or not curing is possible.

Since 1999, the George Family Foundation has been funding several programs at Abbott Northwestern, such as the Virginia Piper Cancer Institute and the Minneapolis Heart Institute®. One funded program was designed to specifically address ways to bring integrative health into the hospital setting. Lori Knutson, a board certified nurse in holistic medicine, was brought in as consultant for that program. Having served as executive director of Sister Kenny Rehabilitation Institute for 15 years, her understanding of rehabilitative care brought a valuable perspective to the process.

Lori first conducted an extensive environmental scan of the organization, which included a patient study that contained questions about current utilization of alternative therapies and how patients had benefitted (or not) as a result. It also involved meetings with physician and nursing groups, pharmacy staff, nutritionists, and others. Lori was introducing the integrative medicine team to people within Abbott Northwestern's system in the hope that a successful program could ultimately be established.

Simultaneously, the George Family Foundation was looking more and more into creating change at the hospital. In 2003, the Foundation was in conversation with Sid Mallory (the president of Abbott Northwestern Hospital Foundation at that time) to find out if they could make a large gift directed to integrative medicine.

Another philanthropist and Abbott Northwestern supporter, Roberta Mann-Benson shared the same passion for integrative medicine and encouraged her family foundation to also make a gift. In 2003, in partnership with the Ted and Roberta Mann Foundation, the George Family Foundation donated $4 million as seed funding for the Institute for Health and Healing (IHH) at Abbott Northwestern Hospital (ANW).

The goal was to weave integrative medicine's philosophy and techniques into daily medical practice to improve patients' lives, help physicians better manage their most complex patients, increase physician and nursing satisfaction in their professions, and add to ANW's reputation as a high-quality, caring institution.

In the beginning, the team met with some resistance from doctors. There was a mixed view on integrative medicine. Some doctors were reluctant to accept it for fear of it becoming interventional care — care that got in the way of traditional Western medicine rather than enhancing the care given by doctors. The challenge was to educate physicians and nurses (thereby changing their perceptions) by putting the patient at the center of their work, and to broaden their practices to incorporate healing as well as curing. Eventually, the doctors began to see it as truly integrative care. According to Penny, Lori was a significant part of this because of the relationships she developed within the hospital system.

In 2002, ANW hospital president Denny DeNarvaez asked Lori to become the new Executive Director of the Institute for Health and Healing.

Lori spent a year building a foundation for the program, garnering support and initial buy-in from doctors and nurses at Abbott Northwestern, and developing the inpatient program first. By 2003, six inpatient teams were developed and each team had three practitioners on it: a nurse with a subspecialty (i.e. oncology, neurology, cardiology) and two others with a specialty in a certain therapy (i.e. massage therapist, reflexologist, acupuncturist, music therapist). The teams were working specifically with the following specialty areas at Abbott Northwestern: cardiology, orthopedic rehabilitation, medical surgical, Women Care (birthing center), oncology, and neurology.

The inpatient teams developed criteria based on individual patient needs. Referrals came from physicians, nurses, and self-referred patients from one of the specialty areas. The teams would meet each morning and determine if referred patients fit the criteria; they would then decide which team would best work with the patient. On average, each team saw six to eight patients a day.

"We trained all of the providers — no matter if they were an acupuncturist, a massage therapist, or a nurse — in acupressure, guided imagery, aromatherapy, and biofeedback. As such, over time they developed more skills than just those for which they were licensed," said Lori. The job description eventually changed for each team member and they were designated as Integrative Health Practitioners.

Penny said, "The program was centered at the patient's bedside; it was literally returning nurses to their roots in a healing and supportive human presence."

The goal was to weave integrative medicine's philosophy and techniques into daily medical practice to improve patients' lives, help physicians better manage their most complex patients, increase physician and nursing satisfaction in their professions, and add to ANW's reputation as a high-quality, caring institution.

Lori acknowledged that the nurses' role was absolutely crucial. "They were the ones who could bridge the medical understanding and the complementary alternative medicine component." The program was strategic in that the IHH hired nurses with a subspecialty (oncology, cardiology), as well as having board certification in holistic nursing. The nurses helped the other therapists know the patient populations medically and helped them understand how their therapies could integrate into the patient's care.

Education has been an important component at the Penny George Institute for Health and Healing since its inception. Lori created the Transformative Nurse Training (TNT) program at Abbott Northwestern, which provided in-service training on holistic nursing to nurses across the system. The program eventually received funding to start a 48-hour transformative nursing training for Abbott Northwestern Hospital nurses and served as a model for an initiative in a Veteran's Administration (VA) hospital in California. The training for the change in this VA system came from ANW nurses.

In 2004, the Institute for Health and Healing opened an outpatient clinic at the ANW campus in Minneapolis. The outpatient teams included physicians, nurse practitioners, massage therapists, music therapists, health psychologists, acupuncturists, nutritionists, and others. In addition to the outpatient care, the clinic offered a variety of classes and programs.

"We provide tools at the Institute to help people develop skills for life," said Penny. "Medical practice in the United States is miraculous in dealing with fixing a targeted issue, but people are unclear of what to do with chronic disease and how to handle it. Integrative medicine puts the patient in the driver's seat of their own care."

The Institute for Health and Healing kept growing. The work eventually expanded to the Unity-Mercy campus, focusing on integrative oncology in partnership with the Virginia Piper Cancer Institute's partner, Minnesota Oncology. Another focus of IHH was to pay attention to the whole continuum of care from prevention to end-of-life. They realized that lifestyle change was a large part of staying healthy and keeping chronic illness at bay. This programming included nutrition, exercise, stress management, and mental health. The IHH redesigned the Wasie Fitness Center at Abbott Northwestern and created LiveWell, an integrated fitness center, which includes the employee health and wellness program at Abbott Northwestern and across the Allina Health system.

"I think the reason that [IHH] was able to grow the way it did and we were able to become an integral piece in the fabric of the organization was, in part, because we spent a great deal of time developing the evidence base behind what we were doing, and creating very significant relationships with administration, with philanthropists, with the medical community," said Lori. "So developing the culture is what has sustained it. From the very beginning of the environmental scan and surveys we did before we started anything, the intention was this was going to be the way care was provided, and the only way it could be – not just to supply services but to integrate into the culture. I think that's the only way it has a future."

In 2006, with the help of a special capital gift from Penny and Bill George, the clinic expanded, doubling the number of treatment rooms and adding additional evening hours. "We have a vision that we will create a healthier nation and healthier communities by transforming the way that we interact with people around their health," said Penny.

In 2008, Ken Paulus and Penny Wheeler from Allina Health led the charge to rename the Institute for Health and Healing to the Penny George Institute for Health and Healing (PGIHH) to honor one of its biggest supporters. Penny said, "Integrative health has the potential to fundamentally change the face of health care today. The Institute is a philosophical and clinical manifestation of that promise."

"We're trying to change not just a hospital and a health system, which is enormous in itself, but we're trying to change American medicine and how health care is conceived and delivered and the consciousness of the American people."

A few years later, the Penny George Institute for Health and Healing expanded even further across the Allina Health care system, but Abbott Northwestern will always be seen as the flagship hospital for the Institute. Penny noted, "They were hugely important in creating a new model of integrative care with medical doctors."

Lori Knutson left PGIHH in 2011. The current Director of Program Development and Administration is Lindsey Niswanger and the Vice President and Medical Director for the PGIHH is Dr. Courtney Baechler.

Abbott Northwestern will always be seen as the flagship hospital for the Institute. Penny George noted, "They were hugely important in creating a new model of integrative care with medical doctors."

Research

Another key component of understanding the role that PGIHH plays on the national healthcare stage is the Integrative Health Research Center (IHRC), which is run by PGIHH. In 2007, Jeffery Dusek, PhD was hired as the Director of Research. Prior to joining PGIHH, Jeff was faculty member at Harvard Medical School, serving as director of Behavioral Sciences Research with the Benson Henry Institute for Mind Body Medicine at Massachusetts General Hospital.

The goal of having a research team was to conduct clinical trials important for the clinic to examine the impact therapies were having on patients.

Since Abbott Northwestern was one of the few hospitals to provide integrative medicine to hospitalized patients, Jeff and his team were conducting observational studies (practice-based research) to advance the study of integrative medicine.

In 2010, Dusek and colleagues utilized data from the Abbott Northwestern electronic medical record to publish results documenting a 55% reduction in pain after ANW inpatients received integrative therapies. The ANW Hospital Foundation funded this work. Publication of that scientific article led to Dusek and his team receiving a $2.6 million grant from the National Institutes of Health (NIH) to conduct the first-of- its-kind evaluation of integrative therapies for hospitalized patients.

As of August 2016, the NIH grant has resulted in publication of 11 scientific articles in peer-reviewed medical journals as well as 14 presentations at international scientific meetings. This research has focused on documenting pain relief from integrative medicine in oncology, cardiovascular, and joint replacement patient populations. Results have been published in several medical journals.

An outreach of the NIH-funded research was to work with Abbott Northwestern Emergency Department (ANW ED) providers to study whether the provision of acupuncture reduces pain and anxiety levels for patients receiving care in the ANW ED. This was an observational study to understand the feasibility of having the acupuncture provider in the fast-paced ED. Before and after receiving acupuncture, the researchers asked patients to report their pain on a 0-10 pain scale. Dusek and colleagues found that the amount of pain reduction (2.37 unit reduction) as a result of receiving acupuncture alone was comparable to acupuncture combined with pain medications including opioids (2.68 unit reduction). IHRC is in the midst of a small randomized trial (funded by the ANW Hospital Foundation) to prepare for a definitive study.

With regard to the use of integrative therapies in oncology patients, IHRC collaborated with the Virginia Piper Cancer Institute on a study focusing on mastectomy patients. Typically, length of stay post-surgery for mastectomy patients is one and a half days. The integrative medicine referral process takes a minimum of two days, so mastectomy patients, even if they were referred, did not often receive in-hospital integrative therapy treatment. The trial recruited patients pre-surgery to receive acupuncture treatment the night after surgery and the next morning. The result was a significant decrease in pain and anxiety. Results of this study were published in the *Oncology Nursing Forum* journal.

Since 2011, the IHRC has been studying quality of life in most Allina ambulatory clinics (oncology, cardiology, neurology, primary care, rehab, etc.). A major goal of the project is to assess how quality of life is impacted by integrative health. As of August 2016, over 50,000 patients have completed a quality of life survey including 4,000 unique PGIHH patients. The PGIHH patients report over 5% increases in physical and mental health components of their quality of life.

As evidenced by its prolific productivity, PGIHH Research is truly a national leader in the study of integrative therapies for hospitalized and clinic patients.

As evidenced by its prolific productivity, Penny George Institute Research is truly a national leader in the study of integrative therapies for hospitalized and clinic patients.

Today

The Penny George Institute for Health and Healing continues to be a groundbreaking institution, leading integrative health practices through its programs and clinics, in education, and in research. According to Dr. Courtney Baechler, Vice President of the PGIHH, 70% of the U.S. population now approves of integrative health care practices. Health providers have also become much more accepting of alternative treatment modalities than they were in 2003. "The George Institute alone has 13 years of research and data substantiating claims about integrative health at the same type of level that we're used to with traditional medicine," said Dr. Baechler, "so that's made physicians more comfortable."

"The mission of the George Institute is to optimize health and well-being by combining the best of Western medicine with practices that come out of ancient healing traditions. There is an ancient wisdom that we need to rediscover."
—*Penny George*

Beyond the training nurses are receiving through the Transformative Nurse Training (TNT) Program, education is now extending out to other health care providers. According to Lindsey Niswanger, Director of Program Development and Administration, the following education programs are in place:

- Aromatherapy, Levels I & II, delivered online via Allina's online learning platform. From 2/1/12 through 8/2/16, 5,550 Allina employees, mostly nurses, have taken Level 1 aromatherapy training, and 2,227 have taken Level 2 aromatherapy training.

- The Institute is partnering with the National Center for Integrative Primary Healthcare to offer the "Foundations in Integrative Health," a 45-hour online training. Approximately 900 Allina Health employees voluntarily registered for the training in 2016.

- Short-term fellowships are given for doctors to gain a better understanding of integrative health in one of the clinics.

In addition, PGIHH continues to be actively involved with ANW through several programs:

- Inpatient integrative health services across the hospital, including acupuncture, massage, and music therapy, along with other supportive modalities

- Outpatient integrative health services at the clinics on the ANW campus and ANW-WestHealth, including integrative medicine consultations, acupuncture, massage, nutrition, spiritual direction, and healthy lifestyle programming, such as Resilience Training, Mindfulness Training, Healing Touch, and more

- The LiveWell Fitness Center (with approximately 470 members) exists as the hub for evidence-based healthy lifestyle programming, such as Integrative Health & Wellness Coaching, Take Action Program for Weight Management, and more

- Collaborative programming with other clinical service lines (e.g., The Mother Baby Center, Joint Replacement Program, Virginia Piper Cancer Institute, Minneapolis Heart Institute®, etc.)

- Art of Healing Programming (e.g., Music on the Mall and collaboration with external groups to provide art therapy to Mother-Baby populations)

The Penny George Institute for Health and Healing began as a small group of individuals who envisioned what health care could be. That vision grew to be the largest hospital-based integrative health program in the United States. "I would like to see continued integration of PGIHH programs and services into standardized care models across the continuum," said Lindsey, "reliably addressing the needs of the whole person – body, mind, and spirit."

People have always been the heart of the work at PGIHH: Patients are seen as a whole person and the interactions with healers are on a human level. "Our practitioners are remarkable healers," said Penny. "They are all credentialed at the highest level, yes, but beyond that there's something special about them, and because of that they function as a team so that the care is much more patient-centered and more coordinated than care that's in silos."

"When we look at chronic disease, 70% of what we see is preventable," said Dr. Baechler. "We obviously need to approach health care through an entirely new lens and perspective. It needs to be individualized to patient needs rather than simply prescriptive [meds, etc.]. What we try to offer people in a more holistic way is how best to meet health needs and give people choices in ways to engage and ways that they can be responsible for those outcomes. It's a profound and empowering experience for the individual."

Resources:

- Allina Health website. http://www.allinahealth.org/Penny-George-Institute-for-Health-and-Healing. Accessed August 15, 2016.

- YouTube video interview with Penny George. https://youtu.be/TJ-rDX-Ba19s. Accessed August 15, 2016.

- George Family Foundation, Establishing an Institute for Health and Healing at Abbott Northwestern Hospital: Strategy and Business Plan Recommendations. January 2005.

- Penny George, interview, August 2016.

- Lori Knutson, interview, August 2016.

- Dr. Courtney Baechler, interview, August 2016.

- Jeffery Dusek, PhD, interview, August 2016.

- Lindsey Niswanger, interview, August 2016.

Curriculum Vitae of Contributors

Dr. Mark Arnesen: Born Owatonna, Minnesota, Carleton College Graduating Summa Cum Laude, Phi Beta Kappa. Attended Mayo Medical School. Residency in Anatomic & Clinical Pathology, Washington University, Seattle, Washington. Diplomate of the American Board of Pathology in Anatomic & Clinical Pathology. Clinical Professor University of Minnesota. 13 publications.

Dr. Bryce Beverlin: University of Minnesota Bachelor of Science in Biology, University of Minnesota Medical School Graduating AOA. Residency in Anesthesiology University of Minnesota, Practiced Anesthesiology at Abbott Northwestern Hospital 1983 – 2013. He authored a number of articles relating to anesthesiology.

Mr. James R. Bulger: Cornell College Iowa, Bachelor of Arts in English; Dominican University of Rover, Forest Illinois; Master of Library & Information Science. Teacher of Humanities, Trinity School at River Ridge Bloomington, MN. Coordinator of Family Life Education, Diocese of St. George's Grenada, West Indies; Knowledge Consultant, Minneapolis, MN. Manager, Library Services, Allina Health System. Three publications.

Dr. Thomas Christiansen: Born St. Louis, MO. Bachelor of Arts, Dennison University. University of Illinois Medical School, AOA. Internship University of Illinois Hospitals. Resident in General Surgery University of Minnesota. Resident in Otolaryngology at University of Minnesota. Member of the American Board of Otolaryngology and Minnesota Academy of Otolaryngology. Clinical Assistant Professor, Department of Otolaryngology University of Minnesota. 13 publications, 12 Lectureships.

Dr. Frazier Eales: High School at Groton School, Groton, Mass; Macalester College, St. Paul; University of Minnesota Medical School. Residency in General Surgery, University of Minnesota; Cardiac Fellowship at University of Minnesota. Board Certified in American Board of Thoracic Surgery. Past President of the Abbott Northwestern Medical Staff, Past President of the Minneapolis Heart Institute®.

Dr. Thomas Flynn: Born Hibbing, MN. Bachelor of Arts, College of St. Thomas Summa Cum Laude, University of Minnesota Medical School AOA. Internship at Barnes Hospital in Internal Medicine, St. Louis; Residency in Internal Medicine, University of Minnesota; Fellowship in Hematology-Oncology, University of Minnesota. Board Certified in Internal Medicine, Hematology, Medical Oncology. Clinical Assistant Professor University of Minnesota. Five abstracts, 12 publications, 8 presentations.

Dr. Robert Ganz: Born Chicago, IL. College at the University of Illinois-Urbana, Magna Cum Laude, Phi Beta Kappa; University of Illinois College of Medicine, Chicago, IL. Internal Medicine Residency University of Illinois Hospital, Chicago, IL; Fellowship Gastroenterology, Northwestern University, Chicago, IL. Diplomate American Board of Internal Medicine; Member of the American Board of Gastroenterology. Associate Professor of Medicine, University of Minnesota. 24 patents; 66 abstracts; 63 lectures.

Dr. Stanley Goldberg: Born Minneapolis. Bachelor of Arts Cum Laude University of Minnesota, University of Minnesota Medical School. Internship MGH; Residency General Surgery Veterans Administration Hospital Minneapolis, MN; Colon & Rectal Surgery University of Minnesota Medical School. Certified Member of American Board of General Surgery and American Board of Colon & Rectal Surgery. Head of Colon and Rectal Surgery Hennepin County Medical Center and University of Minnesota. Co-author of 128 papers, contributor to 73 books, co-author of seven books and videos. Member of multiple fellowships throughout the world.

Dr. Emanuel Gaziano: Born Beckley, West Virginia. Graduate of Western Virginia University, West Virginia University School of Medicine. Internship Hennepin County General Hospital; Residency in OB-GYN University of Minnesota. Certified Member of the American Board of OB-GYN. Professor of OB-GYN, University of Minnesota Medical School, 1994–2013.

Dr. Paul R. Hamann, Bachelor of Science, St. John's University, Collegeville, MN; Master of Science Physiology/Pharmacology, University of North Dakota, Grand Forks, North Dakota; University of Minnesota Medical School, Minneapolis, MN; Master of Science, Administrative Medicine, University of Wisconsin, Madison, WI. Board Certified in American Board of Internal Medicine, American Board of Internal Medicine, Subspecialty Exam in Pulmonary Medicine; Fellow, American College of Chest Physicians. Clinical Associate Professor of Medicine, Department of Medicine, University of Minnesota Medical School.

Ms. Carol Huttner: BSN St. Louis University, St. Louis, MO. Masters in Healthcare and Hospital Administration at Webster College. Abbott Northwestern Hospital Neuro Specialist; Director of Cardiovascular & Critical Care, Patient Care Vice President Abbott Northwestern Hospital; North Central Region President, Specialty Care.

Dr. John Jones: Bachelor of Arts, University of Iowa, College of Liberal Arts; University of Iowa, College of Medicine. Internship at Emmanuel Hospital, Portland, Oregon; Residency in Pathology, Hennepin County Medical Center. Captain U.S. Air Force 2 years. Diplomate of the American Board of Pathology (Anatomic and Clinical); Member of the American Society of Cardiovascular Pathology, Minnesota Society of Pathology, College of American Pathology, American Society of Clinical Pathology. Five publications.

Dr. Arnold Kaplan: Bachelor of Arts/Bachelor of Science, University of Minnesota. Rotating Internship, Mt. Sinai Hospital; Internal Medicine Residency Mt. Sinai Hospital, Veterans Administration Hospital; Gastroenterology Residency, Veterans Administration Hospital. Member of the American Board of Internal Medicine, American College of Physicians; American College of Gastroenterology. Ten publications, 34 lectures/presentations. Clinical Professor of Medicine, University of Minnesota Medical School.

Dr. James Larson: Born Fargo, ND. Bachelor of Arts, Chemistry-Zoology, Concordia College; University of Minnesota Medical School. Residency in Neuro-Surgery and Orthopedic Surgery University of Minnesota, Emergency Medicine Hennepin County Medical Center; Fellowship Traumatology Graz Austria. Diplomate of American Board of Orthopedic Surgery; Member of American Academy of Orthopedic Surgery. 73 presentations locally and nationally.

Dr. Don LeWin: High School: Nichols School Buffalo NY. Princeton University, Medical School State University of NY, Buffalo. Residency Wills Eye Hospital (Philadelphia PA), Fellow – American Board of Ophthalmology, Member of American Eye Study, Fellow – Royal Academy of Medicine, England (Ophthalmology). Chair – Midwest Vitreous Teaching Courses.

Rev. Max Maguire: Wichita State University, San Francisco Theological Seminary, Clinical Pastoral Education at Topeka State Hospital, Menninger Foundation and Virginia Commonwealth/Medical College of Virginia.

Dr. Rajneesh Madhok: Born Agra, India. College at University of North Dakota; University of North Dakota Medical School. Residency in Internal Medicine, Hennepin County Medical Center; Dermatology Residency at Mayo Clinic Graduate School of Medicine. Board Certified American Academy of Dermatology. Clinical Assistant Professor of Dermatology, University of Minnesota Medical School. Four publications.

Elaine Hogan Miller: BS Nursing, University of Connecticut, MS Nursing, University of Minnesota; PhD Nursing, University of Illinois. Worked primarily in cardiovascular patient care at Abbott Northwestern Hospital. Taught Nursing at St. Francis School of Nursing, Hartford, CT; St. Luke's School of Nursing, Fargo ND; Loyola University, Chicago, IL; and Mankato State University, MN.

Dr. Eugene Ollila: Raised in Zim, MN. University of Minnesota Zoology Major; University of Minnesota Medical School. Rotating Internship Hennepin County Medical Center. Private Practice in Prior Lake. U.S. Air Force 2 years. Residency in Internal Medicine, Hennepin County Medical Center. Chief of Internal Medicine department, Abbott Northwestern Hospital, President of the Medical Staff Abbott Northwestern Hospital.

Dr. Ron Peterson: Augustana College, Rock Island IL, Phi Beta Kappa, Summa Cum Laude; Northwestern School of Medicine Chicago, IL, AOA. Residency in OB-GYN, University of Michigan; Fellow American College of OB-GYN. Member American Society of Reproductive Medicine, Minnesota OB-GYN Society.

Dr. Claus Pierach: Maarburg, Glessen, & Munich Germany & Innsbruck Austria; Internal Medicine, University and Clinics Mainz, Germany.

Dr. Ken Preimesberger: Marquette University Medical School; Residency in Diagnostic Radiology, University of Minnesota. Member of the American College of Radiology, American Board of Nuclear Medicine.

Dr. Terry Rosborough: University of Illinois, University of Illinois Medical College and Rush Medical College. Internal Medicine Residency at the University of Minnesota Medical School. Director of Medical Education, Abbott Northwestern Hospital.

Dr. Robert Scott: Born Faribault, MN. Bachelor of Arts, Carleton College, Columbia University College of Physicians and Surgeons, New York, NY. Rotating Internship Minneapolis General Hospital, Internal Medicine Residency, Minneapolis General Hospital. Captain in the U.S. Air Force for two years. Chief resident at Minneapolis General Hospital, chief of staff of Northwestern Hospital, and chief of staff of Abbott Northwestern Hospital.

Dr. John L. Seymour: Born Wilmington, Delaware. Dartmouth College; Dartmouth and Cornell Medical Schools; General Surgery University Medical School and Minneapolis General Hospital. Neuro-Surgery Residency, University of Minnesota Medical School. Certified Board of Neurological Surgery. Associate Professor, University of Minnesota School of Medicine.

Rev. Richard Sellers: Dartmouth College; Masters of Divinity, Union Theological Seminary New York, N.Y.; Masters University of Minnesota Family Social Service. Ordained Minister in the United Church of Christ. Supervisor, Association for Clinical Pastoral Education. Associate Director of Chaplaincy, Abbott Northwestern Hospital; Metro Director, Spiritual Care and Pastoral Education, Allina Health.

Dr. Jennine Speier: Bachelor of Science, Zoology, at the Syracuse University; Masters Physiology, Cornell University, Ithaca NY; University of Minnesota Medical School, Physical Medicine and Rehabilitation, University of Minnesota. Courage Kenny Rehabilitation Institute, Director of Courage Kenny Rehabilitation Institute Research Center. Member of the American Academy of Physical Medicine and Rehabilitation.

Gordon Sprenger: St. Olaf College, Masters Degree in Hospital Administration, University of Minnesota 1961. Hired by Stan Nelson as Assistant Administrator at Northwestern Hospital 1967, President/CEO of Abbott Northwestern Hospital 1970-1992, President/CEO LifeSpan 1982-1992, Executive Officer 1992-1994, President and CEO Allina Health Systems 1994-2003.

Dr. Richard Sturgeon: Born Jamestown ND. University of North Dakota; University of Rochester Medical School. Internship at Hennepin County Medical Center. Medical Staff President Abbott Northwestern Hospital; Vice President Medical Affairs Abbott Northwestern Hospital, Interim President Abbott Northwestern Hospital 2005-2006.

Dr. Thomas Rivers: High School: Muncie, Indiana. Colorado College, Indiana University Medical School Internship Cottage and County General Hospita.l, Santa Barbara, CA. Family Practice Medicine, Muncie Indiana, Mayo Clinic Residency, Department of Rheumatology, ENT Air Force Base, Colorado Springs, Colorado;   Mayo Clinic Urology Residency. Arnett Clinic, Multispecialty Clinic, Lafayette Indiana, Urology Associates, Edina MN, Urology Practice at Methodist Hospital, Fairview Southdale Hospital, and Abbott Northwestern Hospital. Clinical Professor, University of Minnesota Medical School.

Dr. David Tubman: Born Saskatoon, Saskatchewan, Canada. Pre-medical degree at University of Saskatchewan, Saskatoon, Saskatchewan, Canada; Medical Degree: University of Saskatchewan, Saskatoon, Saskatchewan, Canada. Medical/Pathology Internship at Health Sciences Center, Winnipeg, Manitoba, Canada; Radiology Residency Health Sciences Center, Winnipeg, Manitoba, Canada; Neuroradiology Fellowship at McGill University, Montreal Neuro Institute, Montreal, Quebec, Canada. Assistant Professor of Radiology at Health Sciences Center, Winnipeg, Manitoba, Canada and University of Minnesota Hospital. Hospital Affiliations: Health Sciences Center, Winnipeg, University of Minnesota Hospital; Abbott Northwestern Hospital; Minneapolis Children's Medical Center; Shriners Hospital, Minneapolis; Hennepin County Medical Center; United Hospital, St. Paul; St. Paul Ramsey Medical Center, St. Paul; St. Mary's Hospital, Duluth. 13 scientific presentations; four lectureships: Computed Tomography Workshop at Reno, Nevada; EMI Tutorial, Lake Geneva, Wisconsin; Canadian Association of Radiological Technologists; University of Minnesota Continuation Course.

Dr. Robert Van Tassel: Born Eau Claire, WI. College at University of Minnesota, University of Minnesota Medical School. Internship Hennepin County General Hospital, Internal Medicine Residency Hennepin County General Hospital; Fellowship Cardiovascular Medicine University of Minnesota, AOA. Boarded in American College of Cardiology. Member of the American Heart Association. 30 Patents.

Dr. Douglas Yock: Born Minneapolis, MN. St. Olaf College and Harvard University; Summa Cum Laude, Phi Beta Kappa at Harvard; Harvard Medical School, AOA; Stanford University Medical Center, Diagnostic Radiology, University of California, San Francisco, Neuro-Radiology. Certified in the American Board of Radiology and Diagnostic Radiology and Neuro-Radiology.